Methods of Teaching

ELEMENTARY SCHOOL MATHEMATICS

by

WALDEMAR OLSON, Ed. D.

College of Education
University of Florida
Gainesville, Florida

Burgess Publishing Company

426 South Sixth Street • Minneapolis, Minn. 55415

Copyright © 1968 by Burgess Publishing Company

Printed in the United States of America

Library of Congress Catalog Card Number 68-56887

To Eva LaRue and Karen Ann

Preface

This book has been written as a text for courses in teacher education for in-service and pre-service programs. The author has taught the content of this text in classes and workshops for the in-service teacher and to the student preparing to become an elementary teacher. Emphasis is placed on developing the meaning of the concepts and principles of arithmetic and on methods of teaching the content. The reader is guided to discover meanings and generalizations so that he will use "discovery" in his teaching of children.

For the past several years, many teachers have been taking courses in the content and structure of mathematics in the hope that this would solve the dilemma of teaching arithmetic in the elementary school. This generalization seems to be false. Merely taking more courses does not seem to be the total answer to a good mathematics program. This is clearly indicated in the requests from superintendents of schools, supervisors, principals and teachers for help in clarifying meaning and methods for teaching the content of arithmetic. If one can assume that arithmetic deserves to be understood, then it is quite evident that it must be taught to teachers in such a manner that it will produce understanding, interest and security in his ability to teach the content.

Each chapter presenting methods of teaching the fundamental operations of whole numbers, fractions and decimal fractions is divided into four parts:

1. Arithmetic Understanding: The properties, concepts and generalizations in arithmetic for the elementary school are interpreted through language and examples as background information for the teacher.

2. Fundamental Operations: A step-by-step sequence for teaching arithmetic is developed through a series of selected examples and problems. A language is presented which serves as a bond for continuity, relationships and interpretation throughout the four operations in whole numbers, fractions and decimal fractions. Identification of patterns is emphasized to implement understanding of the algorisms and as preparation for establishing ways to estimate answers. Each arithmetical concept is developed from the standpoint of how children may be guided to discover for themselves the meaning involved.

3. Enrichment Experiences: When common algorisms are understood, teachers are provided experiences to discover further patterns which will help them to arrive at the answer in several ways. The activities move from paper-pencil notation to performing the operations mentally. This portion of the chapter provides the teacher with many insights which she can use to encourage the student to work beyond his present level of performance and to generate added interest and enthusiasm for arithmetic.

4. Study Questions: Several questions are stated which will help the teacher to think through the sequential development of the chapter.

The bibliography at the close of every chapter provides the following educational background for strengthening the content of this text:
a. Mathematics background for teachers
b. Philosophy of teaching mathematics
c. Psychology of learning
d. Research on content in the elementary arithmetic program
e. Other techniques for teaching arithmetic
f. Research on teaching arithmetic
g. Various programs providing the new mathematics

The first chapter identifies the teacher's role in arithmetic program and presents several student competencies to be attained. The second chapter introduces numbers and presents a brief study of the concept of sets and operations on sets. The primary objectives of Chapter 7 are two-fold: (1) to develop interest in arithmetic through a study of history of number development, and (2) to test the reader's concepts of base ten by thinking through these same concepts in a base other than ten. Chapter 10 presents geometry as it relates to the elementary school. Content from geometry provides the teacher with information and methods for the study of measurement and non-metric concepts. The remaining chapters develop methodology for teaching arithmetic through language, relationships and discovery.

It is the hope of the author that this book will give to teachers in elementary schools a clearer understanding of arithmetic, ways in which it can be taught and greater enjoyment, appreciation and confidence as they work with children. The success of a student in arithmetic and his attitude toward arithmetic are basically dependent upon his teacher's attitude and the methods which he uses.

Appreciation of the author is extended to colleagues and to the hundreds of teachers, who have taken the courses from which the content of this book has been derived, for their constructive suggestions, enthusiastic responses and encouragement. The children in the elementary schools cannot be ignored. They, too, gave the author confidence and assurance that arithmetic can be made meaningful, interesting and challenging.

Waldemar Olson

Table of Contents

Chapter I

The Changing Program
in Elementary School Mathematics

There probably has been no time during the 20th century when laymen, educators and professional organizations alike were not concerned with the changes taking place in our society. Social changes always bring about modifications in the primary institutions of a country. These modifications must be made quickly within an institution when we live in a dynamic world such as we live in at the present time; otherwise, the institution does not meet the demands of its time and so it must be doomed to failure.

Within the past decade of our century, the tempo of change across the breadth of our country has been fostered by the scientific and technological advancements with all their potentialities for building an even greater society. Education has no choice but to accept the challenge of the times or fail as an institution.

The curriculum of the public school is developed out of the needs of society and the individual. This concept of curriculum development is most evident today in the area of mathematics. Interested laymen, teachers and professional organizations have developed programs which set forth their beliefs concerning new developments in content and in the teaching of mathematics. Major changes advocated center around such topics as providing a precise mathematical language, re-examining grade placement of present mathematical content, addition of mathematical content which will challenge and prepare our youth for our changing times, giving emphasis to concepts, principles, and properties in the teaching of the operations and involving the children in the act of learning through discovering and developing mathematical concepts for themselves. Several of the contributors are:

1. The School Mathematics Study Group (SMSG); Director, E. B. Begle
2. The Science Research Associates (SRA), formerly The Greater Cleveland Mathematics Plan (GCMP); Director, GCMP B. M. Gundlach
3. The University of Illinois Arithmetic Project; Director, David Page
4. The University of Maryland Mathematics Project; Director, J. R. Mayor
5. The Madison Project; Director, Robert B. Davis
6. The Stanford Project; Director, P. Suppes

"New mathematics" means many things. It leaves the idea that the mathematics of the traditional program has been replaced by a content radically new. In the elementary grades, it is difficult to point out any part of the traditional mathematics curriculum and say that "this" has been omitted. However, many new properties, concepts, language and symbols have been added to provide children with tools with which "to think" and "to express" themselves mathematically.

One aspect of the "new mathematics" which is apparent throughout the programs is the discovery approach. Children are guided to use concepts and language previously learned to identify patterns and approaches to new situations and, eventually, to make generalizations which combine many ideas into one general statement.

To meet the challenge of the new look at mathematics, teacher training institutions across the country are recommending 6 to 9 hours of mathematics for the prospective elementary teacher and an opportunity for those who wish to specialize to build a program beyond this minimum. One cannot stop here. Institutions preparing teachers must become more aware of the need for courses in methodology which will provide each teacher with such interpretations and materials which involve the use of mathematics to solve the problems of everyday living for each citizen. Each teacher needs time to become interested, to rid herself of fears, to develop understanding of mathematics, to find security in the teaching of arithmetic, and for life-long inservice experiences to continue updating one's self.

The Teacher and the Program

Good teachers develop in pupils an interest and enthusiasm for arithmetic. The teacher gives to the program living experiences and adapts them to the students' experiences and to their level of maturity. The result for the student is one of accomplishment rather than one of frustration and failure.

The curriculum is the total of all the learning experiences carried on at home and in the school. No textbook can effectively utilize these experiences and make all the adjustments to meet individual differences. The teacher can. Only the teacher can identify the interests, abilities and experiences of the pupils and go beyond the content of text materials to satisfy them. Principles and guidelines which must be supplied by the teacher in planning and guiding number experiences are many. Several of the major principles are:

1. Arithmetic is a way of thinking about a system of ideas, processes, properties and relationships. Thinking is the central theme of the operation. In an environment such as this, children are stimulated to work on their own to discover "why" things happen as they do. They are taught how to think about a problem through a developmental sequence which unites common ideas. It is the task of the children to discover meaning and a way to use this information in solving a particular situation.

2. Content and experiences for each child must be selected on the basis of his experiences and understanding. Many children come to school with number experiences. It is the role of the teacher to evaluate these experiences in the light of the understanding which children have acquired. She places this content into a proposed sequence which seems logical and appropriate for each child. As an example, division is not appropriate if the child cannot subtract. For this reason, the teacher continually plans and revises the content of the arithmetic program so that the needs of each child are met. The content in arithmetic for each grade level, therefore, is determined by the child's understanding, not memorization of concepts and principles.

3. Understanding concepts, processes, properties and relationships is basic to the learning process. Development of ideas through concrete and semi-concrete materials before proceeding to the abstract gives a basis for understanding the abstract. The development of language stresses the relationships which exist as one proceeds from one process to another. To make learning interesting and meaningful is to develop a logical order in thinking which permits transition of concepts understood to new concepts, that is, from counting to addition, to subtraction and so on. This emphasis on interpreting concepts develops the ability to relate, verify and generalize.

4. The pupils are provided opportunities to discover concepts, principles and relationships. They are encouraged to think critically. The process of discovery places upon the student the necessity to recall facts, to identify related principles and to

test his generalization. He sees in new situations some identifying elements already learned and he applies these known ideas as an approach to the solution of the unknown problem. He accomplishes his goal through the use of exploratory materials such as concrete objects, the number line, charts and by manipulation. The teacher is the guide. She accomplishes her purposes through the art of asking questions and challenging the student by suggesting alternate approaches. Discovery is a way of thinking.

5. Repetition is planned to develop and maintain some degree of proficiency. Drill is provided only after the pupil understands the concept. Teaching for meaning does not do away with practice; drill is a means of maintaining skills and techniques already developed. Practice is often effective when it is presented in situations different from the one in which it was learned. In the upper elementary grades, drill in the addition facts can be accomplished through an activity in which numbers are reversed and added until the sum can be read the same from right to left and left to right.

6. Problem solving is a continuous daily experience. Textbook experiences are not sufficient; children and the teacher must supplement texts. Problems related to the environment of the children must be structured so that the children can find common and known experiences within the problem situation. Setting up equations which state the questions asked in the problem are essential and then rewriting the equation to indicate how it is to be solved completes the thought pattern. Problem solving must be daily activity in the arithmetic program.

7. Diagnostic and remedial work is an outgrowth of observed errors in thinking and computation. Wrong answers must direct one to find the reason for the error. Too much emphasis has been placed on the correct answer rather than on the thought process involved. Discovering why the children have wrong answers is the key to remedial work. Guide the children to think about this aspect of their work.

8. Freedom in the approach to a solution is important. There is no one way to solve a problem. The many solutions may be used to create interest and develop a greater depth in the understanding of a concept. Each solution is used to develop deeper insight of the process involved and the existing relationships. The algorism selected by the student at this time may be the only way in which he can solve his problem. If he is forced to another algorism, failure can be the outcome.

9. Repetition will not teach insight and understanding. With understanding, there is little need to memorize. Learnings are presented in a sequential manner. The field of arithmetic presents a systematic organization of its content. A child who understands multiplication of whole numbers sees very little that is new in the multiplication of fractions and decimals. It is the teacher's responsibility to guide and direct her teaching so that children will see arithmetic as a whole.

10. Children learn best when they are actively participating in a learning situation. Provide activities which will arouse their interests in mathematics. As children become involved, the teacher continues to challenge them with questions which guide them through sequences which build new insights and relationships. As they gain new insights, more opportunities for expanding the original concepts are provided. Allow time for children to think and to grow from manipulating objects to abstract algorisms.

11. Mental calculations do not use the same algorisms as paper and pencil activities. Guide children to identify patterns which simplify mental calculations. As common algorisms are taught, the teacher can help the children to identify patterns in

the numbers and to involve the children in using these patterns to structure algorisms which can be solved mentally. As an example, in multiplying 11×15, one can readily identify the partial products in the tens place to be the same digits as in the multiplicand because one multiplies by 1 unit and by 1 ten. Since the partial products are added in the product, the digits in the multiplicand can be added to find the number to be written in the tens place. The product is 165.

Student Competencies to be Attained

The role of the teacher in today's schools consists of guiding the learning of children in its manifold setting. She sets the stage for each child in a way to stimulate him in his desire to grow and prepares carefully the goals to be attained for each child. There is no specific grade level at which each child is expected to attain these competencies. Learning is dependent upon ability and motivation. Some competencies which we seek for our children are:

   I. The development of concepts
     a. The concept of number
     b. The concept of place value.
     c. The concept of a fraction
     d. The concept of measurement
  II. The development of the mathematical processes
     a. The four operations
     b. Language and relationships
     c. Laws, properties and generalizations
 III. The development of skills
     a. Understanding and knowing the basic facts for each operation through language and relationships
     b. Variation in algorisms for solving
     c. The accepted forms for solving
     d. The use of concrete and semiconcrete media
     e. Checking for accuracy
 IV. The development of precision of language
     a. The vocabulary of the processes
     b. Precision of mathematical terms
     c. Reading arithmetic with understanding
     d. Interpreting data in tables and graphs
  V. The development of problem skills: interpreting the problem by the use of
     a. Concrete aids
     b. Semiconcrete materials
     c. A statement of the facts given in the form of an equation
     d. Drawing conclusions and formulating generalizations
 VI. Development of an appreciation and of favorable attitudes toward mathematics
     a. The historical development of numbers
     b. The effect of culture on the growth of mathematics
     c. Discovering patterns in numbers
     d. The excitement and pleasure in working with numbers

The outcome of such a program depends upon how well each child has attained these competencies. The accomplishment of this task depends upon the teaching by teachers who understand children and arithmetic.

Planning a Lesson

A child's understanding of a topic in arithmetic is a matter of slow growth and requires time. The understandings are incomplete at first but gradually deepen and mature with guided experiences. Each teacher must plan each phase step by step so that pupils can move forward with confidence. If the teacher is resourceful, she plans each step carefully. The following organization identifies each stage in constructing a lesson plan. The outline is by no means complete.

I. What I want to teach.

The teacher makes a choice of a topic to be taught: for example, multiplying a 2-digit number by a 1-digit number with regrouping.

II. Why do I want to teach this topic?

The teacher must consider here the understandings which the children have for moving to the topic involving regrouping. She identifies the following reasons for the selection.

a. Children have a background in place value.

b. Children can perform examples in addition requiring regrouping using partial sums.

$$
\begin{array}{r} 57 \\ +36 \\ \hline \end{array}
\qquad
\begin{array}{r} 57 \\ +36 \\ \hline 13 \\ 80 \\ \hline 93 \end{array}
$$

c. Children can regroup in addition.

$$
\begin{array}{r} 1 \\ 69 \\ +27 \\ \hline 96 \end{array}
$$

d. Children can see relationships between addition and multiplication.

$$
\begin{array}{r} 6 \\ \times 3 \\ \hline \end{array}
\longrightarrow
\begin{array}{r} 6 \\ 6 \\ +6 \\ \hline 18 \end{array}
\qquad
\begin{array}{r} 27 \\ \times 3 \\ \hline \end{array}
\longrightarrow
\begin{array}{r} 27 \\ 27 \\ +27 \\ \hline 21 \\ 60 \\ \hline 81 \end{array}
\longrightarrow
\begin{array}{r} 2 \\ 27 \\ 27 \\ 27 \\ \hline 81 \end{array}
$$

e. Children are beginning to think in terms of place value in multiplication which will help them to write the products in terms of place value.

Units × units = units

Units × tens and tens × units = tens

$$
\begin{array}{r} 43 \\ 2 \\ \hline 86 \end{array}
\qquad
\begin{array}{l}
\text{units} \times \text{units} = \text{units} \\
2 \times 3 = 6 \\
\text{units} \times \text{tens} = \text{tens} \\
2 \times 4 = 8
\end{array}
$$

f. Children use the distributive property in learning the basic facts.

III. How will I present the topic?
  a. Using the language of multiplication.

$$3 \times 24 = N$$

3 groups of 24

24 to be added 3 times

  b. The use of the number line and other aids.
  c. Relationships: comparing partial sums and products.
  d. The use of place value.
  e. Use of the distributive property.
  f. Problems: solve in several ways.

IV. Evaluation
  a. Weaknesses in the teaching procedures.
  b. Appraisal of the success in obtaining the goals.
  c. Determining the extent of reteaching.
  d. Children's skill in thinking critically, performance, depth of insight and application.
  e. Has the child established favorable attitudes toward this topic and arithmetic as a whole.
  f. Use homework and assignments as a way to diagnose difficulties rather than a source for grades.

Each teacher must concern herself with the "how" and the "why" of teaching. If this is carefully done, the student will move into new situations, from one operation to another, without realizing that the content being presented is new. This can be accomplished when the program is planned and organized so that pupils can work individually and in small groups.

Understanding how children grow, their differences and how they learn are elements in a teacher's philosophy of education. However, the element which makes a teacher truly great is how she feels toward children; that is, she must have a positive attitude toward the child. The happiest days in the lives of children should be those they spend in school. It is in the power of each teacher to make school fascinating, challenging and interesting for each child.

Selected Text References

1. Corle, Clyde G., *Teaching Mathematics in the Elementary School,* New York: The Ronald Press Company, 1964. Chapters 1 and 2.
2. Dwight, Leslie A., *Modern Mathematics for the Elementary Teacher,* New York: Holt, Rinehart and Winston, Inc., 1966. Chapters 1 and 2.
3. Flournoy, Frances, *Elementary School Mathematics,* New York: The Center for Applied Research in Education, Inc., 1964. Chapter 1.
4. Grossnickle, Foster E., and Leo J. Brueckner, *Discovering Meanings in Elementary School Mathematics,* New York: Holt, Rinehart and Winston, Inc., 1963. Chapters 1 and 2.
5. Marks, John L., C. Richard Purdy and Lucien B. Kinney, *Teaching Elementary School Mathematics for Understanding,* New York: McGraw-Hill Book Company, Inc., 1955. Chapters 1 and 2.
6. Shipp, Donald, and Sam Adams, *Developing Arithmetic Concepts and Skills,* Englewood Cliffs, N. J.; Prentice-Hall, Inc., 1964. Chapter 1.

Selected Readings from the Arithmetic Teacher, an official journal of the National Council of Teachers of Mathematics, 1201 Sixteenth Street, N.W., Washington, D.C. 20036.

1. Adler, Irving, "The Cambridge Conference Report: Blueprint or Fantasy?" *13:*179-186, March 1966.
2. Clark, John R., "Looking Ahead at Instruction in Arithmetic," *8:*388-394, December, 1961.
3. Corle, Clyde G., "The New Mathematics," *11:* 242-247, April, 1964.
4. Fehr, Howard F., "Sense and Nonsense in a Mathematics Program," *13:* 83-91, February, 1966.
5. Inbody, Donald, "Helping Parents Understand New Mathematics," *11:* 530-537, December, 1964.
6. Marks, John, "The Uneven Progress of the Revolution in Elementary School Mathematics," *10:* 474-478, December, 1963.
7. Sueltz, Ben A., "A Time for Decision," *8:* 274-280, October, 1961.
8. Weaver, Fred J., "The School Mathematics Study Group Project in Elementary School Mathematics," *8:* 32-35, January, 1961.

Chapter II

Teaching Beginning Numbers

Children come to school knowing something about enumeration. Some can *say* the names of the numbers in their proper order to 5 or 6; some can *say* the names of the numbers in their proper order to 100. Children talk in terms of fractions. "I'll give you half a piece of this candy." If the teacher listens further, she might hear, "I'll take the largest half" or "I'll give you the largest half." A boy was heard to say that he had 2 pennies in his pocket and that he had 2 more at home. He then added, "I've 4 pennies." The teacher, hearing this, asked, "How many are 2 and 2?" The child was at a loss for an answer because he needed to manipulate pennies or objects to know how many 2 and 2 are. One cannot assume that children understand because they can *say* the numerals. The teacher must find out how deep the meaning goes.

Many children entering school recognize groups of two, three and four. A girl in kindergarten said as she looked at a group of four. "If I put one more with four, that will be how old I am."

The child who comes to school knowing how to add and to subtract must be planned for as carefully as the one who is just beginning numbers. His experiences must be broadened; enrichment activities which will develop insight into the many possible ways of performing the processes must be provided. The process of good teaching is guiding the child *to discover* possible solutions to a problem in arithmetic. In discovering solutions to the problems to be solved, one soon learns that there is *no one* correct way to solve a problem. There may be as many ways as there are children in a class. The solution of the problem might range from manipulating concrete materials (counting objects) to solving the problem mentally. This difference in the approach to the solution of a problem should indicate to the teacher that she is confronted with many levels of arithmetic understanding. Knowing this, the teacher begins to evaluate each student for understanding of arithmetical concepts and processes and then to plan the program in numbers for individuals and small groups.

Readiness Phase

Enumeration

Using number names in their proper order is essential to any progress with numbers. As the child says each number, either with the help of the teacher or alone, he points to each one of the objects he is counting (one-to-one correspondence). For example, if he is counting the children in the first row, he will point at or touch each child as he says, "1, 2, 3" and so on. At this point, the teacher is concerned that the child learns the numeral names in order. The child counts everything in the room: desks, windows, children, pictures, tables, chairs and the numerous objects which the teacher provides. The child is matching a number to a window and so on. This is rational counting.

To strengthen the concept of one-to-one correspondence, students are asked to match objects or elements of one set with objects or elements of a second set. This will involve such activities as giving a sheet of paper to each child or placing a book on each desk. The essential element of this matching is that the pairing comes out even. For every member of Set A, there is a corresponding member in Set B. Match the two teams below. Is a one-to-one correspondence present?

Set A	Set B
Jim	Jack
Bob	Ray
Bill	Rob
John	Mark
Ed	Dave

When the child has learned the names of the numbers, he is ready to think in terms of the real purpose of saying number names, that is, establishing quantity. A child points to some books on a table and says, "I'll count them." He goes through the process of saying, "1, 2, 3" and so on as he touches each book. When he has completed his counting, the teacher may ask, "How many books are there?" "What does the last number name that you say tell you?" The teacher is now developing with the children the concept that one counts to find the number in a given group. Enumeration is counting to find a quantity. What is the cardinal number property of each of the following sets? In using the numeral 4 for Set A, notice that we shift from the concrete to the abstract idea of 4-ness.

Set A	Set B	Set C
□ △	□ △ ○	△ ▯ ○ □
▯ ○	○ ▯	▱ ⊕ ▷ ⋈

By matching (one-to-one correspondence) the elements of Set A with the numbers (1, 2, 3, 4) we shall be able to answer the question "How many?" The last number matched gives the cardinal number of the set.

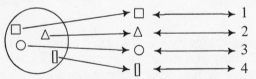

Sets can be any one of many objects and things in the classroom. The door to the classroom can be used as a set with one member, or a basket with two balls used as a set with two members. Children are given blocks of wood or other materials to handle which they will use to establish the concept of number. By grouping the blocks, they can structure sets having different cardinal values. A one-to-one correspondence between the members of two sets leads to the concept of equivalent sets (sets having the same number of members), which in turn establishes the concept that sets having the same number of members must also have the same cardinal number. It is by this means that teachers help children to understand the natural order of numbers. As one looks carefully at the sequence of numbers, it is readily apparent that the sequence builds on the concept of "one more."

○	1	
○ ○	2	2 is 1 more than 1
○ ○ ○	3	3 is 1 more than 2

One cannot stress too much the point that the readiness phase is mostly an oral and a manipulative approach for a large group of children and is not limited to paper and pencil work. As soon as children can say the numerals in their proper order, they are ready to write them. The name of the numeral and the numeral are used together. To know what 3 is, children must be able to hear the word, recognize the word, interpret the meaning of the number as 3 and to write it. It is difficult for many primary children to understand the difference between "numeral" and "number." However, the teacher should know this difference. Numerals are the symbols used to express quantity, while number is the concept, the mathematical idea. Which is larger, numeral 7 or 10? (7). Which is larger, number 3 or 7? (7).

Important Ideas Begun

1. Saying the numeral names in order.
2. The concept of one-to-one correspondence
3. One counts to find how many (cardinal numbers)
4. The last voiced number tells how many in all
5. Writing the numerals

Separating Quantities

A child must have some understanding of quantity before he can separate a smaller number of articles from a larger number of articles. To take 3 blocks from a pile of 8 blocks, he does not count the total pile of blocks, but rather, separates the given quantity of 3 from the group. When children are unsure of themselves, they will ask if this is 3 as they hold up the quantity selected. If children cannot perform this activity, it is an indication that more experiences in establishing one-to-one relationships are necessary.

Practice for this and other activities is contained within the routine of the classroom:

Mike, please get 3 chairs from the group of chairs in the back of the room.
Mary, we are in need of 7 pieces of paper. Please get them from the shelf.
Jim, choose 4 boys for your team.

Comparison

Children begin to compare things long before they come to school. Many come to school using a vocabulary of many and more, larger and smaller, longer and shorter and others. Comparison is necessary in answering the questions of how many more or how many less and how much more and how much less.

How many more chairs are there than children?
How many more children are there in this row than in that row?
I have three more than Jack.
Jack has three less than I.

Sets may be compared directly and the set with more or less identified. Set A can be identified as having two elements more than Set B, or that Set B has two elements less than Set A.

Set A   □   □   □   □   □   □   □
            ↕   ↕   ↕   ↕   ↕
Set B   ○   ○   ○   ○   ○

When children understand counting, we are no longer comparing the sets by matching; each set is counted and the corresponding numbers are compared (5 and 7 are compared). They should note that the cardinal set of 7 is 2 more than the cardinal set of 5.

Set A   □   □   □   □   □   □   □

         ↑   ↑   ↑   ↑   ↑   ↑   ↑

         1   2   3   4   5   6   7

         ↓   ↓   ↓   ↓   ↓

Set B   O   O   O   O   O

The symbols > (greater than) and < (less than) have been introduced to many children by the close of the second grade. Exercises such as the following may be used to strengthen the concept of number:

$$4 \; < \; 7 \longrightarrow 4 \text{ is less than } 7$$
$$12 \; > \; 8 \longrightarrow 12 \text{ is greater than } 8$$
$$\square \; < \; 5 \longrightarrow \text{What number(s) is less than 5?}$$

Grouping

The identification of quantity (2-ness of 2 and so on) is not done by counting but through a recognition of the number of each group. Recognition comes through wide experience in counting and in practice in identifying groups. Having children think through their responses aloud and proving their answers with the use of objects is a good practice. "Show me" pocket charts can be made by the children, and, as the teacher or someone else presents a grouping to the class, the children select the proper number card and place it in the "show me" pocket chart. In this way, the teacher can identify immediately the responses of a particular child. The children can also be asked to write the number on paper or on the chalkboard.

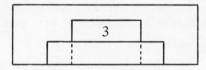

Oral Problems

Short oral statements containing quantities are useful in teaching the child to look for arithmetic meaning in the spoken word. This type of exercise prepares the child for solving written or oral story problems. When children are confronted with written or oral story problems daily, the number meanings they are learning are being put to use. The purpose of learning any number fact (for example, 3 + 4 = 7) is to use it in solving a problem and not to repeat it in a rote fashion. The test of arithmetic understanding lies in one's ability to solve problems and not in one's ability to parrot basic facts. The following statements are significant beginning problems.

Put 4 spools on my desk.
Write the numeral 7 on the chalkboard.
How many ducks are in this picture?
How many balls? Cover 1. How many do you now see?
I am thinking of the number between 4 and 6. What is the number? Point to the number line.
Are 3 apples more than 5 apples?

Important Ideas Begun

1. Separating a smaller group from a larger group.
2. Comparing two groups of objects.
3. Identifying a group without counting.
4. Solving simple oral problems.

Learning Other Names For Numbers

To this point, the pupils have studied the numbers to 10 in four ways.

1. They have found the quantity of a group by counting. They have noted that the last number voiced tells how many are in a particular group. Illustration:

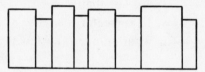

How many books are on this shelf? What does the last number tell us?

2. They have studied quantity in the sense of selecting or reproducing a number quantity from a larger group. Illustration:

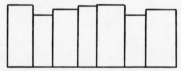

Get 5 books from the set of books on the table.

3. They have compared the sizes of groups, and in each comparison they have answered the questions of how many more or how many less. Illustration:

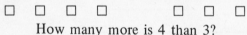

How many more is 4 than 3?

4. They have studied groups in order to recognize quantity without counting. Illustration:

A card may be flashed before a child or a group of students. The question is asked, "How many circles did you see?"

The children are now at a point at which they can begin to analyze each number in relation to the smaller groups which structure it. For example, children learn that 4 is not always 2 and 2, but that it might also be 3 and 1 and 1 and 3. Subtraction is also included in the analysis since 4 is also that number which when 1 is taken away always leaves 3. In the language of sets, we shall discuss the "subsets" of 4. Two and 2, 3 and 1 and 1 and 3 are subsets of 4. The teacher must be aware of the fact that for many children this is an oral approach with very little written activity. It is a time for using concrete materials. Before written work is attempted, this approach is repeated with emphasis on written work.

Relationship between combining sets and addition is developed by manipulating objects and setting up the abstract sentence or equation. Many names for numbers and how they are written are established in this fashion. The number combinations may be called "basic facts," "number pairs" or "subsets." The important concept to establish is that a number can have many names.

$$\square \qquad \triangle \qquad \square\triangle \qquad \text{Union of 2 sets}$$
$$1 \;+\; 1 \;=\; 2 \qquad\quad \text{Number equation}$$

Another name for 2 is 1 and 1, or 2 = 1 + 1.

$$\square \qquad \triangle\text{O} \qquad \square\triangle\text{O} \qquad \text{or} \qquad \triangle\text{O} \qquad \square \qquad \triangle\text{O}\square$$
$$1 \;+\; 2 \;=\; 3 \qquad\qquad\qquad 2 \;+\; 1 \;=\; 3$$

Another name for 3 is 1 + 2 = 3, or 2 + 1 = 3.

Because we cannot think of addition without thinking about subtraction, some examples are included to show the relationship. In subtraction, the action completed in addition is undone. This action is referred to as the "inverse operation." For every basic fact in addition, there are two corresponding subtraction facts when the addends are different. If they are alike, there is but one fact.

$$\begin{array}{cc} 1 & 2 \\ \underline{+\,1} \longrightarrow & \underline{-\,1} \\ 2 & 1 \end{array} \qquad \text{Note that the sum becomes the minuend and an addend becomes the subtrahend.}$$

$$\begin{array}{ccc} 2 & 3 & 3 \\ \underline{+\,1} \longrightarrow & \underline{-\,2} \quad \text{and} & \underline{-\,1} \\ 3 & 1 & 2 \end{array}$$

When pictures are used to illustrate, they may be crossed out to indicate that the object was removed.

$$2 \;-\; 1 \;=\; 1 \qquad\qquad 3 \;-\; 1 \;=\; 2$$
$$\text{O} \quad \boxtimes \qquad\qquad\quad \text{O} \quad \text{O} \quad \boxtimes$$

Children have used many different aids in developing the meanings of numbers. Beginning with concrete aids such as blocks, a 10-button abacus, milk caps and so on, they are guided by the teacher to discover meanings about a number, for example, 4. The various ways in which the questions are asked will give varied language experiences for the child. Hearing these questions orally many times over will eventually help him in interpreting meanings in the fundamental processes of arithmetic.

The teacher asks, "What happens to 4 when it is divided into two equal groups?" The children manipulating their concrete aids, divide 4 into two equal groups. They discover that it is 2 and 2. The teacher discusses this operation with the children. "Have you ever divided an apple into two parts?" "Have you ever divided marbles into two groups?" "Have you divided candy with your friend?" "What do you remember about these parts?" "Are these parts always the same size?" Use a cardboard and 4 clothespins to show the subsets of 4.

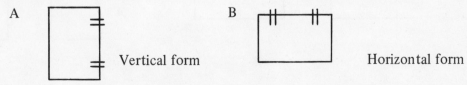

A   Vertical form   B   Horizontal form

What is 4 now? How can we tell this story? The children are guided to see that in A and B the oral statement is 2 and 2 is 4. Children often ask how to write the story on the chalkboard. The teacher carefully writes the vertical form for A and the horizontal form for B but does not *require* the children to do so.

A   2

        2

        4   B   2 and 2 is 4   Read, "2 and 2 is 4."

The verb *is* emphasizes the relationship of 2 and 2 to 4: 2 and 2 *is* another name for 4. However, the statement 2 and 2 *are* 4 is also used. The language used to express these findings is important. The following statements can also be used to describe this division of 4.

1. Two groups of 2 is 4. *Two groups of 2 is 4* emphasizes that 2 and 2 is another name for 4. (How many groups of 2 are there? Two.) The teacher realizes that this is the language of multiplication, but does not point this out unless questioned by a child. It is important for children to hear the statement because of the verbal distinction between addition and multiplication.
2. Two 2's are 4. (Explanation the same as No. 1 above.)
3. How many 2's are 4? Two.

To complete the analysis of 4, children are asked to *tell* another story about 4. Using their concrete materials, they discover that 4 is also:

A
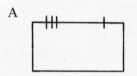
Read: 3 and 1 is another name for 4.
        3 and 1 is 4.
        3 + 1 = 4

B
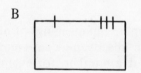
Read: 1 and 3 is another name for 4.
        1 and 3 is 4.
        1 + 3 = 4

Guide the children to discover the commutative property of addition by asking them to look at the arrangement of the clothespins as the card is reversed. Does the sum change when the order of the objects are changed? 3 + 1 = 4 and 1 + 3 = 4.

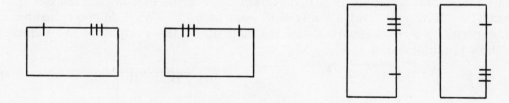

The teacher continues to broaden the language of oral arithmetic by developing with the children the following statements:

1. 3 and what number is 4?   3 + □ = 4.
2. What number and 1 is 4?   □ + 1 = 4.
3. I am thinking of two numbers which make 4. What are they? This is a good question because it permits several answers: 2 + 2 = 4, 3 + 1 = 4, 1 + 3 = 4.

To vary the activity from counting blocks, counting frames, a cardboard and clothespins and cutouts, the students should be introduced to the "whole number line." Each of the subsets for 4 should be represented. After which numeral does 4 come? Before what numeral does 4 come?

The Whole Number Line

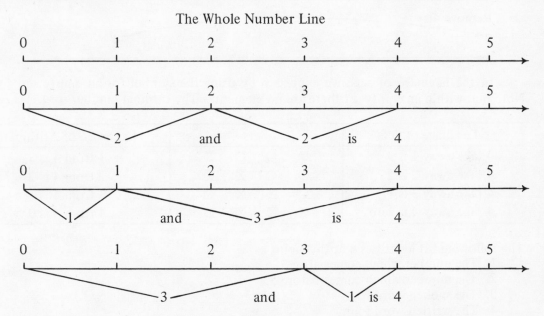

The wise teacher will encourage the children to discover the commutative property with other numbers. There is no point to dwell on the name of the property at this time. In addition to the property, children may discover the generalization that when 1 is added to a number, 6 + 1, the sum is always the next number in the counting series, 6 + 1 = 7. What number added to 3 is 4? Check the number line using questions such as: How many more than 3 is 4? How many less than 4 is 3? What is the next number in the counting series when 1 is added to 3? Many of these patterns are identified during the oral approach, but they can be left until the development of the fundamental operations for emphasis.

Subtraction is the operation which "undoes" addition. Sometimes the discussion comes about by the loss of a stick, a block or a clothespin. The teacher takes this opportunity to introduce the relationship of addition and subtraction by guiding the children to discover number stories with respect to subtraction. They manipulate objects to discover the basic subtraction facts and then use the number line for verification. At what point on the number line does one stop if 1, 2, 3 or 4 objects are removed?

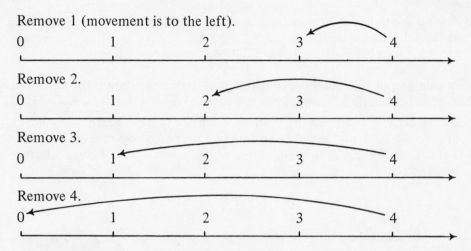

Remove 1 (movement is to the left).

Remove 2.

Remove 3.

Remove 4.

In the language of sets, we express 0 by using the symbol for an empty set, Note that within an empty set there are no elements. The cardinal number for } { is zero.

Language of Sets	Sets				Language of Arithmetic
4 take away 1 is 3	O	O	O	⊠	1 from 4 is 3
4 take away 2 is 2	O	O	⊠	⊠	2 from 4 is 2
4 take away 3 is 1	O	⊠	⊠	⊠	3 from 4 is 1
4 take away 4 is zero	⊠	⊠	⊠	⊠	4 from 4 is 0

The following list identifies 4 at this point as:
1. The number which comes after 3.
2. The number which comes before 5.
3. The spoken word four.
4. The written word four.
5. The numeral 4.
6. 2 and 2, two groups of 2, two 2's.
7. 3 and 1 and 1 and 3.

Good teaching is guiding children to *discover* meanings. The teacher challenges each child by asking similar questions about the other numbers until all have been studied between 1 and 10 and the teens.
1. How can we find out about 6?
2. What happens if we divide 6 into two equal groups?
3. How is the story stated?
4. Can it be said in more than one way?

$$\begin{array}{ccccccc} 3 & 4 & 2 & 5 & 1 & 6 & 0 \\ \underline{3} & \underline{2} & \underline{4} & \underline{1} & \underline{5} & \underline{0} & \underline{6} \\ 6 & 6 & 6 & 6 & 6 & 6 & 6 \end{array}$$

The odd numbers are treated in the same manner as even numbers except for the first step of division. The children discover that 3, 5 (any odd number) cannot be divided equally into two groups. The pattern of odd numbers discovered by children because of previous experiences in dividing even numbers is:

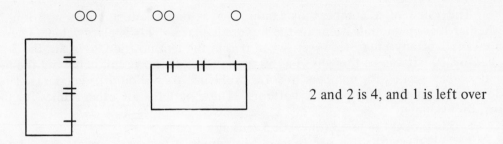

2 and 2 is 4, and 1 is left over

Now ask the children to group 5 into two groups. How many ways can you group 5?

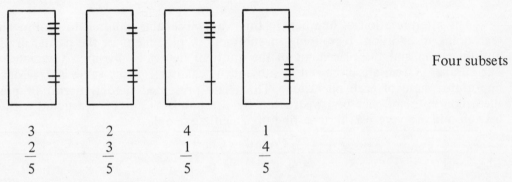

Four subsets

3	2	4	1
2	3	1	4
5	5	5	5

As the numbers increase along the whole number line, the number of basic facts increase up to and including 10. There are more basic facts or subsets in 6 than in 4; there are more basic facts in 10 than in 9.

5 basic facts in 6   3 basic facts in 4

3	4	2	5	1		2	3	1
3	2	4	1	5		2	1	3
6	6	6	6	6		4	4	4

8 basic facts for 9   9 basic facts for 10

5	4	6	3	7	2	8	1		5	6	4	7	3	8	2	9	1
4	5	3	6	2	7	1	8		5	4	6	3	7	2	8	1	9
9	9	9	9	9	9	9	9		10	10	10	10	10	10	10	10	10

Readiness for the subsets in addition with sums more than 10 begins with a systematic study of the numbers that we call the teens. These are discussed in Chapter III, Addition of Whole Numbers. The analysis of the teens as the children explore them is identical with the study of the basic facts in numbers 10 or less.

In our Hindu Arabic numeration system (Decimal System), 10 is the base. The base is simply the first collection of ones in any number series. In the units place, the collection repeats itself each time there are 10 units. 1, 2, 3, 4, 5, 6, 7, 8, 9, 10. The first collection, 10, states that there are no ones in the unit position and that there is one group of 10. The collection of 10 is used to form the next number in our series: 10 and 1 more are 11, 10 and 2 more are 12. This continues until 10 and 9 are reached. The next addition of 1 to 9 makes a collection of 10. There are now two collections of 10. This is written 20 (2 tens, no ones). When there is a collection of 10 tens, the collection is called 1 hundred.

The value of a number, for example, 5, is dependent upon its position, that is, whether it is in the units, tens or the hundreds place. This is place value. The number 5 means 5 of anything. However, when it is in the tens position, as in 50, the 5 is multiplied by 10. It can be thought of as 50 ones or as 5 tens. As children write the numerals and as they work with numbers to solve problems, they should be encouraged to break down each number into possible patterns. These patterns are other names for the number, for example:

1. 53—thought of as 53 (ones) or 5 tens and 3 ones.
2. 242—thought of as 242 (ones); 2 hundreds, 4 tens and 2 ones; or 24 tens and 2 ones.
3. 305—thought of as 305 (ones); 3 hundreds, no tens and 5 ones; or 30 tens and 5 ones.

The interpretation of numbers in this way will enable children to find meaning for regrouping in addition, regrouping in subtraction, placement of the partial products in multiplication and the placement of the quotient figures in division. Characteristics of our number system are discussed in subsequent chapters. Place value is developed as an important phase of each operation. The chart presented here is useful in presenting these concepts and can be constructed by the pupils. Charts constructed with flannel background are very useful in setting up specific examples.

Counting Chart									
1	2	3	4	5	6	7	8	9	10
11	12	13	14	15	16	17	18	19	20
21	22	23	24	25	26	27	28	29	30
31	32	33	34	35	36	37	38	39	40
41	42	43	44	45	46	47	48	49	50
51	52	53	54	55	56	57	58	59	60
61	62	63	64	65	66	67	68	69	70
71	72	73	74	75	76	77	78	79	80
81	82	83	84	85	86	87	88	89	90
91	92	93	94	95	96	97	98	99	100

1. Note the placement of the numbers.
2. What is 23? (2 tens and 3 ones).
3. What number comes after 16? 29?

Cardinal and Ordinal Numbers

Number names and their symbols express two ideas, cardinal and ordinal. The cardinal idea is that of *quantity*, how many in a group. The ordinal idea is that of place, (position) and indicates *which one*.

Cardinal ideas:
How many chairs do we need?
How many children are there in our room?
Mary is 7 years old.
Jack is 58 inches tall.
My book weighs 2 pounds.
I have 2 hands.

Ordinal ideas:

My telephone number is Geranium 6–4532.
Jill's room number is 37.
Set the dial to Channel 12.
Find page 13 in our reader.
My birthday is July 4th.
I am third in line for a drink of water.

Some Important Ideas Begun

1. One-to-one correspondence.
2. Number sequence.
3. Meaning of numeral and number.
4. Number as a set.
5. The concept of "family."
6. Combining sets.
7. Separating sets.
8. Cardinal and ordinal numbers.
9. Writing the equation.
10. Relationship of addition and subtraction

Sets In The Elementary School

Sets have already been introduced in the previous presentation. It is not the purpose here to discuss sets in detail, but to help one recall previous work with sets. This can also be said about the basic mathematics involved in such a text as this. No effort is made to develop mathematical concepts in their abstract form except where it is necessary in the "methods" development; this writer is dealing with methodology.

Set is an undefined term in mathematics just as *point, line* and *plane* are undefined. Each of us has an idea of what the word means. It implies to us a group of books on a shelf, a set of dishes or a collection of objects. In each case, a description has been stated. The collection of objects described in a set is called *members* or *elements* of the set. *Braces* are used to enclose the members of the set.

Braces → $\{ \ \square \quad \triangle \quad \bigcirc \ \}$ Members or elements of the set

Language: The set whose members (or elements) are a square, a triangle and a circle.

$\{ \ \square \quad \triangle \quad \bigcirc \ \}$ Members or elements of the set

Language: The set whose members are Dick, Jane, Lois, and Frank.

$\{ \ \text{Dick} \quad \text{Jane} \quad \text{Lois} \quad \text{Frank} \ \}$

Language: The set of whole numbers whose members are

$\{ \ 0, \ 1, \ 2, \ 3 \ \text{and} \ 4 \ \}$

Common Properties of Sets

1. **Number property:** The capital letter N written to the left of the set asks the question, "How many elements (members) are there in the set:"

$N \ \{ \ \square \ \bigcirc \ \triangle \ \}$

$N \ \{ \ \square \ \bigcirc \ \triangle \ \} \ = 3$

There are 3 elements in the set.

$$N \left\{ 2, 4, 6, 8 \right\} = 4$$

There are 4 elements in the set.

2. **Equivalence**: Sets having the same number of elements (the same number property) are equivalent.

$$A = N \left\{ \bigcirc \ \square \right\} = 2$$
$$B = \overline{N} \left\{ \triangle \ \triangledown \right\} = 2$$

Set A is equivalent to Set B. There is a one-to-one correspondence between the elements.

3. **Equal sets**: Two sets composed of identical elements.

$$\text{Set A} = \left\{ 1, 2, 3, 4 \right\}$$
$$\text{Set B} = \left\{ 3, 1, 4, 2 \right\}$$

Set A = Set B (Set A is equal to Set B). The order in which the elements appear does not affect the set. Since Set A = Set B, there is in reality only one set of members.

4. **Subsets**:   A set which is contained in another set.

a. Set A $= \left\{ 1, 2, 3 \right\}$

Set B $= \left\{ 1, 2, 3, 4, 5, 6 \right\}$

Set A is a subset of Set B. Set A $\subset$ Set B. The symbol for "is a subset of" is $\subset$.

b. Set A = The students in the third grade.

Set B = The boys in the third grade.

$$B \subset A$$

Language: Set B is a proper subset of Set A. Set B is a proper subset because Set A contains members not included in Set B.

c. Set C $= \left\{ 1, 2, 3 \right\}$. How many subsets in Set C?

$$\left\{ 1 \right\} \quad \left\{ 1, 2 \right\} \quad \left\{ 1, 2, 3 \right\}$$
$$\left\{ 2 \right\} \quad \left\{ 2, 3 \right\} \qquad \left\{ \ \right\} \qquad \text{empty set}$$
$$\left\{ 3 \right\} \quad \left\{ 1, 3 \right\}$$

Note that any set is a subset of itself. An empty set, $\left\{ \ \right\}$, is a subset of every set.

d. The number of subsets in a set. An empty set is a subset of every set except itself. A set with two elements, $\left\{ 1, 2 \right\}$ has four subsets.

$$\left\{ \ \right\}, \quad \left\{ 1 \right\}, \quad \left\{ 2 \right\}, \quad \left\{ 1, 2 \right\}$$

A set with three elements, a, b, c, has eight subsets. The base in each case is 2 (a single element set has two subsets). The power to which the base (2) is raised is determined by the number of elements in the set.

Therefore,

$$\text{Set A} = \left\{ a, b, c \right\} = 2^3 \text{ or 8 subsets.}$$
$$\text{Set B} = \left\{ \square \ \triangle \ T \ Z \right\} = 2^4 = 16 \text{ subsets.}$$

Operations on Sets

1. **Sets may be combined.** The symbol for the union of two sets is ∪. The union of two sets is a set composed of all elements contained in the two sets. This idea may be stated in the following form.

    Set A = {Bill, John, Mary}

    Set B = {Jim, Lois}

    A ∪ B = {Bill, John, Mary, Jim, Lois}

Language: The union of set A and set B is set C. The members of each set may be listed in describing the sets and their union.

Examples:

What is the union of set A and set B if

A = {△ ∟}

B = {○ □ ⊤}

A ∪ B = {△ ∟ ○ □ ⊤}

What is the union of set R and set W if

R = {1, 2, 3, 4, 5}

W = {6, 7, 8, 9}

R ∪ W = {1, 2, 3, 4, 5, 6, 7, 8, 9}

Language: The union of set R and set W is the set whose elements are 1, 2, 3, 4, 5, 6, 7, 8, 9.

What is the union of set T and Set S if

T = {3, 5, 7}

S = {2, 4, 6}

T ∪ S = {2, 3, 4, 5, 6}

What is the pattern in each of the previous sets? Do the sets have any elements in common? Sets which do not have any elements in common are called disjoint sets. Addition is related only to the union of disjoint sets.

There can be sets which have elements in common. In sets N and O, one of the members is common to both sets.

Example:

Set N = {Bill, George, Fred}

Set O = {Jack, Fred, Mike}

N ∪ O = {Bill, George, Fred, Jack, Mike}

Fred is a member of each set.

2. **Intersection of sets:** An operation which identifies the common elements in two sets. The symbol for intersection is ∩.

Set A		Set B		Set C
{Alice, Bob, Jim}	∩	{Fred, Bob, Ed}	=	{Bob}

If Sets A and B name two committees, Bob is the member common to each committee.

Language: The intersection of Set A, whose members are Alice, Bob, and Jim, and Set B, whose members are Fred, Bob and Ed, is Set C, whose member is Bob.

Set A ∩ Set B = Set C

A ∩ B = C. The intersection of Set A and Set B is Set C.

Set W   Set P   Set R

$\{\square \llcorner \triangle\}$ ∩ $\{\top \llcorner \triangle \bigcirc\}$ = $\{\llcorner \triangle\}$

Set R is the intersection of Set W and Set P.

Set A   = $\{3, 6, 9, 12\}$

Set B   = $\{6, 8, 10, 12\}$

A ∩ B = $\{6, 12\}$

Set A   = $\{5, 7, 9, 11\}$

Set B   = $\{6, 8, 10, 12\}$

A ∩ B = $\{\quad\}$

The intersection of Set A and Set B. is an empty set. (No common elements.)

3. **Sets may be separated.**

a. Application of one-to-one comparison:

Set A   = $\{\square \quad \square \quad \square \quad \square \quad \square\}$

Set B   = $\{\square \quad \square \quad \square\}$

Set B is compared with a subset of Set A. The number of elements not in the subset is Set C, $\{\square, \square\}$.

Set B ∪ Set C = Set A

$\{\square\square\square\} \cup \{\square\square\} = \{\square\square\square\square\square\}$

The cardinal number of each set is:

N $\{\square\square\square\square\square\}$ - N $\{\square\square\square\}$ = N $\{\square\square\}$

5 - 3 = 2

3 + 2 = 5

Set B ∪ Set C = Set A.

b. Take-away approach: On the take-away approach, instead of matching objects and objects, a subset of a set is removed by counting.

Set A = $\{\triangle \triangle \triangle \atop \triangle \triangle \triangle\}$

Count out 4 from Set A.

$\{\triangle \triangle \triangle \atop \triangle \triangle \triangle\}$

The set $\{\triangle \triangle\}$ remains.

The cardinal number for each set is:

6 - 4 = 2

Definition of Terms and Their Symbols

1. **Empty set:** A set which does not contain any elements. An empty set is a subset of every set except itself. Its symbols are { } or ϕ.

2. **Finite set:** A set whose elements may be counted or it may be an empty set.

3. **Infinite set:** A set which cannot be counted. (Not finite.)

4. **Braces:** Symbols used to enclose sets.

5. **Subsets:** If every element of a Set A is also an element of a Set B, then Set A is a subset of Set B. If Set A contains fewer members than Set B, Set A is a proper subset of Set B.

Application of Sets

1. **Identifying sets:**

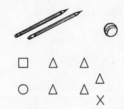

Ask the children to identify each kind of object.

Ask the pupils to draw a line around all the pencils, the ball and so on.

Place cutouts on a flannel board. Group the objects which are alike by using a string. Are the shapes within the string alike?

Discuss sets of objects which children find in the room. How many members are there in each set?

2. **Counting:**

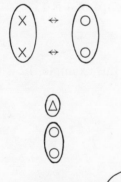

Matching two sets, one-to-one correspondence, to determine equivalent sets. Is the set of circles equivalent to the crosses? (Yes.)

To develop the concept of 1.

How many members (objects) in this set? Write the numeral 1.

How many members in this set? Write the numeral 2.

Draw a line around each designated set

2,   1,   3,   4

3. **Combining sets:**

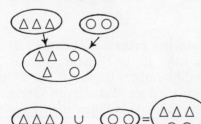

Ask the children to combine two sets of object by moving objects from one set to the other.

$$3 + 2 = 5$$
3 and 2 is 5

4. Separating sets:

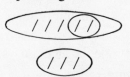

Remove 2 pencils from the set.

$5 - 2 = 3$

5 minus 2 is 3.

5. Combining equivalent sets (multiplication):

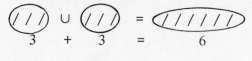

$3 \quad + \quad 3 \quad = \quad 6$

Repeated addition.

Introduce the symbol for union of sets, $\cup$.

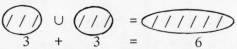

$3 \quad + \quad 3 \quad = \quad 6$

Multiplication

How many sets are there?

How many in each set?

$2 \times 3 = 6$

Two sets of 3 is 6.

Two groups of 3 is 6.

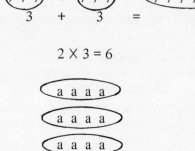

How many sets are there?

How many in each set?

Three sets of 4 is 12.

Three groups of 4 is 12.

6. Intersection of two sets:

Finding a common denominator:

Find the first five multiples of 3 and 4. In this example, 12 is the lowest common denominator.

Example:

$1 \times 3 = 3$	$1 \times 4 = 4$
$2 \times 3 = 6$	$2 \times 4 = 8$
$3 \times 3 = 9$	$3 \times 4 = 12$
$4 \times 3 = 12$	$4 \times 4 = 16$
$5 \times 3 = 15$	$5 \times 4 = 20$

Set A = 3, 6, 9, 12, 15

Set B = 4, 8, 12, 16, 20

Set A $\cap$ Set B = 12

Set has a special usage in the elementary mathematics program. It defines a collection or a group of objects in a concise and meaningful way. In the elementary grades, one speaks of the "set of whole numbers," the "set of odd numbers below 16" or a "set of numbers from 5 to 15," giving the restrictions of a specified set. Placing restriction upon sets has some of the elements of challenge and can stimulate children with a desire to learn.

The concept of "group" as used throughout this book could have been called "set." These terms have been used interchangeably to reinforce this idea. The teacher and the children should discuss "Why is this a group?" "Why do you wish to call this a set?" If she wishes to place some emphasis on sets in her teaching, she can relate the language of sets to the content of each chapter which follows. For example, in combining a group of three objects and a group of four objects, she can develop the concept of addition through the union of sets as:

Set A   Set B   Set C

$$ (\triangle\ \square\ \bigcirc)\quad \cup\quad (\triangle\ \diamond\ \mathsf{T}\ \mathsf{L})\quad =\quad (\triangle\ \square\ \bigcirc\ \triangle\ \diamond\ \mathsf{T}\ \mathsf{L}) $$

The union of Set A and B is Set C. If she wishes to introduce the concept of quantity (cardinality), the equation $3 + 4 = 7$ can be developed.

There are many words in arithmetic which, when understood, help to clarify thinking and expression. Good judgment in the selection and development of the vocabulary in arithmetic is essential. The following chapters present and clarify terms with which the teacher should be familiar in order to develop a significant program in arithmetic.

Questions, Activities and Discussion Topics

1. What is the distinction between even and odd numbers?
2. What teaching aids would you use to develop the concept of subsets?
3. Numbers have many names. Explain this statement.
4. What is the distinction between "numeral" and "number"?
5. How can you develop the concept of quantity with children in kindergarten and the first grade?
6. Check several series of textbooks used by children in the public schools for their treatment of beginning numbers. Are there greater emphases on certain aspects of their approach?
7. Make up five sets using set notation. For each of these sets, write an equivalent set, an equal set and a subset.
8. Solve for the total number of subsets in each of the five sets in Question 7.
9. Discuss the idea of subsets as applied to the basic facts in addition.
10. What daily experiences involve one-to-one correspondence?

Selected Text References

1. Banks, J. Houston, *Elementary School Mathematics*, Boston: Allyn and Bacon, Inc., 1966. Chapter 1.
2. DeMay, Amy J., *Guiding Beginners in Arithmetic*, Evanston, Ill.: Row, Peterson and Company, 1957. Chapters 1–5.
3. Dwight, Leslie A., *Modern Mathematics for the Elementary Teacher*, New York: Holt, Rinehart and Winston, Inc., 1966. Chapter 4.
4. Grossnickle, Foster E., and Leo J. Brueckner, *Discovering Meanings in Elementary School Mathematics*, New York: Holt, Rinehart and Winston, Inc., 1963. Chapter 5.
5. Kramer, Klaas, *The Teaching of Elementary School Mathematics*, Boston: Allyn and Bacon, Inc., 1966. Chapter 6.
6. Spencer, Peter Lincoln, and Marguerite Brydegaard, *Building Mathematical Competence in the Elementary School*, New York: Holt, Rinehart and Winston, Inc., 1966. Chapters 4 and 6.
7. Swenson, Esther, *Teaching Arithmetic to Children*, New York: The Macmillan Company, 1964. Chapter 4.

Selected Readings from the <u>Arithmetic</u> <u>Teacher</u>

1. Beard, Virginia, "Mathematics in Kindergarten," *9:* 22–25, January, 1962.
2. Botts, Truman, "Numbers, Sets and Counting," *8:* 281–286, October, 1961.
3. Brace, Alec, and L. Doyal Nelson, "The Preschool Child's Concept of Number," *12:* 126–133, February, 1965.
4. Clary, Robert C., "Teaching Aids for Elementary School Arithmetic," *13:* 135–136, February, 1966.
5. Fisher, Alan A., "The Peg Board—A Useful Aid in Teaching Arithmetic," *8:* 186–188, April, 1961.
6. Heard, Ida Mae, "Developing Concepts of Time and Temperature," *8:* 124–126, March, 1961.
7. Michalov, Mary, "The Versatile Number Runner," *8:* 182–186, April, 1961.
8. Rasmussen, Don, and Lore Rasmussen, "The Miquon Mathematics Program," *9:* 188–192, April, 1962.

Chapter III

Addition of Whole Numbers

Addition is the process of putting together two or more disjoint sets. In the discussion of sets, this "putting together" is called "union" and the symbol used to designate this action is ∪. Both addition and union are operations but addition is an operation on numbers while union is an operation on sets. Numbers are added, but sets are combined.

We have seen that numbers are ordered and related in a specific way. It is possible to describe any two numbers by using the terms "greater than," "less than" or "equal to." $(13 > 8)$, $(7 < 18)$ and $(6 = 6)$. If we begin with 0 and add 1, the collection is 1. Each time 1 is added to a number, the collection is the next number in the set of numbers. The elements for the set of natural numbers begin with the number 1 and they are spoken of as the set of counting numbers. The set of whole numbers begins with 0, for example, 0, 1, 2, 3, 4 and so on.

The concept of putting like things together is present throughout arithmetic. The reason for finding a common denominator in the addition of fractions with different denominators is to conform to this concept.

$$\begin{array}{r} 1/2 \\ +\ 1/3 \\ \hline \end{array} \rightarrow \begin{array}{r} 3/6 \\ 2/6 \\ \hline 5/6 \end{array}$$

Addition and multiplication are binary operations because only two terms can be combined at a time. If three addends are to be added, we may add any two and then add the sum to the third addend. For example, in $4 + 7 + 6$, we may add $4 + 7 = 11$. We then add $11 + 6 = 17$. Parentheses are used to indicate the pair of addends to be added first, for example, $(4 + 7) + 6 = 11 + 6 = 17$. Addition as an operation is a way of thinking about adding two numbers to produce a third.

The addition process must obey certain properties and principles. To understand addition, one must understand these laws so well that they are a part of the approach in interpreting the process. An understanding of these laws has much to do with the manner in which addition is taught. The following properties and principles are presented as a review of background in arithmetic for the teacher.

Commutative Property of Addition

The order in which two numbers are added does not affect the sum. Many teachers in the past used the coined expression "reversing numbers" in explaining this action:

$$6 + 7 = 7 + 6 \qquad\qquad 36 + 43 = 43 + 36$$
$$13 = 13 \qquad\qquad\qquad 79 = 79$$

The idea may be generalized in the following form:

a + b = b + a   when a and b are elements of the set of whole numbers

Associative Property of Addition

Since addition is a binary operation, if three or more addends are to be added, pairs to be added must be selected in sequence. This property involves the grouping of the addends without changing the order.

$$(8 + 13) + 4 = 8 + (13 + 4)$$

If the order of numerals is changed, before the pairing, the commutative property has been introduced. The following steps interpret the thought process involved:

8 + (9 + 2) = N	Associative property
8 + 2 + 9 = N	Commutative property
(8 + 2) + 9 = N	Associative property
10 + 9 = 19	

This idea may be generalized in the following form:

(a + b) + c = a + (b + c) when a, b and c are elements of the set of whole numbers

Closure Property of Addition

When addition is applied to the set of whole numbers, the sum is always a member of this set. With any number that we select from the set of whole numbers, if we add another number from this set, the sum will also be a member of this set. The set of numbers in the set of whole numbers is infinite.

$$5 + 6 = 11, \qquad 35 + 14 = 49, \qquad 365 + 481 = 846$$

If a and b are members of the set of whole numbers, a + b will be a member of this set. We then say that the set of whole numbers is closed with respect to addition.

Identity Element

When 0 is added to any number, the sum is the number. Zero is the identity element for addition.

$$4 + 0 = 4, \quad 23 + 0 = 23, \quad 0 + 62 = 62$$

The idea may be generalized in the following form:

a + 0 = a and 0 + a = a

Expanded Notation

Numbers have many names. When 36 is written as 30 + 6 or 20 + 16, we have given other names to 36. The number 36 has been expanded.

Even Numbers

If a set of objects can be divided into two equivalent subsets, subsets having the same cardinal numbers, then the set is even. The sum of two even numbers is an even number and the sum of two odd numbers is an even number.

$$2 + 4 = 6, \qquad 14 + 28 = 42, \qquad 236 + 124 = 360$$
$$3 + 7 = 10, \qquad 17 + 29 = 46, \qquad 175 + 267 = 442$$

Odd Numbers

If a set of objects cannot be divided into two equivalent subsets, the set is odd. The sum of an even number and an odd number is an odd number.

$$4 + 7 = 11, \qquad 21 + 16 = 37, \qquad 167 + 214 = 381$$

Compensation

The principle of balancing the addends by adding a number to one addend and subtracting the same number from the second addend is compensation.

$$8 + 7 = (8 + 2) + (7 - 2) = 10 + 5 = 15$$
$$324 + 187 = (324 - 13) + (187 + 13) = 311 + 200 = 511$$

The set of digits for a given number system determines the number of possible combinations that occur for that system. Since there are 10 basic digits in our number system — 0, 1, 2, 3, 4, 5, 6, 7, 8, 9 — the number of combinations possible is 100. In the first row of the chart below, 0 has been added to itself and the remaining 9 digits. In speaking of the 100 combinations, it is common practice to call them the "basic addition facts." Recently, emphasis has been given to the term "subset," since each combination is a subset of the 10 basic digits. Later in the chapter, the basic facts are presented in another form.

ONE HUNDRED BASIC FACTS

```
 0    0    0    0    0    0    0    0    0    0
 0    1    2    3    4    5    6    7    8    9
---  ---  ---  ---  ---  ---  ---  ---  ---  ---
 0    1    2    3    4    5    6    7    8    9

 1    2    3    4    5    6    7    8    9
 0    0    0    0    0    0    0    0    0
---  ---  ---  ---  ---  ---  ---  ---  ---
 1    2    3    4    5    6    7    8    9

 1    1    1    1    1    1    1    1    1
 1    2    3    4    5    6    7    8    9
---  ---  ---  ---  ---  ---  ---  ---  ---
 2    3    4    5    6    7    8    9   10

      2    3    4    5    6    7    8    9
      1    1    1    1    1    1    1    1
     ---  ---  ---  ---  ---  ---  ---  ---
      3    4    5    6    7    8    9   10

      2    2    2    2    2    2    2    2
      2    3    4    5    6    7    8    9
     ---  ---  ---  ---  ---  ---  ---  ---
      4    5    6    7    8    9   10   11

           3    4    5    6    7    8    9
           2    2    2    2    2    2    2
          ---  ---  ---  ---  ---  ---  ---
           5    6    7    8    9   10   11

           3    3    3    3    3    3    3
           3    4    5    6    7    8    9
          ---  ---  ---  ---  ---  ---  ---
           6    7    8    9   10   11   12

                4    5    6    7    8    9
                3    3    3    3    3    3
               ---  ---  ---  ---  ---  ---
                7    8    9   10   11   12
```

```
  4     4     4     4     4     4
  4     5     6     7     8     9
 ───   ───   ───   ───   ───   ───
  8     9    10    11    12    13

        5     6     7     8     9
        4     4     4     4     4
       ───   ───   ───   ───   ───
        9    10    11    12    13

        5     5     5     5     5
        5     6     7     8     9
       ───   ───   ───   ───   ───
       10    11    12    13    14

              6     7     8     9
              5     5     5     5
             ───   ───   ───   ───
             11    12    13    14

              6     6     6     6
              6     7     8     9
             ───   ───   ───   ───
             12    13    14    15

                    7     8     9
                    6     6     6
                   ───   ───   ───
                   13    14    15

                    7     7     7
                    7     8     9
                   ───   ───   ───
                   14    15    16

                          8     9
                          7     7
                         ───   ───
                         15    16

                          8     8
                          8     9
                         ───   ───
                         16    17

                                9
                                8
                               ───
                               17

                                9
                                9
                               ───
                               18
```

Presentation Of Addition

The readiness program has presented the meaning of numbers through the oral study of sets; that is, each number, for example, 5, has been analyzed in terms of its subsets in addition and subtraction. Although these operations of addition and subtraction are not separated in the teaching process, they are discussed individually for a clearer look at each process.

The procedure now is for the child to rediscover the number stories and to write these facts. Each child will have available to him for rediscovering the facts, the number line, blocks, popsicle sticks, counting frame, abacus, tens chart and whatever aids he might construct.

If one starts with 4, ask the children to show or to tell something that they remember about 4. The usual response is the story that 2 and 2 is 4. If other responses are forthcoming, each one is considered with the pupils. The grouping and the basic fact are written on the chalkboard or on paper by the students.

Grouping   □ □   2

                □ □   + 2   Basic fact

                         4

The plus sign (+) is explained to mean "and" or "to add." The following questions are useful in getting at the meaning.

1. What is the arrangement of the blocks?
2. Why did I write one 2 above the other?
3. How do we read or say the number fact?
4. What is 2 and 2?
5. Can you tell something else about this arrangement of blocks? (Can be read as two groups of 2, or two 2's. You will note that this is the language of multiplication. It is introduced to give the pupils listening acquaintance with the phraseology. It is building a language for multiplication.)

Next, the children are asked whether they can discover another arrangement which will show that 2 and 2 is 4. Several children are asked to draw the grouping that they have discovered on the chalkboard and to write the basic fact below the grouping.

□ □   □ □

2   +   2   =   4

(The equals sign (=) is explained to mean "is" or "equals.")

The following statements make good practice excercises for all the basic facts:

1. Two and what number is 4?

     2 + □ = 4

2. What number and 2 is 4?

     □ and 2 = 4

3. Two and 2 are how many?

     2 + 2 = □

(The square or box (□) is explained to mean "what number." One can also think of the box as a place holder.)

Other groupings of 4 to be rediscovered:

△ △ △   3   △   1

   △   + 1   △ △ △   + 3

           4   4

△ △ △   △   △   △ △ △

  3   +   1   =   4   1   +   3   =   4

Chart 2 presents another form in which the basic facts may be studied. Can you identify any patterns?

Chart 1 shows how to read Chart 2.

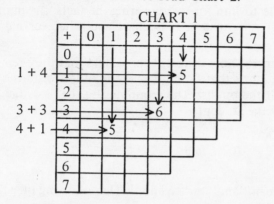

CHART 1

CHART 2

+	0	1	2	3	4	5
0	0	1	2	3	4	5
1	1	2	3	4	5	
2	2	3	4	5		
3	3	4	5			
4	4	5				
5	5					

Ask children to construct problems orally using these number facts. Children must solve problems everyday to learn the skills involved and as they learn to write, the problems can be written and exchanged among the class members for solving.

Examples: Mary had 3 pencils. Jane has 1 pencil. If they put the pencils together, how many are there?

Bill has 2 wagon wheels. Jack has 2 wagon wheels. How many wheels have the two boys?

The number of basic facts for 4 in addition and subtraction is 6, 3 for each process. This is true only when the 0 is omitted. If the 0 facts are included, the number of facts in each process is one more than the "set." This generalization holds true for all numbers from 1 through 9.

SET OF 4

Without 0 Facts		With 0 Facts	
Addition	Subtraction	Addition	Subtraction
2 + 2 = 4	4 - 2 = 2	2 + 2 = 4	4 - 2 = 2
3 + 1 = 4	4 - 3 = 1	3 + 1 = 4	4 - 3 = 1
1 + 3 = 4	4 - 1 = 3	1 + 3 = 4	4 - 1 = 3
(3 facts for each process)		0 + 4 = 4	4 - 0 = 4
		4 + 0 = 4	4 - 4 = 0
		(5 facts for each process)	

SET OF 5

Without 0 Facts		With 0 Facts	
Addition	Subtraction	Addition	Subtraction
3 + 2 = 5	5 - 3 = 2	3 + 2 = 5	5 - 3 = 2
2 + 3 = 5	5 - 2 = 3	2 + 3 = 5	5 - 2 = 3
4 + 1 = 5	5 - 4 = 1	4 + 1 = 5	5 - 4 = 1
1 + 4 = 5	5 - 1 = 4	1 + 4 = 5	5 - 1 = 4
(4 facts for each process)		0 + 5 = 5	5 - 0 = 5
		5 + 0 = 5	5 - 5 = 0
		(6 facts for each process)	

In a similar manner, children are guided to discover the teens, 11 through 18. The chart on subsets (below) summarizes the subsets for each of the numbers from 2 through 18. Note that 0 has been omitted from this chart.

SUBSETS FOR EACH OF THE NUMBERS FROM 2 THROUGH 18

2	3	4	5	6	7	8	9	10	11	12	13	14	15	16	17	18
1	2	2	3	3	4	4	5	5	6	6	7	7	8	8	9	9
1	1	2	2	3	3	4	4	5	5	6	6	7	7	8	8	9
		1	3	2	4	3	5	4	6	5	7	6	8	7	9	8
		2	1	3	2	4	3	5	4	6	5	7	6	8	7	9
			1	4	2	5	3	6	4	7	5	8	6	9	7	
			3	1	4	2	5	3	6	4	7	5	8	6	9	
				1	5	2	6	3	7	4	8	5	9	6		
				4	1	5	2	6	3	7	4	8	5	9		
					1	6	2	7	3	8	4	9	5			
					5	1	6	2	7	3	8	4	9			
						1	7	2	8	3	9	4				
						6	1	7	2	8	3	9				
							1	8	2	9	3					
							7	1	8	2	9					
								1	9	2						
								8	1	9						
									1							
									9							

1. How many basic facts for 2? 7? 11? 13? 18?
2. Can you identify a pattern?
3. What are the basic facts (subsets) for 12? 16? 18?

6	7	5	8	4	9	3
6	5	7	4	8	3	9
12	12	12	12	12	12	12

8	9	7
8	7	9
16	16	16

Recall that the addition of two 1-digit numbers and their sum is a basic fact.

9
9
18

Only the combination of 9 and 9 is 18.

The family approach does not limit the teaching to a single process at a time. It is necessary to *divide* 16 into two equal groups before one can consider the basic fact 8 + 8 = 16. *Multiplication* is involved when the subsets are referred to as two groups of 8 or 2 eights, and subtraction, the undoing of addition is always present in the loss of blocks, bottle caps and so on. Once there is understanding, practice which can be carried on in small groups or individually is important in order to establish the recall of the basic facts at a moment's notice. With knowledge of some of the basic facts, children are ready to add 2-digit numbers. Some children knowing only 10 or 12 basic facts are ready to add 2-digit numbers without regrouping.

To look for patterns in numbers should become second nature to the teacher and the children. Challenge the children to look for patterns within the 100 basic facts. Each child can find a great deal of interest in studying the following chart. Ask him to generalize about each pattern that he observes. Identify the facts on either side of the diagonal, subsets for 6, and the patterns for each row and column. Several patterns are discussed below.

+	0	1	2	3	4	5	6	7	8	9
0	0	1	2	3	4	5	6	7	8	9
1	1	2	3	4	5	6	7	8	9	10
2	2	3	4	5	6	7	8	9	10	11
3	3	4	5	6	7	8	9	10	11	12
4	4	5	6	7	8	9	10	11	12	13
5	5	6	7	8	9	10	11	12	13	14
6	6	7	8	9	10	11	12	13	14	15
7	7	8	9	10	11	12	13	14	15	16
8	8	9	10	11	12	13	14	15	16	17
9	9	10	11	12	13	14	15	16	17	18

The 19 Zero Facts

The teaching of the zero facts is, perhaps, best left until there is a need for them in the solution of problems. The first introduction to 0 usually comes in writing 10, 20 and so forth. The two meanings of 0—that it is a place holder (writing 0 in the ones place puts the 1 in the tens place) and that there is no unit in the units place—are then discussed with the children. In solving problems, the 0 is not encountered until the addition of a 2-digit number and a 1-digit number as 10 + 6, or in the addition of 2-digit numbers (12 + 10, 10 + 20, 20 + 34). Actually, 0 should be treated like any other number. The symbol "0" is of the same importance as a place holder as the 6 in 26. Without the 6, the 2 tens would not be identified. All numbers are place holders. In addition, the symbols 1 through 9 indicate a quantity which is defined by position. The 0 indicates a lack of quantity.

The generalization to discover for 0 is: if a number is added to 0 or a 0 is added to a number, the sum is always the number. Zero is the identity element for addition.

THE ZERO FACTS

0	0	0	0	0	0	0	0	0	0
0	1	2	3	4	5	6	7	8	9
0	1	2	3	4	5	6	7	8	9

1	2	3	4	5	6	7	8	9
0	0	0	0	0	0	0	0	0
1	2	3	4	5	6	7	8	9

The 17 Ones Facts

If the teaching of the zero facts is delayed until the writing of 2-digit numbers, establishing the generalization for adding 1 can be a starting point. The generalization to discover for 1 is: when adding 1 to any number, the next number in the counting series is the answer. What is the number if 1 is added to 4? Using a number line, a large ruler, a large calendar, the 100 chart and other aids, the pupils discover that the number is 5. Counting any group is an addition because a 1 is added to each previous number. Help the children to identify this in the chart below.

THE ONES FACTS

1	1	1	1	1	1	1	1	1
1	2	3	4	5	6	7	8	9
2	3	4	5	6	7	8	9	10

2	3	4	5	6	7	8	9
1	1	1	1	1	1	1	1
3	4	5	6	7	8	9	10

(Note: Adding 1 to 0 has been considered with the zero facts.)
What is the sum of any number and 1?

The Doubles

The sums of consecutive doubles increase by 2. Children who have had experiences in dividing sets into two equal groups seem to identify these sums quickly. Dividing candy, marbles and toys with a friend has given them this experience, too. In studying the basic facts, we observe that the first division of even numbers always results in two equal groups, the doubles or the twins for that particular number. In 4, the doubles are 2 and 2. The number line, 100 board and the counting frame can be used to clarify what is taking place when counting by 2. The sums of the doubles are the numbers used in counting by twos to 18. The division of "even" numbers into two groups makes the doubles.

0 Included in zero facts	1 Included in ones facts
0	1
0	2

THE DOUBLES

2	3	4	5	6	7	8	9
2	3	4	5	6	7	8	9
4	6	8	10	12	14	16	18

Paired Facts (The Commutative Property)

Two groups are to be identified in this pattern of basic facts. The *near doubles* have the sum of 1 more than the smaller double or 1 less than the sum of the larger double.

Generalization: Since 3 is 1 more than 2, 3 > 2, 1 is added to the sum of the smaller double.

$$\begin{array}{r} 2 \\ +\ 3 \\ \hline 5 \end{array}$$

$2 \to 2 + 2 = 4$ (Sum of the smaller double)

Then $4 + 1 = 5$

Generalization: Since 2 is 1 less than 3, 2 < 3, 1 is subtracted from the sum of the larger double.

$$\begin{array}{r} 2 \\ +\ 3 \\ \hline 5 \end{array}$$

$2 \to 3 + 3 = 6$ (Sum of the larger double)

Then $6 - 1 = 5$

There are nine pairs (18 facts) of near doubles.

$$\begin{array}{cc} 0 & 1 \\ 1 & 0 \\ \hline 1 & 1 \end{array} \qquad \begin{array}{cc} 1 & 2 \\ 2 & 1 \\ \hline 3 & 3 \end{array}$$

These facts have been considered with the zero facts and the ones facts. Observe how the commutative property is an aid to learning these facts.

2	3	3	4	4	5	5	6	6	7	7	8	8	9
3	2	4	3	5	4	6	5	7	6	8	7	9	8
5	5	7	7	9	9	11	11	13	13	15	15	17	17

How can we know that $3 + 4 = 7$ if we know that $3 + 3 = 6$? Since 4 is one more than 3, adding 1 to 6 is the same as saying the next number to 6 in the counting series.

The second group involving the commutative property contains 21 pairs of related facts when the zero and the ones facts are omitted. There is no one generalization which applies to this group.

1. In adding 2 to a number, the sum is found by skipping a number in the counting series. $(5 + 2) =$

   $5 + 2 = 7$

2. Add a number to 9 in order to group by 10. The sum may be found by first thinking of 9 as 10 and adding the second number. Because 1 was added to 9 to make 10, 1 is subtracted from the sum to arrive at the corrected sum.

   $9 + 6 = \square$

   $9 + 1 = 10, \ 10 + 6 = 16$

   Then $16 - 1 = 15$ – compensation

   Therefore $9 + 6 = 15$

3. Grouping to form 10 may be used when the sum is 11 or more.

   $$\begin{array}{l} 8 + 7 = \\ 8 + 2 = 10 \\ 7 - 2 = \ \underline{\ 5\ } \\ 15 \end{array}$$

As understanding develops, children can move to the use of the equation for the solution. The steps emphasize the concept of renaming numbers.

$$8 + 7 = \square$$
$$8 + (2 + 5) = \square \quad \text{Renaming 7}$$
$$(8 + 2) + 5 = \square \quad \text{Regrouping to make 10 and the associative property}$$
$$10 \quad + 5 = 15$$

Therefore, $8 + 7 = 15$

4. The idea of doubles may be used to find the sum. In the grouping $7 + 5 = \square$, $5 + 5$ may be thought of as the double. The difference between 5 and 7 is 2.

$$5 + 5 = 10$$
$$10 + 2 = 12$$

Then $7 + 5 = 12$

The sevens may be used as well. $7 + 7 = 14$. The difference between 7 and 5 is 2. Because 7 is greater than 5 ($7 > 5$), 2 is subtracted from 14.

$$7 + 7 = 14$$
$$14 - 2 = 12$$

Then $7 + 5 = 12$

Using the Basic Facts in 2-Digit Addition

The children who have learned several basic facts are ready to use them in 2-digit addition. The two meanings to discover in this early presentation are the following:

1. Three and 2 are always 5 regardless of the place in a number.

Units	Tens Place	Hundreds Place
3	30	300
2	20	200
5	50	500

2. The quantity given to the basic facts depends upon the position in the number.

Units	Tens Place	Hundreds Place
3	30	300
2	20	200
5 ← 5 ones	50 ← 5 tens	500 ← 5 hundreds
	(The 5 in the tens place is multiplied by 10.)	(The 5 in the hundreds place is multiplied 100.)

Structure several problems for the children. Ask them to solve the problems in any way they can. Example: We have 23 red chairs and 12 green chairs in our room. How many chairs do we have in all?

Possible solutions which children may identify.

1. Use of the number line:

```
 0    1    2    3    4    5    6    7    8    9   10   11   12   13   14   15
16   17   18   19   20   21   22  (23)  24   25   26   27   28   28
30   31   32   33   34  (35)  36   37 , etc.
```
(Count 12 more from 23 = 35)

2. Use of the 100 chart:

1	2	3	4	5	6	7	8	9	10
11	12	13	14	15	16	17	18	19	20
21	22	㉓	24	25	26	27	28	29	30
31	32	33	34	㉟	36	37	38	39	40
41	42	43	44	45	46	47	48	49	50, etc.

(Count 12 more from 23 = 35)

3. Use of the counting frame:

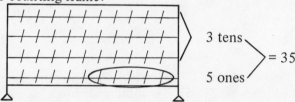

3 tens
5 ones
= 35

Analyzing each number: 23 = 2 tens and 3 ones

12 = 1 ten and 2 ones

How many tens?   (3)

How many ones?   (5)

4. Use of the place value chart (analyze each number):

Tens	Ones
2	3
1	2
3	5

3 tens, 5 ones = 35

5. Children must learn many names for numbers as they continue to study the concept of number. The number 23 may be thought of as 23 ones. In writing 23, the number may be written 20 + 3, 10 + 10 + 3, 10 + 13 and so on. This is called renaming a number or expanded notation.

$$
\begin{array}{r} 23 \\ +\ 12 \\ \hline 35 \end{array}
\longrightarrow
\begin{array}{r} 20 + 3 \\ 10 + 3 \\ \hline 30 + 5 \end{array}
$$

The pattern observed in the expanded notation emphasizes place value. As children add, they should say 3 units and 2 units are 5 units, 2 tens and 1 ten are 3 tens to keep them aware of the importance of place value. If the child thinks tens when he is adding tens, he is more likely to write the sum in the tens place. The following sequence will help children to discover that one adds tens and tens and ones and ones when adding 2-digit numbers.

$$
\begin{array}{r} 10 \\ +\ 20 \\ \hline 30 \end{array}
\longrightarrow
\begin{array}{l} 1 \text{ ten} \\ 2 \text{ tens} \\ \hline 3 \text{ tens} \end{array}
$$

$$
\begin{array}{r} 12 \\ +\ 24 \\ \hline 36 \end{array}
\longrightarrow
\begin{array}{l} 1 \text{ ten and } 2 \text{ ones} \\ 2 \text{ tens and } 4 \text{ ones} \\ \hline 3 \text{ tens and } 6 \text{ ones} \end{array}
$$

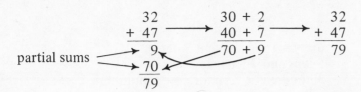

partial sums → 9
→ 70
79

Regrouping

In learning the basic facts with sums above 10, it should be pointed out to children that the sum can be interpreted to mean units or 1 ten and units. In the example 8 + 4 = 12, as one hears 12, he has an option to visualize the sum 12 as 12 units or as 1 ten and 2 units. When 12 is written, the interpretation is that of 1 ten and 2 units.

Children have had many experiences with addition before one attempts regrouping. They have solved single digit examples and problems, they have added 2-digit and 1-digit numbers, 2-digit and 2-digit numbers and have done some work with 3-digit numbers. They have become aware of such properties of addition as commutivity and associativity. As they discovered the subsets for 10 and the numbers through 18, they learned to think in tens and so many units. In the example 8 + 4, they obtained the sum through:

1. The use of objects: O O O O   O O
                           O O O O   O O   counting

2. The use of objects and regrouping to form 1 ten and 2 units:

(O O O O   OO) → 10 + 2 = 12

3. The use of numbers based on Number 2 above:

$$8 + 4 =$$
$$8 + (2 + 2) = \quad \text{Renaming}$$
$$(8 + 2) + 2 = \quad \text{Associative property}$$
$$10 + 2 = 12$$

There are several algorisms which children will discover when they begin addition requiring regrouping. In writing the basic facts such as 7 + 5 = 12, they have thought it through in terms of tens and ones and written the sum. It is not surprising, then, to find students using this very approach in solving for the sum. They identify the basic fact in the units place and write the sum directly as in the following examples.

18   8 + 5 = 13
+ 5
13   Regrouping is not necessary
10   One uses partial sums
23

36
+ 18
14 ← 6 + 8 = 14
40 ← 3 tens and 1 ten = 4 tens
54

```
  356
+ 279
   15        6 + 9 = 15 (1 ten and 5 ones)
  120        5 tens and 7 tens = 12 tens
+ 500        3 hundreds + 2 hundreds = 5 hundreds
  635
```

The way in which a problem is solved by a pupil is the core of teaching at this time. The several solutions presented indicate levels of thinking by the children and each solution becomes a part of the class discussion. The discovery of the basic properties by the children and the depth of the discussion to be carried on is at the discretion of the teacher. It is she who knows the mathematical understanding of each child. It becomes increasingly important that children be given time to think, to ask questions and to suggest ways to clarify a problem. From the algorisms provided by the students, a series of steps in the development of the concept of regrouping can be established. The example below provides such a sequence.

	Place Value	Expanded Notation
28	2 tens + 8 ones	20 + 8
+ 34	+ 3 tens + 4 ones	+ 30 + 4
	5 tens + 12 ones =	50 + 12 = 62
	6 tens + 2 ones = 62	

	Partial Sums		Regrouping
28	28	28	8 + 4 = 12
+ 34	+ 34	+ 34	regroup 12 to
	12 (8 + 4)	62	1 ten and 2 ones
	50 (20 + 30)		
	62		

An individual who does not learn to regroup can complete his addition by using partial sums.

Importance of Endings in Addition

The addition of a 2-digit number and a 1-digit number without the usual method of regrouping is addition by endings. As the children learn the basic subsets of any number through 18, they should become aware of the number in the units place and the number of tens formed by regrouping the units. Whenever two 1-digit numbers are added and regrouping is involved, only one group of 10 can be formed. In the following examples, how many tens can be carried to the tens place? Always 1. What number is always in the units place for 8 + 7? 9 + 4? 7 + 9? Using these two concepts, we can add using endings.

```
  18        Because 8 + 7 ends in 5 and one 10 is carried,
+  7        one can start at the left and say "25."


  39
+  4        Think from left to right; think 43.
```

What is the sum in each of the following examples?

```
  27      47      87      45      65      85
+  5    +  5    +  5    +  9    +  9    +  9
```

The table below will give children practice in addition by endings. They may wish to construct their own tables.

+	7	8	15	26	29
25	32				
35					
45					
55					
65					

In column addition, it becomes necessary to look at 3 or more addends. Can one use the statement, "When 2 numbers are added, the greatest number of tens to carry is 1," to generalize the addition of 3 addends? About 4 addends? In the examples below, observe that the number of tens to carry range from 0 to 2.

$$
\begin{array}{ccc}
 & \overset{1}{} & \overset{2}{} \\
13 & 15 & 19 \\
14 & 16 & 16 \\
+\ 11 & +\ 12 & +\ 18 \\
\hline
8 & 43 & 53
\end{array}
$$

For children who have had some experience with the equation forms, an extension of their addition skills can be provided by challenging them to solve examples in this manner. To facilitate understanding, compare the equation solution with the solution in the expanded form.

1. $18 + 5 = \square$
    $(10 + 8) + 5 =$ renaming 18
    $10 + (8 + 5) =$ associative property
    $10 + 13 = 23$

2. $18 + 5 = \square$
    $(10 + 8) + 5 =$ renaming 18
    $(10 + 8) + (2 + 3) =$ renaming 5
    $(10 + (8 + 2) + 3 =$ associative property
    $(10 + 10) + 3 =$ associative property
    $20 + 3 = 23$

3. $18 + 5 = \square$
    $18 + (2 + 3) =$ renaming 5
    $(18 + 2) + 3 =$ associative property
    $20 + 3 = 23$

4. $28 + 34 = \square$
    $(20 + 8) + (30 + 4) =$ renaming or expanding
    $20 + (8 + 30) + 4 =$ associative property
    $20 + (30 + 8) + 4 =$ commutative property
    $(20 + 30) + (8 + 4) =$ associative property
    $50 + 12 = 62$

$$
\begin{array}{cc}
(20 + 30) + (8 + 4) = & \quad 20 + 8 \\
\quad 50 \quad + \quad 12 = 62 & +\ 30 + 4 \\
 & \overline{\ 50 + 12}
\end{array}
$$

Work with addition extended to 3-digit numbers

No regrouping:

Expanded notation

423	400 + 20 + 3	600
+ 251	+ 200 + 50 + 1	70
	600 + 70 + 4 = 674	+ 4
		674

Place value

	4 h + 2 t + 3 u	600
	+ 2 h + 5 t + 1 u	70
	6 h + 7 t + 4 u = 674	+ 4
		674

$534 + 243 = (500 + 30 + 4) + (200 + 40 + 3)$ = Expanded notation

$(500 + 200) + (30 + 40) + (4 + 3)$ = Commutative and associative properties

$700 + 70 + 7 = 777$

Regrouping:

Place value   Partial sums

376	3 h + 7 t + 6 u	376	
+ 298	+ 2 h + 9 t + 8 u	+ 298	
	5 h + 16 t + 14 u =	14	(6 + 8)
	5 h + 17 t + 4 u =	160	(7 t + 9 t)
	6 h + 7 t + 4 u	500	(5 h + 2 h)
		674	

Expanded notation   Regrouping

467	400 + 60 + 7	11
+ 358	+ 300 + 50 + 8	467
	700 + 110 + 15 =	+ 358
	700 + 120 + 5 =	825
	800 + 20 + 5 = 825	

$374 + 287 = (300 + 70 + 4) + (200 + 80 + 7)$ = Expanded notation

$(300 + 200) + (70 + 80) + (4 + 7)$ =

500   +   150   +   11   = 661

Regrouping from the units place to the tens place involves nothing different from work done previously. The only variation is the thought process in regrouping tens to hundreds and then adding the hundreds. Three concepts are involved in regrouping in any example:

1. An understanding of place value.
2. An understanding of regrouping.
3. An understanding of the commutative and associative properties of addition.

Provide opportunities for children to explore the relations between the different algorisms. They should see that only the name of the number and the approach varies. We are still operating under the concept that there is no one way to solve an example.

As children begin to see patterns in numbers, they can break away from performing addition in a stereotyped manner. Adding from left to right adds interest and emphasizes the need to recognize place value. Challenge the children to perform addition in this manner.

$$
\begin{array}{r}
28 \\
+\ 37 \\
\hline
15 \\
50 \\
\hline
65
\end{array}
\qquad\longrightarrow\qquad
\begin{array}{r}
28 \\
+\ 37 \\
\hline
50 \\
15 \\
\hline
65
\end{array}
\quad
\begin{array}{l}
(20 + 30) \\
(8 + 7)
\end{array}
$$

$$
\begin{array}{r}
358 \\
+\ 276 \\
\hline
14 \\
120 \\
500 \\
\hline
634
\end{array}
\qquad\longrightarrow\qquad
\begin{array}{r}
358 \\
+\ 276 \\
\hline
120 \\
500 \\
14 \\
\hline
634
\end{array}
\quad
\begin{array}{l}
(50 + 70) \\
(300 + 200) \\
(8 + 6)
\end{array}
$$

Column Addition

Column addition, adding three or more digits, may be a part of the child's activities as early as the readiness program. Children, telling stories about 4, show the following groupings along with the basic facts.

$$
\begin{array}{r}
2 \\
1 \\
+\ 1 \\
\hline
4
\end{array}
\qquad
\begin{array}{r}
1 \\
2 \\
+\ 1 \\
\hline
4
\end{array}
\qquad
\begin{array}{r}
1 \\
1 \\
+\ 2 \\
\hline
4
\end{array}
\qquad
\begin{array}{r}
1 \\
1 \\
1 \\
+\ 1 \\
\hline
4
\end{array}
$$

As they learn to write the symbols, problem situations are provided to give them experience in working with such groupings. The same kind of thinking is required in column addition as in adding two 1-digit numbers, that is, combining groups.

In column addition, children must develop the skill of thinking mentally the sum of the first two numbers as they add the third number.

$$
\begin{array}{r}
3 \\
2 \\
+\ 4 \\
\hline
\end{array}
$$

To find the answer, the child thinks 2 and 3 is 5. If he cannot hold the 5 in his mind, as he adds the 4, he must use some device to help him. He can count on his fingers, he can use checks on his paper or he can write 5 along side the 2. A great deal of practice is necessary to develop the skill of retaining the unwritten or thought number, the 5 in this example. Oral practice will develop this skill more readily than performing the activity using paper and pencil because the pupil is compelled by the situation *to think* the partial sum and the other number to be added. However, both activities should be provided. The first activity in column addition is with sums of 10 or less.

Examples:

$$
\begin{array}{r}
3 \\
4 \\
+\ 2 \\
\hline
\end{array}
$$

1. $(3 + 4) + 2\ =\ 9$ Associative property
    $3 + (4 + 2)\ =\ 9$ Associative property
    $3 + 2 + 4\ =\ \square$ Commutative property (order of 4 and 2 changed)
    $(3 + 2) + 4\ =\ 9$ Associative property

3	2.	(2 + 4) + 3 = 9 Associative property
4		2 + (4 + 3) = 9 Associative property
+ 2		2 + 3 + 4 = □ Commutative property
		(2 + 3) + 4 = 9 Associative property

3.   Omit saying the numbers; say only the sums.

3, 7, 9 or 2, 6, 9

Observe the practices of the children and discover the reasons for their particular way to approach the solution.

Column addition involving sums more than 10; for example, 7 + 8 + 6 requires knowledge and skill in the use of the higher decade facts as 15 + 6. The following solutions indicate ways in which children may add a column of numbers:

7	1.	7 + 6 + 9 = □
6		(7 + 6) + 9 = □ Associative property
+ 9		13 + 9 = 22
	2.	9 + 6 + 7 = □
		(9 + 6) + 7 = □ Associative property
		15 + 7 = 22
	3.	9 + 6 + 7 = □ Making tens
		9 + (1 + 5) + 7 = □ Renaming 6
		9 + (1 + 5) + (5 + 2) = □ Renaming 7
		(9 + 1) + (5 + 5) + 2 = □ Associative property
		10 + 10 + 2 = 22

4.   Think: 7 + 6 = 13, 13 + 9 = 22.

5.   Think: 7, 13, 22. Repeat only the sums.

In which example is addition easier?   2 + 3 + 4 = □ or 7 + 4 + 8 = □? Adding a 1-digit number to only a 1-digit hidden number is easier than adding a 1-digit number to a 2-digit hidden number: 2 + 3 is a 1-digit hidden number. 7 + 4 is a 2-digit hidden number.

The techniques applicable to single column addition are also applicable to 2- or more column addition. Note the use of the associative property in the following examples.

6	6 + 3 + 7 = □
3	(6 + 3) + 7 = 9 + 7 = 16
+ 7	6 + (3 + 7) = 6 + 10 = 16
5	5 + 2 + 4 = □
2	(5 + 2) + 4 = 7 + 4 = 11
+ 4	5 + (2 + 4) = 5 + 6 = 11

```
  56
  23
+ 47
  16  ←
 110  ←——→ Finding partial sums
 126
```

37
14
+ 39
90

Columns are added separately and regrouped. The number carried may be indicated in the tens position. $7 + 4 + 9 = 20$. Twenty is 2 tens and no ones. $3 + 1 + 1 = 7$. $7 + 2$ (2 is the number of tens carried) $= 9$. The number carried may be added first as: $2 + 3 + 1 + 3 = 9$ tens

A philosophy of this text is that there is no one way to solve for an answer. As progress is made by children, the teacher can stimulate each child to move towards more and more mental activity. The suggestions and examples in the activities to broaden the scope of each fundamental operation presented at the close of several chapters are to challenge a child or children in this direction. The challenge can come in the form of research carefully planned by the teacher. This work will substitute for the class assignments normally given. The emphasis is always on discovery by the pupil. Another way to add a column of 2-digit addends may be accomplished by thinking tens and units as in the following sequences.

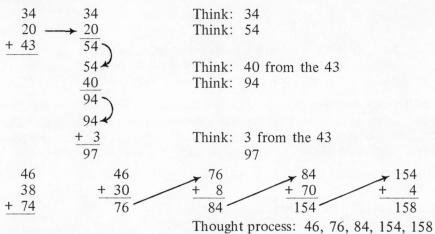

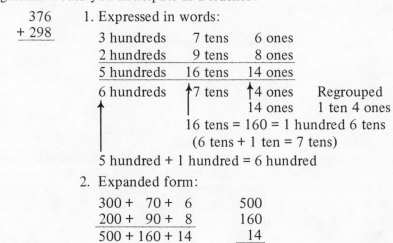

Thought process: 46, 76, 84, 154, 158

Addition of 3-place Numbers with Regrouping

When the concepts in regrouping 10 are understood, the pupils are ready to solve examples including regrouping of tens and hundreds in the same example. Ask the pupils to solve $376 + 298$ in as many ways as they can and defend their choice of algorism. What algorisms would you anticipate as a teacher?

376
+ 298

1. Expressed in words:

3 hundreds	7 tens	6 ones
2 hundreds	9 tens	8 ones
5 hundreds	16 tens	14 ones
6 hundreds	7 tens	4 ones

Regrouped
14 ones   1 ten 4 ones

16 tens = 160 = 1 hundred 6 tens

(6 tens + 1 ten = 7 tens)

5 hundred + 1 hundred = 6 hundred

2. Expanded form:

300 + 70 + 6   500
200 + 90 + 8   160
500 + 160 + 14   14
                      ‾‾‾‾
                      674

3. Partial sums (from either left or right):

```
  376
+ 298
```

     14 → 14 ones → 1 ten 4 ones

   160 → 16 tens → 1 hundred 6 tens

   500 →   5 hundreds

   674

4.
```
  11
  376
+ 298
  674
```
     The writing of the number carried (crutch) is not necessary.

5. Observe the pattern of numbers. Any two columns may be taken.

```
  376
+ 298
```

   14   (6 + 8)   Units + units equal units, but 14 is 1 ten and 4 ones.

 660   37 + 20 = 57, 57 + 9 = 66 tens. 66 tens is 660.

 674

Many activities can be suggested to develop a meaningful approach to addition. By asking the proper questions and by encouraging the children to identify patterns already known to them, the teacher can guide the children in the formation of desired concepts. What known ideas can a child apply to solve the following example?

1. Adding each column:

```
  315             315              11
  413             413            315
+ 256    ──→    + 256    ──→     413
                  14           + 256
                  70 ←── Partial sums  984
                 900
                 984
```

2. By thinking the sums, the two right hand columns can be added first and then the hundreds column added.

```
  315
  413        15 + 10 + 3 + 50 + 6 are added as units and regrouped
+ 256
  984        (3 + 4) + 2
```

Multiple Counting

Activities in multiple counting may be used to build strength in recognizing the basic facts. Too often multiple counting involves counting by 2's, 5's and 10's, always starting with 2, 5 and 10. Count by 2's starting with 1, count by 5's starting with 1, 2, 3 and 4 and by 10's starting with 1, 2, 3, 4 and so on. Help the children to identify various patterns in terms of key facts as they count in this manner.

1. Count by twos starting with any odd number. What number is skipped each time? Example: 7, 9, 11, 13, 15, 17, 19, 21 and so on. What key facts are encountered?

$$\begin{array}{r} 7 \\ + 2 \\ \hline 9 \end{array} \qquad \begin{array}{r} 9 \\ + 2 \\ \hline 11 \end{array} \qquad \begin{array}{r} 11 \\ + 2 \\ \hline 13 \end{array} \qquad \begin{array}{r} 13 \\ + 2 \\ \hline 15 \end{array}$$

2. Count by fives starting with a number other than 5. Example: 2, 7, 12, 17, 22 and so on. What key facts are encountered?

$$\begin{array}{r} 2 \\ + 5 \\ \hline 7 \end{array} \qquad \begin{array}{r} 7 \\ + 5 \\ \hline 12 \end{array} \qquad \begin{array}{r} 12 \\ + 5 \\ \hline 17 \end{array} \qquad \begin{array}{r} 17 \\ + 5 \\ \hline 22 \end{array}$$

3. Count by fours, sixes, nines and so on.

Important Ideas Begun in Addition

1. Meaning of addition.
2. Interpretation of and application of the commutative, associative, identity element and closure properties of addition.
3. Place value and addition.
4. Regrouping.
5. Equation form.

Activities to Broaden the Scope of Addition

To teach children in any area of the curriculum one must first establish common elements such as depth of understanding, desire and interest on the part of the learner. Too often children are directed to memorize concepts, principles and generalizations and this is accepted as learning. This book is written on the premise that learning takes place when children are permitted to think through solutions to problem situations using their experiences, language and understandings already learned to discover new ideas. To foster learning, children should be guided in a manner which will stimulate interest for learning.

The activities presented in this section are best taught at a time when a pupil or several children indicate to the teacher their understanding of certain basic principles. With few exceptions, these activities are not taught to a total classroom. The emphasis is upon individual growth. These activities are divided into two classifications, those which are used to build interest and have little use beyond this and those activities which will generate interest and desire to perform arithmetic at a mental level.

Excess of Nines

Excess of 9's or casting out 9's provides practice in manipulating numbers and it is in this respect that casting out 9's might be most beneficial. The method is challenging to the pupil. It should not be required as proof. The activities to broaden the scope of working in arithmetic should develop the quality of choice by the pupil in his approach to a solution or in checking his work.

To develop the concept of excess of 9's at the elementary level stimulates the children to observe what happens to 10, 100, 1000 and so on when each number is divided by 9. What is the remainder when 100 is divided by 9? When 10 is divided by 9? What is the remainder in the units place when 9, 8, 7 and so on are divided by 9?

1. What is the excess of 9 in 10? $10 \div 9 = 1$ and a remainder of 1. The remainder in each case is the excess. What is the excess of nines in 30? If there is 1 excess in 10, there must be 3 in 30.

2. What is the excess of nines in 100? $100 \div 9 = 11$ and a remainder of 1. The excess in 100 is 1. In 1,000? In 10,000? How many excesses in 500? 3,000?

3. To arrive at the excess in any number, add the digits horizontally and find the excess of the sum.

$$\begin{array}{r} 673 \\ 425 \\ 310 \\ + 243 \\ \hline 1651 \end{array}$$

The addend $673 = 6 + 7 + 3 = 16$. (Divide the sum by 9)

$$\begin{array}{r} 1 \quad \leftarrow \quad \text{Not considered because it tells how many nines} \\ 9\overline{)16} \\ 9 \\ \hline 7 \quad \leftarrow \quad \text{Considered because 7 is the excess} \end{array}$$

The addend $425 = 4 + 2 + 5 = 11$ (Divide the sum by 9)

$$\begin{array}{r} 1 \\ 9\overline{)11} \\ 9 \\ \hline 2 \quad \leftarrow \quad \text{The excess} \end{array}$$

The addend $310 = 3 + 1 + 0 = 4$ (Divide the sum by 9)

$$\begin{array}{r} 0 \qquad \text{No nines in 4} \\ 9\overline{)4} \\ 0 \\ \hline 4 \quad \leftarrow \quad \text{Excess} \end{array}$$

The addend $243 = 2 + 4 + 3 = 9$ (Divide the sum by 9)

$$\begin{array}{r} 1 \\ 9\overline{)9} \\ 9 \\ \hline 0 \quad \leftarrow \quad \text{Excess} \end{array}$$

Total the excesses and divide the sum by 9:

Excess from addend 673 $\rightarrow$ 7
Excess from addend 425 $\rightarrow$ 2
Excess from addend 310 $\rightarrow$ 4
Excess from addend 243 $\rightarrow$ $\underline{0}$
                                                      13 $\leftarrow$ Total excesses

$$\begin{array}{r} 1 \\ 9\overline{)13} \\ 9 \\ \hline 4 \quad \leftarrow \quad \text{Excess of nines in 13} \end{array}$$

$$\begin{array}{r} 673 \\ 425 \\ 310 \\ \underline{243} \\ 1651 \quad \leftarrow \quad \text{Total of the excess of 9 in the sum is} \end{array}$$

$$1 + 6 + 5 + 1 = 13$$

$$
\begin{array}{r}
1 \\
9\overline{)13} \\
9 \\
\hline
4
\end{array}
\quad \leftarrow \quad \text{Excess of nines in 13}
$$

Since the sum 1651 also has an excess of nines equal to the excess of nines from the horizontal total excesses, the sum is probably correct. If the sum 1651 were written 1615 (digits misplaced), the excess would still be 4. This is the reason for saying the answer is *probably correct*.

Left-to-Right Addition

It has been pointed out that there is no one correct way to find the answer to a problem. The use of different approaches adds enchantment, enjoyment and challenge to arithmetic.

Example: Left to right:

$$
\begin{array}{r}
4\,5 \\
1\cancel{3}\cancel{4}2 \\
758 \\
+\ 694 \\
\end{array}
$$

6 + 7 = 13; think 13 hundreds and write 13. The sum is written above the example. 9 + 5 = 14; think 14 tens. 14 tens = 1 hundred, 4 tens. Add the 1 hundred to the 3 hundred, scratch the 3 and write the corrected number above the 3.

4 + 8 = 12, think 12 as 1 ten and 2 ones. Add 1 ten to 4 tens, scratch the 4 tens and write 5.

Read the sum as 1452.

The example can also be solved in the following manner (recognition of place value):

$$
\begin{array}{lll}
\begin{array}{r}
1.\ 758 \\
694 \\
\hline
1300 \\
140 \\
12 \\
\hline
1452
\end{array}
&
\begin{array}{r}
2.\ 758 \\
694 \\
\hline
13 \\
14 \\
12 \\
\hline
1452
\end{array}
&
\begin{array}{r}
3.\ 758 \\
694 \\
\hline
144 \\
12 \\
\hline
1452
\end{array}
\end{array}
$$

Reversing 2-Digit Numbers

An activity which will create interest and also perform the function of practice of the basic addition facts involves the reversal of digits and adding until the sum can be read from right to left and left to right.

Examples:

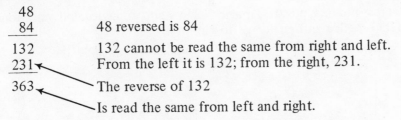

$$
\begin{array}{r}
48 \\
84 \\
\hline
132 \\
231 \\
\hline
363
\end{array}
$$

48 reversed is 84

132 cannot be read the same from right and left. From the left it is 132; from the right, 231.

The reverse of 132

Is read the same from left and right.

$$
\begin{array}{r}
79 \\
\underline{97} \longleftarrow \text{The reverse of 79}\\
176 \\
\underline{671} \longleftarrow \text{The reverse of 176}\\
847 \\
\underline{748} \\
1595 \\
\underline{5951} \\
7546 \\
\underline{6457} \\
14003 \\
\underline{30041} \\
44044 \qquad \text{Read the same from left and right}
\end{array}
$$

Stimulate the children to compare and check results. One can challenge the children by such statements as, in 89, the final sum is a number in the trillions. Can you find it?

Principle of Compensation

Children in the primary grades become acquainted with this principle when they develop understanding of place value. Basic facts are learned by grouping to form tens.

1.

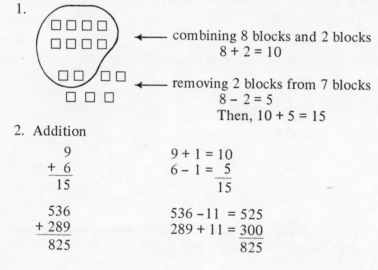

← combining 8 blocks and 2 blocks
 8 + 2 = 10

← removing 2 blocks from 7 blocks
 8 – 2 = 5
 Then, 10 + 5 = 15

2. Addition

$$
\begin{array}{r}
9 \\
\underline{+\ 6} \\
15
\end{array}
\qquad
\begin{array}{l}
9 + 1 = 10 \\
6 - 1 = \underline{\ 5} \\
15
\end{array}
$$

$$
\begin{array}{r}
536 \\
\underline{+\ 289} \\
825
\end{array}
\qquad
\begin{array}{l}
536 - 11\ = 525 \\
289 + 11 = \underline{300} \\
825
\end{array}
$$

Games

The use of cross-number puzzles, magic squares and triangles and variations in the use of charts offers practice and challenge to children.

Magic Square

```
8 3 4 |       15's
1 5 9 |
6 7 2 ↓
  ←
  15's
```

Magic Triangle

```
        8
      5   3
    2   9   4
   ─────────→
 15's         15's
```

Charts: Complete the basic facts.

+	0	1	2	3	4	5
0	0			3		5
1	1	2				
2			4	5		
3	3					
4	4					
5	5					

Read the left column as the first addend and the top row as the second addend.

+	0	1	2	3	4	5
0			0+2 2			
1		1+1 2				
2						
3			3+2 5			
4						
5					5+4 9	

Rearrange the sticks so that 1 or more can be moved leaving a count of 9 on each of the four sides. There are 24 sticks in all. The size of each set may vary. Note that there are three original sets with three elements in each set. How many can you remove and still count 9 on each side? Can you find the arrangement when 1, 3 or 4 are removed?

/ / /   / / /   / / /⁹   / /   / /   / / / / /
/ / /   / / /   / /   / /
/ / /   / / /   / / /   / / / / /   / /   / /
⁹   2 were removed

Chapter Summary

Many of the procedures described for learning addition are techniques for developing meaning in arithmetic. Effectiveness for developing this meaning depends upon the experiences that the teacher is able to provide each child and the order in which these experiences are developed. Specifically, the order is from working with concrete materials to manipulation of symbols.

Sequence of steps in teaching addition:

1. **Number readiness:** Many children come to school knowing how to "say" the numbers to 10 and beyond. The teacher uses whatever background the child has as a starting point to develop concepts of number.

   a. Thinking in "sets," "collections" and "groups" to develop number concept. The common property of each set is number.

One-to-one correspondence. The two sets are equivalent.

Nonequivalent sets. The number property for each set is different.

To think in the abstract, that is, 4, and to write the symbol 4. When the child relates 4 to 3, 4 to 5, 2 to 1, etc., he begins to see the order of the whole numbers in the total series of numbers.

   b. Discovering the "subsets" or "basic facts" from "sets" or "families." Other names for numbers are discovered as subsets of a set.

$$2 + 1 = 3$$
$$2 + \square = 3$$

$$1 + 2 = 3$$
$$1 + \square = 3$$

2. **Addition without regrouping:**

<u>Addition of tens:</u>

```
  20       25
+ 10     + 30
  30       55
```

<u>Partial Sums:</u>

```
   34
 + 13
    7
   40
   47
```

<u>Place Value:</u>

```
  3 tens 4 ones
+ 1 ten  3 ones
  4 tens 7 ones = 47
```

<u>Expanded Notation:</u>

```
  30 + 4
+ 10 + 3
  40 + 7 = 47
```

<u>Equation:</u>

$$36 + 12 = (30 + 6) + (10 + 2) = \text{Expanded notation}$$
$$(30 + 10) + (6 + 2) = \text{Commutative and associative properties}$$
$$40 \quad + \quad 8 \quad = 48$$

<u>Place Value:</u>

```
  324     3 h 2 t 4 u
+ 252     2 h 5 t 2 u
          5 h 7 t 6 u = 576
```

<u>Expanded Notation:</u>

```
300 + 20 + 4
200 + 50 + 2
500 + 70 + 6 = 576
```

ADDITION   53

3. **Techniques for teaching sums of 10 or more**:

   a. ○ ○ ○ ○   ○ ○ → $\overline{(○○○○\qquad ○)○}$ $10 + 2 = 12$
      ○ ○ ○ ○   ○ ○ $\underline{(○○○○\qquad ○)○}$

         8   +   4   =   8 + (2 + 2)   =   Renaming 4

        (8 + 2) + 2   =   Associative property

           10   + 2   =   12

   b.   8   8 + 2 = 10   To form a group of 10
        $\underline{+\ 7}$ $\underline{7 - 2 =\ \ 5}$ To keep a balance in the addends
                      15

        Therefore, $8 + 7 = 15$

   c.   7   6 + 6 = 12   7   7 + 7 = 14
        $\underline{+\ 6}$ 12 + 1 = 13 $\underline{+\ 6}$ 14 − 1 = 13

4. **Addition with regrouping**:

Basic Fact:	Partial Sums:	Expanded Notation:
8	18	10 + 8
$\underline{+\ 5}$	$\underline{+\ 5}$	$\underline{+\qquad 5}$
13	13	10 + 13 = 23
	$\underline{10}$	
	23	

Regrouping:	Equation:
$\overset{1}{18}$	$18 + 5 =$
$\underline{\ 5}$	$18 + (2 + 3) =$ Renaming 5
23	$(18 + 2) + 3 =$ Associative property
	20 + 3 = 23

Partial Sums:	Place Value:	Expanded Notation:
37	3 t + 7 u	30 + 7
$\underline{+\ 26}$	$\underline{+\ 2\ t + 6\ u}$	$\underline{+\ 20 +\ 6}$
13	5 t + 13 u = 63	50 + 13 = 63
50		
63		

Regrouping:	Equation:
$\overset{1}{37}$	$37 + 26 = (30 + 7) + (20 + 6) =$ Expanded notation
$\underline{26}$	$(30 + 20) + (7 + 6) =$ Commutative and
63	associative properties
	50 + 13 = 63

Partial Sums:	Place Value:
476	4 h + 7 t + 6 u
$\underline{+\ 398}$	$\underline{+\ 3\ h + 9\ t + 8\ u}$
14	7 h + 16 t + 14 u = Regroup
160	8 h + 7 t + 4 u = 874
$\underline{700}$	
874	

Expanded Notation:	Regrouping:

$$400 + 70 + 6$$
$$+ 300 + 90 + 8$$
$$\overline{700 + 160 + 14} = 874$$

$$\overset{1\ 1}{476}$$
$$+ 398$$
$$\overline{874}$$

Study Questions

1. Make a simple abacus. Use it to illustrate regrouping in addition.
2. Explain and illustrate the commutative, associative and closure properties in addition of whole numbers.
3. Demonstrate the concept of regrouping using the place value chart.
4. Illustrate the series of steps to be used in presenting the addition of 2-digit numbers involving regrouping.
5. Check the addition in the following example using the excess of nines.

$$426$$
$$350$$
$$+ 281$$

6. Check several arithmetic series for their presentation of addition.
7. Solve using the equation form:
   a. $27 + 8 =$
   b. $36 + 29 =$
8. Solve using the principle of compensation:
   a. $267 + 179 =$
   b. $3646 + 2797 =$
9. If you have read Chapter VII, "Numeration Systems and Bases," construct an abacus for some base that you choose and apply the concepts of regrouping that you have learned in Base 10.
10. Prepare a large chart of the 100 basic addition facts which can be used to illustrate their structure. How can the chart be used?

Selected Text References

1. Banks, J. Houston, *Elementary School Mathematics*, Boston: Allyn and Bacon, Inc., 1966. Chapter 2.
2. Flournoy, Frances, *Elementary School Mathematics*, New York: The Center for Applied Research in Education, Inc., 1964. Chapters 2–4.
3. Grossnickle, Foster E., and Leo J. Brueckner, *Discovering Meanings in Elementary School Mathematics*, New York: Holt, Rinehart and Winston, Inc., 1963. Chapters 6, 7 and 17.
4. Hollister, George E., and Agnes G. Gunderson, *Teaching Arithmetic in the Primary Grades*, Boston: D. C. Heath and Company, 1964. Chapter 6.
5. Kramer, Klaas, *The Teaching of Elementary School Mathematics*, Boston: Allyn and Bacon, Inc., 1966. Chapter 10.
6. Marks, John L., C. Richard Purdy and Lucien B. Kinney, *Teaching Elementary School Mathematics for Understanding*, New York: McGraw-Hill Book Company, Inc., 1966. Chapters 5 and 6.
7. Swain, Robert L., and Eugene D. Nichols, *Understanding Arithmetic*, New York: Holt, Rinehart and Winston, Inc., 1965. Chapter 5.

Selected Readings from the Arithmetic Teacher

1. Adkins, Bryce E., "Adapting Magic Squares to Classroom Use," 10: 525–532, November, 1965.
2. Kaliski, Lotte, "Arithmetic and the Brain-Injured Child," 9: 245–251, May, 1962.
3. Machlin, Ruth, "The Use of Overlay Charts," 8: 433–435, December, 1961.
4. Paschal, Billy J., "Teaching the Critically Disadvantaged Child," 13: 369–374, May, 1966.
5. Philips, Jo, "Basic Laws for Young Children," 12: 525–532, November, 1965.
6. Rivera, Emilio, "Adding by Endings: Some Important Considerations," 12: 204–206, March, 1965.
7. Stutler, Mary S., "Arithmetic Concepts in First Grade," 9: 81–85, February, 1962.
8. Volpel, Marvin C., "The Hundred Board," 6: 295–301, December, 1959.

Chapter IV

Subtraction of Whole Numbers

Subtraction is the process of separating a group of objects from a larger group of similar objects. This process has the opposite action of addition. The two processes are related; in knowing that $5 + 3 = 8$ one can reason that $8 - 3 = 5$ and $8 - 5 = 3$. The sign (–) is read "minus" or "from." In solving problems, the relationship of addition and subtraction becomes evident. In the problem, "John has 16 pennies and he spends 5 pennies for a pencil. How many pennies does he have left?", several questions bring out this relationship.

How many pennies did John have? Is a sum given? Yes.

How many pennies did John spend? Is an addend given? Yes.

How many pennies remained? Is this the missing addend? Yes.

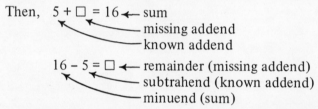

Then, $5 + \square = 16 \leftarrow$ sum
      — missing addend
      — known addend

$16 - 5 = \square \leftarrow$ remainder (missing addend)
      — subtrahend (known addend)
      — minuend (sum)

Three common algorisms for subtraction are decomposition, additive and equal additions. The most common method taught in the public schools is the decomposition or take-away form. The algorism $43 - 15$ may be read "43 minus 15" or "15 from 43."

1. The additive form of subtraction makes use of the language of addition. For example, the elements of $8 + 5 = 13$ are used to determine the subtraction facts.

$$\begin{array}{r} 8 \\ + 5 \\ \hline 13 \end{array}$$
 8 and 5 is 13
 8 and what number is 13? What number and 5 is 13?

$$\begin{array}{r} 13 \\ - 8 \\ \hline 5 \end{array}$$
 The language of additive subtraction for this example is 8 and what number is 13? $8 + \square = 13$. $8 + 5 = 13$. Therefore, the difference is 5.

$$\begin{array}{r} 13 \\ - 5 \\ \hline 8 \end{array}$$
 5 and what number is 13? $5 + \square = 13$. $5 + 8 = 13$. Therefore, the difference is 8.

$$\begin{array}{r} 52 \\ - 16 \\ \hline 36 \end{array}$$
 $6 + \square = 12$. $6 + 6 = 12$.
 $1 + \square = 4$. $1 + 3 = 4$.
 Regrouping is done as in decomposition.

2. The equal additions form in subtraction is based on the Principle of Equal Additions. In subtraction, this means that the same number can be added to the subtrahend

and the minuend without changing the remainder. Examples:

$$\begin{array}{r} 13 \\ -\ 7 \\ \hline 6 \end{array} \longrightarrow \begin{array}{l} \text{Add 10 to 13} \\ \text{Add 10 to } 7 \\ \text{Difference} \end{array} \longrightarrow \begin{array}{r} 23 \\ -\ 17 \\ \hline 6 \end{array} \longrightarrow \begin{array}{l} (13+10)-(7+10)= \\ 23\quad-\quad 17\quad=6 \end{array}$$

$$\begin{array}{r} 34 \\ -\ 17 \\ \hline 17 \end{array} \longrightarrow \begin{array}{l} 34+3 \\ 17+3 \\ \text{Difference} \end{array} \longrightarrow \begin{array}{r} 37 \\ -\ 20 \\ \hline 17 \end{array} \longrightarrow \begin{array}{l} (34+3)-(17+3)= \\ 37\quad-\quad 20\quad=17 \end{array}$$

The answer in each example, respectively, is: 6 and 17. The addition to the minuend and the subtrahend of 10 in one example and 3 to the second example did not change the difference.

The generalization can be stated as: $(a+d)-(b+d)=c$
$$a-b\ =c$$

The equal additions method uses only 10 and powers of 10 to balance the operation of subtraction. Examples:

$$\begin{array}{r} 53 \\ -\ 29 \\ \hline 24 \end{array}$$

$$\begin{array}{r} {\scriptstyle 10} \\ 5\ 3 \\ -\ \ 2\ 9 \\ \hline 4 \end{array} \qquad \text{Step 1.} \quad \text{In the set of whole numbers, 9 cannot be subtracted from 3. To solve, add 10 units to the 3 units. } (10+3=13).\ \text{Then } 13-9=4.$$

$$\begin{array}{r} {\scriptstyle 1} \\ 5\ 3 \\ -(1+2)\ 9 \\ \hline 2\ 4 \end{array} \qquad \text{Step 2.} \quad \text{Ten units are added to the units place in the minuend in Step 1. To compensate for this, add 1 ten to the 2 tens in the subtrahend (2 tens + 1 ten = 3 tens). Then } 5-3=2.$$

$$\begin{array}{r} {\scriptstyle 10} \\ 625 \\ -\ 386 \\ \hline 9 \end{array} \qquad \text{Step 1.} \quad \text{Add 10 units to 5; } 10+5=15. \\ \text{Then } 15-6=9.$$

$$\begin{array}{r} {\scriptstyle 1} \\ 62\ 5 \\ -\ 39\ 6 \\ \hline 9 \end{array} \qquad \text{Step 2.} \quad \text{Since 10 units are added to the units in the minuend, compensate by adding 1 ten to the 8 tens in the subtrahend. } (8+1=9.)$$

$$\begin{array}{r} {\scriptstyle 10\ 1} \\ 62\ 5 \\ -\ 39\ 6 \\ \hline 39 \end{array} \qquad \text{Step 3.} \quad \text{Nine tens cannot be subtracted from 2 tens. Add 10 tens to 2 tens in the minuend (10 + 2 = 12 tens). Then 12 tens} - \text{9 tens = 3 tens.}$$

$$\begin{array}{r} {\scriptstyle 1\ 1} \\ 62\ 5 \\ -\ 49\ 6 \\ \hline 2\ 39 \end{array} \qquad \text{Step 4.} \quad \text{Since 10 tens were added to the 2 tens in the minuend, add 1 hundred to the 3 hundred in the subtrahend. Then } 6-4=2.\ \text{Remainder, 239.}$$

The decomposition form is the most common approach to the teaching of subtraction. The teacher must acquaint herself with the additive and the equal additions forms so that she can recognize these approaches when working with children who use them. A basic philosophy of this book is that there is no *one* correct procedure or algorism for arriving at a solution. Therefore, for some students all forms may be taught to broaden the scope of their knowledge of subtraction. Enrichment gives each individual an opportunity of choice in solving problems.

Number Properties Pertaining to Subtraction

A review of the properties and principles of subtraction are presented here for the teacher who feels insecure in the structure of arithmetic and as a summary for those with some background in mathematics. There is no attempt to place this content into any form of methodology. Approaches to teaching these properties and principles of subtraction will come later.

1. **Commutative property (the rule of order)**: In addition, the order in which two numbers from the set of whole numbers are added does not affect the sum. In the following examples, the differences are not the same when the order is changed. The number $^-2$ is not the same number as 2. Therefore, subtraction is not commutative. $a - b \neq b - a$

$$\begin{array}{r} 5 \\ -3 \\ \hline 2 \end{array} \qquad \begin{array}{r} 3 \\ -5 \\ \hline ^-2 \end{array}$$

2. **Closure**: In subtraction of whole numbers, the difference is not always a member of the given set.

    Given: The set of whole numbers 0, 1, 2, 3, 4 . . .

$$\begin{array}{r} 8 \\ -5 \\ \hline 3 \end{array} \qquad \begin{array}{r} 5 \\ -8 \\ \hline ^-3 \end{array}$$

In the first example, the difference, 3, is a member of the set of whole numbers. However, in $5 - 8 = {}^-3$, $^-3$ is not a member of this set. The set of whole numbers is not closed to subtraction.

To give subtraction the property of closure, a set of new numbers, the negative numbers, was added to 0 and the set of counting numbers. This new set, the integers, is closed to subtraction. The differences, 5 and $^-5$, are members of the new set.

$$\begin{array}{r} 13 \\ -8 \\ \hline 5 \end{array} \qquad \begin{array}{r} 8 \\ -13 \\ \hline ^-5 \end{array}$$

3. **Associative property**: In general, subtraction is not associative. In the examples which follow, note the differences in the answers as regrouping is carried out.

$(12 - 6) - 2 = 4$	Associative property
$12 - (6 + 2) = 4$	Addition of the subtrahends
$12 - (6 - 2) = 8$	Associative property does not hold

The subtrahends cannot be subtracted in the last equation. The generalization can be stated in the following ways:

$(a - b) - c = \text{difference}$

$a - (b + c) = \text{difference}$

4. **Zero in subtraction**: Zero is not an identity element in subtraction. Zero used in the subtrahend acts as though it were an identity element because the difference is the minuend. Zero operates as an identity element when it is in the right hand position as $6 - 0 = 6$.

5. **Principle of equal additions**: The difference does not change if the same number is added to the minuend and the subtrahend. Examples:

$$\begin{array}{r} 13 \\ -\ 7 \\ \hline \end{array} \qquad \begin{array}{l} (13 + 3) - (7 + 3) = \\ \quad 16\ -\ 10\ \ = 6 \end{array}$$

$$\begin{array}{r} 423 \\ -189 \\ \hline \end{array} \qquad \begin{array}{l} (423 + 11) - (189 + 11) = \\ \quad 434\ -\quad 200\ \ = 234 \end{array}$$

If $a - b$, then $(a + n) - (b + n) = c$

6. **Principle of equal subtraction**: The difference does not change if the same number is subtracted from the minuend and the subtrahend. Examples:

$$\begin{array}{r} 13 \\ -\ 7 \\ \hline \end{array} \qquad \begin{array}{l} (13 - 3) - (7 - 3) = \\ \quad 10\ -\ 4\ \ = 6 \end{array}$$

$$\begin{array}{r} 612 \\ -284 \\ \hline \end{array} \qquad \begin{array}{l} (612 - 12) - (284 - 12) = \\ \quad 600\ -\quad 272\ \ = 328 \end{array}$$

If $a - b = c$, then $(a - n) - (b - n) = c$

Operations Using Negative Numbers

We have said with respect to whole numbers that $a - b = c$ and $b + c = a$ if a is greater than b.

$$\begin{array}{r} 21 \\ -\ 8 \\ \hline 13 \end{array} \qquad \begin{array}{r} 13 \\ +\ 8 \\ \hline 21 \end{array}$$

To operate on numbers when a is less than b, a new set of numbers was invented so that subtraction would always be possible (closure). The new set is the negative numbers and, when they are combined with the set of whole numbers, they make up the set of integers.

NUMBER LINE – INTEGERS

$$\overset{\longleftrightarrow}{\ ^-8\ \ ^-7\ \ ^-6\ \ ^-5\ \ ^-4\ \ ^-3\ \ ^-2\ \ ^-1\ \ 0\ \ 1\ \ 2\ \ 3\ \ 4\ \ 5\ \ 6\ \ 7\ \ 8\ }$$

In addition of whole numbers, the action or movement on the line is to the right. Subtraction, the inverse of addition, moves in the opposite direction, to the left. Examples:

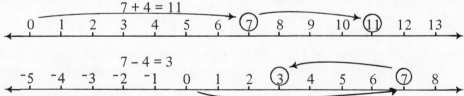

Presentation of Subtraction

The idea of taking groups apart is not new to children. They have shared, given away and lost objects and materials in their daily experiences. From these experiences, they may have begun to identify questions which subtraction asks. Subtraction is a way of thinking about separating two numbers to find a third. Given a sum and an addend, one subtracts to find the missing addend.

Problem 1.   Jack has 7 marbles. He gives 4 marbles to Bob. How many marbles has Jack left? (The sum and an addend are present in this example.)

$$4 + \square = 7 \qquad 7 - 4 = 3$$

Question asked: <u>How many are left or remain?</u>

Problem 2.   Mary has 6 dolls. Her friend Jane has 4 dolls. How many more dolls has Mary than Jane? How many less dolls has Jane than Mary?

$$6 - 4 = 2$$

John weighs 68 pounds. His friend Paul weighs 73 pounds. How much more does Paul weigh than John?

$$73 - 68 = 5$$

Question asked: <u>How many more or less?</u> <u>How much more or less?</u>

Problem 3.   A pocket knife costs 78¢ in one store. In another store, the same knife costs 73¢. What is the difference in the price?

$$78 - 73 = 5$$

In the example of John's weight is 68 pounds and Paul's weight is 73 pounds, the question could have been "What is the difference?"

$$73 - 68 = 5$$

Question asked: <u>What is the difference?</u>

Problem 4.   Dick needs 15¢ to buy a toy automobile. He has 11¢. How much more does he need to purchase the automobile? (The sum and the addend are present in this example.)

$$11 + \square = 15 \qquad 15 - 11 = 4$$

To give each student a book, the teacher asked for 28 books. The storeroom has only 23 books. How many more books are needed? (The sum and the addend are present in this example.)

$$23 + \square = 28 \qquad 28 - 23 = 5$$

Questions asked: <u>How many more are needed?</u> <u>How much more is needed?</u>

Learning the Basic Facts

The family of 4 has been analyzed in terms of its subsets using concrete and semi-concrete materials. The procedure now is to help the children to recall the basic facts learned in subtraction, to discover the unknown subtraction number stories, to interpret and use the language of subtraction and to write these stories.

Ask the pupils to show or tell something that they remember about 3. Have the pupils use blocks of wood or clothespins on a cardboard to show that 1 has been taken away from 3.

Continue to explore the concept of separating sets. Originally, the sets were combined in the union of sets and then written to perform addition. Now as the sets are separated, help the children to see that the set is being separated into subsets again. Write the subtraction fact and the related addition fact for 3.

⊞ ⊞ ⊞   A set of blocks

□ □ ⊡   Separate 1 block from the set

3 – 1 = 2   3 minus 1 is 2

2 + 1 = 3   Related addition fact

In addition to these statements, the children are helped to think more critically about their findings if the teacher will continue to ask such questions as the following:

1. What is 3 minus 1?
2. What number must be added to 2 to give 3?
3. What number plus 2 is 3?
4. How did you get your answer? Show us.
5. What are the other names for 3?

The subtraction facts for 3 are:

Without zero facts (number facts 1 less than family)	With zero facts (number facts 1 more than family)
3 – 1 = 2 3 – 2 = 1	3 – 0 = 3 3 – 1 = 2 3 – 2 = 1 3 – 3 = 0

Continue in this way with other number facts to be developed

As the children continue to explore the separation of sets and to write the basic facts, both the vertical and the equation form are presented. In this early presentation which emphasizes the question "How many remain?", the identification of the sum and the given addend will strengthen the relationships between addition and subtraction.

Problem: John had 7¢ when he left home. On the way to school he spent 5¢. How much money does he have left?

Place 7 clothespins on a cardboard. Ask the children to respond to the following statements and then write the equation on the chalkboard. The cardboard may be held in either the horizontal or the vertical position. Take 5 clothespins away. How many remain?

$$7 – 5 = 2 \qquad 5 + 2 = 7$$

Help the children to discover relationships between the addition facts and the subtraction facts. Direct their study in a way to discover the generalization that for every addition fact there are two subtraction facts.

$$\begin{array}{c} 4 \\ + 3 \\ \hline 7 \end{array}$$ and its reverse $$\begin{array}{c} 3 \\ + 4 \\ \hline 7 \end{array}$$ have 2 addends in common and the sum

7 ←—The sum in the addition fact (minuend)
– 4 ←—One of the addends in the addition fact (subtrahend)
3 ←—The second addend in the addition fact (remainder)

$$7 \leftarrow \text{The sum in the addition fact}$$
$$-\ 3 \leftarrow \text{One of the addends in the addition fact}$$
$$4 \leftarrow \text{The second addend in the addition fact}$$

The 100 Basic Subtraction Facts

The structure of the 100 basic subtraction facts provides several generalizations helpful in learning the combinations. The pupils should not be required to use just one approach but guided to discover that a combination of several methods is the more feasible approach in learning the basic facts. In accepting the philosophy that there is "no one correct procedure" for solving problems, many solutions will be discovered and many children will find success in the more simple solutions. The teacher must provide experiences so that children can discover generalizations present in the 100 basic subtraction facts. Although the generalizations are listed, one does not begin with the rule. Questions such as the following will guide children in their thinking about the basic facts.

If you have 3 baseball bats and you give 1 to your friend, how many will you have left? Tell me what you are thinking. Show, using an aid, what you are thinking. Can you write this equation? As you work other problems similar to the one above, are you beginning to identify a pattern? What happens whenever 1 is subtracted from a number?

1. Generalization: If 0 is subtracted from a number, the answer is the number (minuend).

1	2	3	4	5	6	7	8	9
$-\ 0$	$-\ 0$	$-\ 0$	$-\ 0$	$-\ 0$	$-\ 0$	$-\ 0$	$-\ 0$	$-\ 0$
1	2	3	4	5	6	7	8	9

2. Generalization: When the subtrahend is 1, the answer is 1 less than the minuend.

2	3	4	5	6	7	8	9	10
$-\ 1$	$-\ 1$	$-\ 1$	$-\ 1$	$-\ 1$	$-\ 1$	$-\ 1$	$-\ 1$	$-\ 1$
1	2	3	4	5	6	7	8	9

3. Generalization: When the subtrahend and the minuend are alike (doubles), the answer is 0.

0	1	2	3	4	5	6	7	8	9
$-\ 0$	$-\ 1$	$-\ 2$	$-\ 3$	$-\ 4$	$-\ 5$	$-\ 6$	$-\ 7$	$-\ 8$	$-\ 9$
0	0	0	0	0	0	0	0	0	0

There is no one generalization which applies to the remaining facts. Pupils will discover that in:

1. Subtracting an even number from an odd number, the difference is always an odd number. Example:
$$9 - 6 = 3$$

2. Subtracting an odd number from an even number, the difference is always an odd number. Example:
$$12 - 7 = 5$$

3. Subtracting an even number from an even number or an odd number from an odd number, the difference is always an even number. Example:
$$14 - 8 = 6, \qquad 17 - 9 = 8$$

4. Knowing $14 - 7 = 7$ (from $7 + 7 = 14$), then $13 - 7 = 6$ because 13 is 1 less than 14.

5. Knowing $14 - 7 = 7$, then $15 - 7 = 8$ because 15 is 1 more than 14.

There may be little value in presenting the following chart since the basic facts are not taught in table form. However, in looking at the total collection of basic facts, patterns are more easily identified. Children find it interesting to look for patterns and to generalize about them. This involves them in the process of learning.

THE 100 BASIC SUBTRACTION FACTS

0	1	2	3	4	5	6	7	8	9
- 0	- 0	- 0	- 0	- 0	- 0	- 0	- 0	- 0	- 0
0	1	2	3	4	5	6	7	8	9

1	2	3	4	5	6	7	8	9	10
- 1	- 1	- 1	- 1	- 1	- 1	- 1	- 1	- 1	- 1
0	1	2	3	4	5	6	7	8	9

2	3	4	5	6	7	8	9	10	11
- 2	- 2	- 2	- 2	- 2	- 2	- 2	- 2	- 2	- 2
0	1	2	3	4	5	6	7	8	9

3	4	5	6	7	8	9	10	11	12
- 3	- 3	- 3	- 3	- 3	- 3	- 3	- 3	- 3	- 3
0	1	2	3	4	5	6	7	8	9

4	5	6	7	8	9	10	11	12	13
- 4	- 4	- 4	- 4	- 4	- 4	- 4	- 4	- 4	- 4
0	1	2	3	4	5	6	7	8	9

5	6	7	8	9	10	11	12	13	14
- 5	- 5	- 5	- 5	- 5	- 5	- 5	- 5	- 5	- 5
0	1	2	3	4	5	6	7	8	9

6	7	8	9	10	11	12	13	14	15
- 6	- 6	- 6	- 6	- 6	- 6	- 6	- 6	- 6	- 6
0	1	2	3	4	5	6	7	8	9

7	8	9	10	11	12	13	14	15	16
- 7	- 7	- 7	- 7	- 7	- 7	- 7	- 7	- 7	- 7
0	1	2	3	4	5	6	7	8	9

8	9	10	11	12	13	14	15	16	17
- 8	- 8	- 8	- 8	- 8	- 8	- 8	- 8	- 8	- 8
0	1	2	3	4	5	6	7	8	9

9	10	11	12	13	14	15	16	17	18
- 9	- 9	- 9	- 9	- 9	- 9	- 9	- 9	- 9	- 9
0	1	2	3	4	5	6	7	8	9

Using the Basic Facts of Subtraction

Story problems must be used consistently while the pupils are learning the basic facts. They should have many experiences in translating story problems through the following steps.

1. The written problem, stating the problem orally or having the problem read for the pupils. Problem: Jack had 7 marbles. He gave 3 marbles to his friend. How many marbles does he have left?

2. Use concrete materials in solving the problem. Use buttons, sticks, blocks of wood and so on. Problem: Jack places 7 objects on his desk. He gives 3 to his friend. By counting the buttons, sticks and blocks that are left, he discovers how many he has left. State the number fact: 7 take away 3 is 4.

3. Use semiconcrete materials in solving the problem.
Drawing: ○ ○ ○ ○ ○ ⊗ ⊗   Jack crosses out the number which he gave away. He counts the zeros which are not crossed out to find how many he has left. State the number fact: 7 take away 3 is 4.

4. Set up the mathematical questions using numbers in the vertical form. Example:

$$3 + \square = 7 \quad \text{(One addend and the sum are given)}$$

$$\text{Then} \quad \begin{array}{r} 7 \\ -\ 3 \\ \hline 4 \end{array}$$

5. Set up the mathematical questions using numbers in the equation form. Example:

$$3 + \square = 7 \quad \text{(One addend and the sum are given)}$$
$$7 - 3 = 4 \quad \text{(Equation form)}$$

When children have learned several basic facts, they are ready to use them in solving problems having minuends and subtrahends with 2 digits. Problem: John has 20 marbles. He gives 10 marbles to his friend. How many marbles does John have left?

Solutions suggested by the students:

1. The number line: Count 10 spaces to the left of 20.

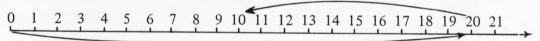

2. The counting frame: Place 20 beads to the right, then count 10 and move to the left leaving 10. In the place value form, the numbers must be read as 2 tens minus 1 ten and not 2 – 1. This is to emphasize place value.

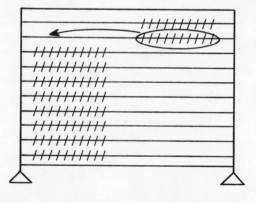

Tens	Units
2	0
- 1	0
1	0

3. Place value: 20 $\longrightarrow$ 2 tens + 0 units

                – 10   1 ten + 0 units

                              1 ten + 0 units

4. Inverse relationship between addition and subtraction:

              10   20

           + 10 $\longrightarrow$ – 10

              20   10

Tens tables similar to the hundred basic facts table can be constructed by the children. In this chart, the minuend is within the chart. The vertical column at the left names the subtrahend while the top row names the difference. The chart illustrates 7 tens – 4 tens = 3 tens or 70 – 40 = 30.

SUBTRACTING TENS

– +	0	10	20	30	40	50	60	70	80	90
0	0	10	20	30	40	50	60	70	80	90
10	10	20	30	40	50	60	70	80	90	100
20	20	30	40	50	60	70	80	90	100	110
30	30	40	50	60	70	80	90	100	110	120
40	40	50	60	70	80	90	100	110	120	130
50	50	60	70	80	90	100	110	120	130	140
60	60	70	80	90	100	110	120	130	140	150
70	70	80	90	100	110	120	130	140	150	160
80	80	90	100	110	120	130	140	150	160	170
90	90	100	110	120	130	140	150	160	170	180

Many students already understand the distributive property of multiplication over addition. The study of equations has developed the concept of expanded notation and the renaming of numbers so that the following approach will challenge them to further study in subtraction of tens.

$$30 + 20 = (3 \times 10) + (2 \times 10)$$
$$= (3 + 2) \times 10 \quad \text{Distributive property}$$
$$= 5 \times 10 \quad \text{Multiplication}$$
$$= 50$$

$$50 - 30 = (5 \times 10) - (3 \times 10)$$
$$= (5 - 3) \times 10 \quad \text{Distributive property}$$
$$= 2 \times 10 \quad \text{Multiplication}$$
$$= 20$$

Subtraction by Endings

Children who can identify basic facts and who can complete the subtraction without too much difficulty are ready to move into a solution involving greater mental activity. Subtraction by endings consists in subtracting a 1-digit number from a 2-digit number in one mental operation. If the pupil thinks 4 from 6 is 2, 0 from 1 is 1, he is using decomposition. If he thinks 4 from 16 in one operation because he recognizes the elements in the tens and the units places, he is subtracting by endings.

$$\begin{array}{r} 16 \\ -\ 4 \\ \hline \end{array}$$ He observes that there is no regrouping
He thinks from left to right, one, two = 12

A table for subtraction by endings can be structured by the pupils. Note that several generalizations applicable to the 100 basic subtraction facts such as subtracting ones and doubles are also applicable to this table.

11	12	13	14	15	16	17	18	19
− 1	− 1	− 1	− 1	− 1	− 1	− 1	− 1	− 1

12	13	14	15	16	17	18	19
− 2	− 2	− 2	− 2	− 2	− 2	− 2	− 2

13	14	15	16	17	18	19
− 3	− 3	− 3	− 3	− 3	− 3	− 3

14	15	16	17	18	19
− 4	− 4	− 4	− 4	− 4	− 4

15	16	17	18	19
− 5	− 5	− 5	− 5	− 5

16	17	18	19
− 6	− 6	− 6	− 6

17	18	19
− 7	− 7	− 7

18	19
− 8	− 8

19
− 9

Meanings and relationships are best discovered by pupils when they are guided through a sequence of problem situations which are gradual in development. The sequence as developed here is not meant to be presented to children. These suggestions are made to teachers to acquaint them with solutions which children will present as they are guided to think about a problem. Several approaches are presented to make certain that the process becomes meaningful to children.

The subtraction of tens from tens has been developed. The examples to follow set the stage for teaching subtraction through 3-digit numbers without regrouping.

1. Establish the concept that 3 from 5 is always 2 regardless of its place in a number. To arrive at the true quantity, multiply by the place value. A 2 in the tens place equals $2 \times 10 = 20$.

$$
\begin{array}{ccccc}
5 & 50 & 5 \text{ tens} & 50 \\
\underline{-\ 3} & \underline{-\ 30} \longrightarrow & \underline{-\ 3 \text{ tens}} \longrightarrow & \underline{-\ 30} \\
2 & & 2 \text{ tens} & 20
\end{array}
$$

2. Establish the concept that units and units and tens and tens are subtracted.

Place Value   Expanded Notation

$$
\begin{array}{cc}
25 & 2\,t + 5\,u \\
\underline{-\ 3} \longrightarrow & \underline{-\quad\ 3\,u} \\
& 2\,t + 2\,u = 22
\end{array}
\qquad
\begin{array}{cc}
20 + 5 & 25 \\
\underline{-\quad\ 3} \longrightarrow & \underline{-\ 3} \\
20 + 2 = 22 & 22
\end{array}
$$

$$
\begin{array}{cc}
57 & 5\,t + 7\,u \\
\underline{-\ 4} \longrightarrow & \underline{-\quad\ 4\,u} \\
& 5\,t + 3\,u = 53
\end{array}
\qquad
\begin{array}{cc}
50 + 7 & 57 \\
\underline{-\quad\ 4} \longrightarrow & \underline{-\ 4} \\
50 + 3 = 53 & 53
\end{array}
$$

Equation

$$
\begin{aligned}
25 - 3 \ = \ &(20 + 5) - 3 && \text{Renaming 25 (expanded notation)} \\
&20 + (5 - 3) && \text{To subtract units from units} \\
&20 + 2 = 22 && \text{Tens and units are added}
\end{aligned}
$$

$$
\begin{aligned}
57 - 4 \ = \ &(50 + 7) - 4 = && \text{Renaming 57 (expanded notation)} \\
&50 + (7 - 4) = && \text{To subtract units from units} \\
&50 + 3 = && \text{Tens and units are added}
\end{aligned}
$$

In the previous subtraction in which a 1-digit number is subtracted from a 2-digit number, children discovered that they can first subtract the units and then add the difference to the tens. Understanding the subtraction involved in $40 - 10 = \square$ and $37 - 3 = \square$, they are now ready for 2-digit subtraction.

The addition of 2-digit numbers without regrouping should be reviewed. In this discussion, the children will recall or rediscover that they can find the sum of $43 + 4$ and the sum of $56 + 30$ by adding units and adding tens and then adding the two sums. Expanded notation emphasized the addition of tens and tens and units and units. The properties of commutivity and associativity were used to explain the procedure. Since these properties do not pertain to subtraction, the children will add units and tens in the answer to arrive at the difference.

Subtraction of 2-Digit Numbers (no regrouping):

Place Value   Expanded Notation

$$
\begin{array}{cc}
53 & 5\,t + 3\,u \\
\underline{-\ 20} \longrightarrow & \underline{-\ 2\,t + 0\,u} \\
& 3\,t + 3\,u = 33
\end{array}
\qquad
\begin{array}{cc}
50 + 3 & 53 \\
\underline{-\ 20 + 0} \longrightarrow & \underline{-\ 20} \\
30 + 3 = 33 & 33
\end{array}
$$

Substantiate the answer using a place value chart:

Tens	Units	
¦¦¦¦¦	¦¦¦	Remove 20
¦¦¦	¦¦¦	Remaining objects
3 t	+ 3 u	= 33

Place Value   Expanded Notation

$$47 \longrightarrow 4\,t + 7\,u$$
$$- 23 \qquad\ \ - 2\,t + 3\,u$$
$$\overline{\qquad\qquad\ \ 2\,t + 4\,u = 24}$$

$$40 + 7 \longrightarrow 47$$
$$- 20 + 3 \qquad - 23$$
$$\overline{20 + 4 = 24 \qquad 24}$$

Children who show insight into the solution of these examples can proceed with the equation form. They should compare the equation with the place value and the expanded notation form to see that in each case tens and tens and ones and ones are subtracted and the two answers are added.

Equation Form

$$68$$
$$- 45$$

$$68 - 45 = (60 + 8) - (40 + 5)$$
$$= (60 - 40) + (8 - 5) \qquad \text{collecting tens and units}$$
$$= \quad 20 \ + \ 3 \ = \ 23$$

$$45 \longrightarrow 40 + 5 \qquad 68 \longrightarrow 60 + 8$$
$$+ 23 \qquad\ + 20 + 3 \qquad - 45 \qquad - 40 + 5$$
$$\overline{68} \qquad\ \overline{60 + 8 = 68} \qquad\quad \overline{20 + 3 = 23}$$

By observation and manipulation, children discover that tens are subtracted just as ones are subtracted. As practice is carried to 3- and 4-digit numbers in subtraction, children discover that hundreds and thousands are subtracted just as tens and ones are subtracted. Have the pupils tell what they are thinking while they solve examples similar to the following using the expanded form and the common algorism.

$$236 \longrightarrow 200 + 30 + 6 \longrightarrow 236$$
$$- \ \ 4 \qquad - \qquad\qquad\ \ 4 \qquad\qquad - \ \ 4$$
$$\overline{\qquad\quad 200 + 30 + 2 = 232 \qquad \overline{232}}$$

$$478 \longrightarrow 400 + 70 + 8 \longrightarrow 478$$
$$- \ 50 \qquad - \qquad\quad\ 50 + 0 \qquad\quad - \ 50$$
$$\overline{\qquad\quad 400 + 20 + 8 = 428 \qquad \overline{428}}$$

$$687 \longrightarrow 600 + 80 + 7 \longrightarrow 687$$
$$- 372 \qquad - 300 + 70 + 2 \qquad - 372$$
$$\overline{\qquad\quad 300 + 10 + 5 = 315 \qquad \overline{315}}$$

Decomposition (regrouping)

Decomposition is necessary when there are more units in one or more places in the subtrahend than in the corresponding places in the minuend.

Minuend $\longrightarrow$ 635   7 is greater than 5 in the units place

Subtrahend $\longrightarrow$ 287   8 is greater than 3 in the tens place

Prepare for decomposition by reviewing with the pupils the thought process in subtracting 7 from 13. Ask the pupils to demonstrate the subtraction as shown below:

$$13$$
$$- \ 7$$

The 13 represents a collection of 13 objects (not 1 ten and 3 ones). Separate 7 from the set of 13.

O   O   O   O   O   O   O   O
O   O   O   O $\longrightarrow$ O   O   ⊗   ⊗
O   O   O   O   ⊗   ⊗   ⊗   ⊗

Shown on the abacus:

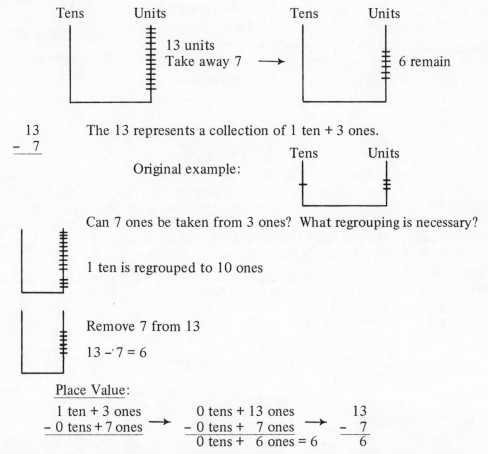

13   The 13 represents a collection of 1 ten + 3 ones.
− 7

Original example:

Can 7 ones be taken from 3 ones? What regrouping is necessary?

1 ten is regrouped to 10 ones

Remove 7 from 13

13 − 7 = 6

Place Value:

1 ten + 3 ones	0 tens + 13 ones	13
− 0 tens + 7 ones	− 0 tens + 7 ones	− 7
	0 tens + 6 ones = 6	6

Stress the similarity of the following examples: What is similar in each example? What is the basic fact to be identified? Prove your work using the abacus and the place value chart.

15
− 9   Think 1 ten and 5 ones as 15 ones

15   Ones
− 9   Ones
6   Ones

Expanded Notation

25
− 9   Think 2 tens and 5 ones as 1 ten and 15 ones

10 + 15
−   9
10 +   6 = 16

Expanded Notation

45
− 9   Think 4 tens and 5 ones as 3 tens and 15 ones

30 + 15
−   9
30 + 6 = 36

Children may be interested in performing the operation by subtracting the subtrahend from the 10 or tens instead of the basic fact as above. Many children having difficulty recalling the basic facts do learn readily to subtract from tens. In this instance, the tens are thought of as units.

$$\begin{array}{c} 13 \\ -\ 8 \\ \hline \end{array} \longrightarrow \begin{array}{c} 10+3 \\ -\ 8 \\ \hline 2+3=5 \end{array} \longrightarrow \begin{array}{l} 10\ \text{units} - 8\ \text{units} = 2\ \text{units} \\ 2\ \text{units} + 3\ \text{units} = 5\ \text{units} \end{array}$$

$$\begin{array}{c} 23 \\ -\ 7 \\ \hline \end{array} \longrightarrow \begin{array}{c} 10+13 \\ -\ 7 \\ \hline 3+13=16 \end{array} \longrightarrow \begin{array}{c} 13+10 \\ -\ 7 \\ \hline 13+3=16 \end{array} \longrightarrow \begin{array}{c} \overset{1\ 1}{23} \\ -\ 7 \\ \hline 16 \end{array}$$

$$\begin{array}{c} \overset{3\ 1}{42} \\ -\ 9 \\ \hline \end{array} \qquad \begin{array}{c} 30+12 \\ -\ \ \ \ 9 \\ \hline \end{array} \longrightarrow \quad \text{Think 12 as } 10+2. \text{ Subtract 9 from 10, then add 2.}$$

$$\begin{array}{c} 30+10+2 \\ -\ \ \ \ \ \ 9 \\ \hline 30+\ \ 1+2 = 33 \end{array}$$

Teachers must remember that these are techniques to use in helping children to learn the basic facts as well as procedures for solving examples when the facts cannot be recalled. Then, too, many children can subtract without using "crutches." They perform their work mentally and make no record of their activity. The variations among pupils should indicate to every teacher that all children cannot be taught as one class. A class must be divided into several sections to care for the individual needs.

In subtraction involving regrouping with 2–digit numbers, numbers are expanded to establish place value and the basic subtraction facts.

$$\begin{array}{c} 23 \\ -\ 17 \\ \hline \end{array} \longrightarrow \begin{array}{c} 10+13 \\ -(10+7) \\ \hline 6 \end{array}$$

$$\begin{array}{c} 54 \\ -\ 29 \\ \hline \end{array} \longrightarrow \begin{array}{c} 40+14 \\ -(20+9) \\ \hline 20+\ 5\ =\ 25 \end{array}$$

Common algorism:

$$\begin{array}{c} 54 \\ -\ 29 \\ \hline \end{array} \longrightarrow \begin{array}{c} \overset{4\ 1}{54} \\ -\ 29 \\ \hline 25 \end{array}$$

Step 1. Substitute 10 ones for 1 ten. The minuend is now thought of as 4 tens and 14 ones.

Step 2. Take 9 from 14 $(14 - 9 = 5)$ or $(10 - 9) + 4 = 5$.

Step 3. 4 tens – 2 tens = 2 tens.

Equation form:

$$54 - 29 = N$$
$$(50 + 4) - (20 + 9) = N \qquad \text{Expanded notation}$$
$$(50 - 20) + (4 - 9) = N \qquad \text{Collecting like terms}$$
$$(40 - 20) + (14 - 9) = N \qquad \text{Regrouping}$$
$$\ \ \ \ 20\ \ \ \ +\ \ \ \ 5\ \ \ = 25$$

$$76 - 38 = N$$
$$(70 + 6) - (30 + 8) = N$$
$$(70 - 30) + (6 - 8) = N$$
$$(60 - 30) + (16 - 8) = N$$
$$\ \ \ 30\ \ \ \ +\ \ \ \ 8\ \ \ = 38$$

$$\begin{array}{c} 76 \\ -\ 38 \\ \hline \end{array} \longrightarrow \begin{array}{c} 70+6 \\ -30+8 \\ \hline \end{array} \longrightarrow \begin{array}{c} 60+16 \\ -30+\ 8 \\ \hline 30+\ 8 = 38 \end{array}$$

A sequence can be developed with the pupils to establish the language involved in solving examples having 3-digit numbers. The following examples illustrate the sequence:

1. Pattern to identify: Regroup 1 ten to 10 ones

474
– 248

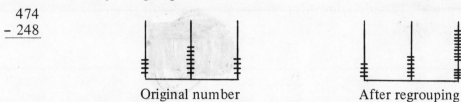

Original number   After regrouping

Expanded notation to emphasize to children what is taking place:

473	$400 + 70 + 3$	$400 + 60 + 13$
– 248	$-(200 + 40 + 8)$	$-(200 + 40 + \ 8)$
		$200 + 20 + \ 5 \ = \ 225$

2. Pattern to identify: Regroup 1 hundred to 10 tens

527
– 283

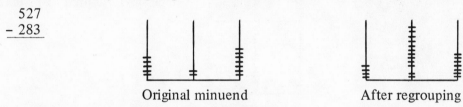

Original minuend   After regrouping

Expanded notation to emphasize the regrouping:

527	$500 + 20 + 7$	$400 + 120 + 7$
– 283	$- 200 + 80 + 3$	$-(200 + \ 80 + 3)$
		$200 + \ 40 + 4 \ = \ 244$

3. Patterns to identify: Regroup 1 ten to 10 ones, 1 hundred to 10 tens.

724
– 276

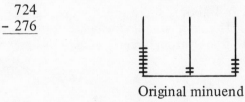

Original minuend

Step 1. First regrouping: How many ones? How many tens?

6 ones from 14 ones equals 8 ones

$$\begin{array}{r} {\scriptstyle 1\ 1} \\ 7\not{2}4 \\ -\ 276 \\ \hline 8 \end{array}$$

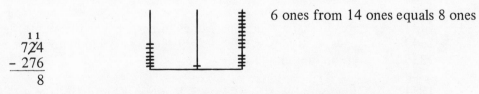

Step 2. Second regrouping: How many tens? Hundreds?

7 tens from 11 tens = 4 tens

$$\begin{array}{r} {\scriptstyle 6\ 1\ 1} \\ 7\not{2}4 \\ -\ 276 \\ \hline 448 \end{array}$$

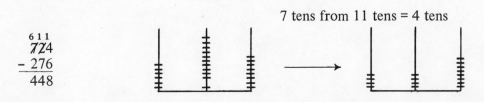

Step 3.   724   700 + 20 + 4   700 + 10 + 14   600 + 110 + 14
          – 276   – 200 + 70 + 6   – 200 + 70 + 6   – 200 + 70 + 6
                                                                      400 + 40 + 8 = 448

Step 4.   Pattern to identify: Regroup 1 hundred to 10 tens.

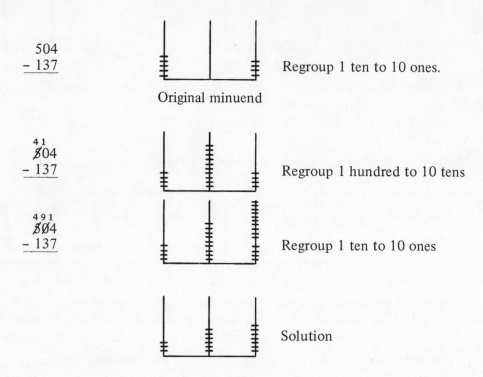

504
– 137   Regroup 1 ten to 10 ones.

                    Original minuend

 4 1
 5̸04
– 137   Regroup 1 hundred to 10 tens

 4 9 1
 5̸0̸4
– 137   Regroup 1 ten to 10 ones

                                               Solution

Another approach to solving Problem 4 above, and a much more logical procedure, is to think of 504 as 50 tens and 4 ones. The understanding which children have in reading numbers will determine their ability to think through regrouping in this manner.

 4 9 1
 5̸0̸4
– 137   50 tens – 1 ten = 49 tens

The technique of reading the minuend when it contains zeros as so many hundreds, tens and units, is logical and meaningful. The following examples illustrate this point further.

         5 9 9 1
1.   6̸0̸0̸7   Read 6007 as 600 tens 7 ones. Regroup 1 ten from 600 tens to 10
     – 2649   ones, 600 tens – 1 ten = 599 tens. This eliminates the need to re-
      3358   group in each place.

         3 9 12 1
2.   4̸0̸3̸1   Regroup 1 ten to 10 ones. Regroup 1 hundred from 40 hundreds
     – 1256   to 10 tens. 40 hundreds – 1 hundred = 39 hundreds.
      2775

Important Ideas Begun

1. Subtraction is the inverse operation of addition.
2. There are three forms of subtraction.
3. Skills in teaching the basic facts.
4. Expanded notation to strengthen the concept of place value.
5. Properties of subtraction.
6. Expanded notation to rename numbers.

The algorisms that we have been using lead directly to the use of the common algorism. However, another approach which will challenge children to think about subtraction in another way is to rename the subtrahend so that one of its numbers is the same as the units digit in the minuend.

In solving $15 - 9 = \square$, instead of thinking 9 from 15 or $(10 - 9) + 5$, rename the subtrahend so that the units digit in the *minuend* is subtracted leaving 0.

$15 - 9 = N$	
$15 - (5 + 4) = N$	Renaming 9 to contain a 5
$(10 + 5) - (5 + 4) = N$	Renaming 15 to contain a 5
$10 + (5 - 5) - 4 = N$	
$(10 + 0) - 4 = N \qquad 5 - 5 = 0$	
$\quad 10 \quad - 4 = 6$	

$23 - 7 = N$	
$23 - (3 + 4) = N$	Renaming 7 to contain a 3
$(20 + 3) - (3 + 4) = N$	Renaming 23 to contain a 3
$20 + (3 - 3) - 4 = N$	
$(20 + 0) - 4 = N$	
$\quad 20 \quad - 4 = 16.$	

Children will find ways to solve an equation other than those normally presented when they are challenged. The previous equation may be written in the following way:

$23 - 7 = N$	
$23 - 3 - 4 = N$	3 and 4 are subtrahends
$(23 - 3) - 4 = N$	
$\quad 20 \quad - 4 = 16$	Always subtracting from tens

$56 - 8 = N$	
$56 - 6 - 2 = N$	Renaming 8
$(56 - 6) - 2 = N$	
$\quad 50 \quad - 2 = 48$	Subtracting from tens

Activities to Broaden the Scope of Subtraction

The following activities can be used for drill of facts, to create interest and to add new ways to perform subtraction. In no case should these activities be required of all pupils. Challenge the children to do research on these and other activities so that they may develop deeper insights.

1. **Counting backwards**: Count backwards by twos starting with 21. What number is skipped each time? Example:

21, 19, 17, 15, 13, 11, 9, 7, 5, 3, 1

What key facts are encountered?

a. $\begin{array}{r} 21 \\ -\ 2 \end{array}$ $\longrightarrow$ $\begin{array}{r} 10+11 \\ -\qquad 2 \\ \hline 9 \end{array}$

b. $\begin{array}{r} 19 \\ -\ 2 \end{array}$ $\longrightarrow$ $\begin{array}{r} 10+9 \\ -\qquad 2 \\ \hline 7 \end{array}$

2. **Excesses of nines (casting out nines)**: A common check for accuracy in subtraction is made by adding the subtrahend and the difference. The sum is the minuend. For most children in Grades 5 and 6, this is the procedure used to check the work. Casting out nines can be used to challenge the pupils who do the ordinary things well. Example:

$\begin{array}{r} 3428 \\ -\ 2103 \\ \hline 1325 \end{array}$ Add: $3+4+2+8=17$ Excess of nines is 8
                Add: $2+1+0+3=\ 6$ Excess of nines is 6
                Add: $1+3+2+5=11$ Excess of nines is 2

To find the excess of nines in each case, divide by 9.

$\begin{array}{r} 1 \\ 9\overline{)17} \\ 9 \\ \hline 8 \end{array}$ The number of nines is not considered

$\leftarrow$ Considered because it is in excess of nines in 17

$\begin{array}{r} 0 \\ 9\overline{)6} \end{array}$ No nines in 6

$\leftarrow$ The excess

$\begin{array}{r} 1 \\ 9\overline{)11} \\ 9 \\ \hline 2 \end{array}$ The number of nines is not considered

$\leftarrow$ The excess of nines in 11

Then $3428 \longrightarrow 17$ Excess $\longrightarrow 8$
       $\dfrac{-2103 \longrightarrow\ 6}{1325 \longrightarrow 11}$ $\dfrac{\text{Excess} \longrightarrow -6}{\longrightarrow \text{Excess } 2 \leftrightarrow 2}$

Subtract 6 from 8 = 2. Excess in the difference is 2. Since the difference has an excess of 2 and the difference of the two excesses is 2, the difference 1325 is probably correct.

3. **Rounding off the subtrahend (concept of compensation)**: If the same number is added to the minuend and the subtrahend, the difference is unchanged. Examples:

$\begin{array}{r} 13 \\ -\ 7 \end{array}$ $\begin{array}{r} 13+3=16 \\ -\ 7+3=10 \\ \hline \end{array}$ $\begin{array}{r} 342 \\ -\ 187 \end{array}$ $\begin{array}{r} 342+13=355 \\ -\ 187+13=200 \\ \hline \end{array}$

$$(a+n)-(b+n)=c$$
$$a\ -\ b\ =c$$

The number added in each case is the difference between the subtrahend and the next multiple of 10. This technique brings subtraction into the realm of mental activity. As the spread between the subtrahend (163) and the multiple of 10, 200, increases, it becomes more desirable to use the common algorism. Illustration:

$$\begin{array}{r} 481 \\ -\ 163 \\ \hline \end{array}$$
The difference between 200 and 163 is 37. The addition of 481 and 37 can be more cumbersome than the normal subtraction. The final subtraction in the problem is 518 – 200 = 318.

4. **Reversing digit numbers**: This activity provides an opportunity for the pupil to *identify patterns* from which a generalization can be stated. It also provides, under a pleasant situation, an excellent review of regrouping and place value in subtraction. The exercise can be used to introduce arithmetic at the beginning of the fifth and sixth grades instead of the usual review. The teacher can introduce this activity if she knows that the children can regroup in subtraction.

Consider any 3-digit number. Reverse the number; write the larger number as the minuend.

$$\begin{array}{r} 753 \\ -\ 357 \\ \hline \end{array} \qquad \begin{array}{r} 864 \\ -\ 468 \\ \hline \end{array} \qquad \begin{array}{r} 362 \\ -\ 263 \\ \hline \end{array} \qquad \begin{array}{r} 622 \\ -\ 226 \\ \hline \end{array}$$

When the pupils have become acquainted with the technique of setting up examples, ask them to construct several and to solve them. Generate interest in looking for patterns which will lead to the solution of an example. Ask such questions as: "If you tell me what the *units* digit is in the difference in your example, I will tell you your answer." Example:

$$\begin{array}{r} 753 \\ -\ 357 \\ \hline \end{array}$$
The pupil says 6. Using 6 as your guide, the answer to the problem is 396.

Solution: After solving several examples, children soon identify the following patterns:

    a. The middle number is always 9. Why is this so? (Regrouping.)

    b. The sum of the digits in the units and the hundreds place is always 9. (Can be stated as the difference between the units digit and 9.)

Ask the question in different ways:

    a. What are the digits in the units place in the minuend and the subtrahend? By knowing 7 and 3, the subtraction can be completed mentally (13 – 7).

    b. What are the digits in the hundreds place in the minuend and the subtrahend? Because of the regrouping necessary, it is no longer 7 and 3 which the pupil states, but 6 and 3.

5. **Reversing 4-digit numbers**: This is a good practice for reviewing the basic facts in subtraction. Children who understand the process of finding the excess of nines will be challenged with this activity. Ask the children to find a pattern which will identify a number "crossed out" in the difference. This is a challenge to their discovery technique.

Procedure: a. Ask the children to construct and solve several examples.

$$\begin{array}{r} 7513 \\ -\ 3157 \\ \hline 43\cancel{5}6 \end{array}$$
b. Ask the children to "cross out" any one digit in the difference. (5 has been crossed out in the example.)

c. Ask a child to tell or write on the board the digits not "crossed out" (4, 3, 6).

d. The teacher, or a pupil knowing the pattern, then tells the number crossed out.

e. Challenge the pupils to discover why it was possible to state the number which was "crossed out."

Solutions: a. Add the remaining numbers in the answer.

b. Add 4 + 3 + 6 = 13.

c. Find excess of nines in 13. ⟶ $9\overline{)13}$

$$\begin{array}{r} 1 \\ 9\overline{)13} \\ \underline{9} \\ 4 \ \text{Excess} \end{array}$$

d. Subtract 4 from 9 = 5. 5 is the number "crossed out."

6. **Signed digits (negative numbers):** Subtract the smaller number from the larger number in each place. Use an Integer Number Line to complete the subtraction for each place. Procedure:

$$\begin{array}{r} 467 \\ -\ 129 \\ \hline 34\overline{2} \end{array}$$

7 from 9 = $\overline{2}$. $\overline{2}$ is a signed number. It indicates that the subtrahend was larger than the minuend. The others are positive: 6 – 2 = 4, 4 – 1 = 3.

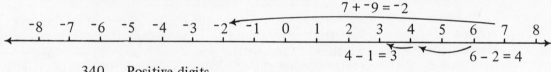

$$\begin{array}{r} 340 \\ +\ \overline{}2 \\ \hline 338 \end{array}$$ Positive digits
Negative digit

To complete the operation, the signed number, $\overline{2}$, is added to the positive number, 340.

$$\begin{array}{r} 4562 \\ -\ 2937 \\ \hline 24\overline{3}\overline{5} \end{array}$$ The negative numbers are 4 and 5

2030 ← The positive numbers
$+\ \ ^-405$ ← The negative numbers
1625

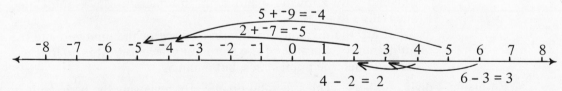

Generalization: In the addition of the positive and the negative numbers, observe that one always subtracts from a 10 or a power of ten. Basic facts other than 10 are not encountered, for example, 12 – 7.

7. **Making change:** This method is useful in making change when the minuend is a $1.00, $10.00, $100.00 and so on. The subtraction is performed as a mental process. Procedure:

$$\begin{array}{r} \$1.00 \\ -\ .37 \\ \hline \end{array}$$ think ⟶ $$\begin{array}{r} .90 \\ -\ .37 \\ \hline \$\ .63 \end{array}$$ $$\begin{array}{r} \$10.00 \\ -\ \ 2.76 \\ \hline \$\ 7.24 \end{array}$$ think ⟶ $$\begin{array}{r} 9.90 \\ -\ 2.76 \\ \hline \$\ 7.24 \end{array}$$

8. **Subtraction by complements (subtrahend):** The complement of a number is the difference between a number and the next power of 10. This exercise provides practice and fun in manipulating numbers. Procedure:

$$\begin{array}{r} 4,763 \\ -\ 2,847 \\ \hline \end{array}$$ The complement of 2,847 is 7,153 (10,000 – 2,847).
Add. 4,763 + 7,153 = 11,916

$$\begin{array}{r} 4,763 \\ +\ 7,153 \\ \hline 11,916 \\ -10,000 \\ \hline 1,916 \end{array}$$ Because 10,000 is the power of 10 used in finding the complement, subtract it from the sum, 11,916. The remainder is the difference.
4,763 – 2,847 = 1,916

9. **Extending the use of the number line:**

WHOLE NUMBER LINE

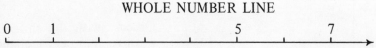

Point to divisions on the number line and ask the children to name and to write in the correct numeral. What is the second point to the right of 0? Write 2 as $^+2$ to emphasize positive numbers. The $^+2$ is read positive 2.

The number line above is drawn in a horizontal position. Now draw a number line in a vertical position. Point to the divisions on the number line and ask the children to name and to write in the correct number. Where is $^+1$?

Combine the two number lines and construct the following graph. The horizontal number line (the first □ in the equation) is the base; the vertical number line (the second □ in the equation) is the vertical scale to the left. Read the horizontal scale first. The equation □ + □ = 5 has two missing elements. If these replacements make the equation true, it is called a truth set or solution set. Identify the pattern for the set of 5. Note that this graph is similar to the 100 basic addition chart.

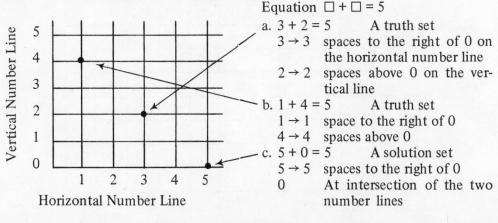

Horizontal Number Line

Equation □ + □ = 5

a. 3 + 2 = 5   A truth set
   3 → 3   spaces to the right of 0 on the horizontal number line
   2 → 2   spaces above 0 on the vertical line

b. 1 + 4 = 5   A truth set
   1 → 1   space to the right of 0
   4 → 4   spaces above 0

c. 5 + 0 = 5   A solution set
   5 → 5   spaces to the right of 0
   0   At intersection of the two number lines

THE INTEGER NUMBER LINE

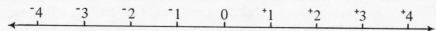

Point to the divisions on the number line and ask the children to name and to write in the correct number.

a. What is the second point to the right of 0? What is this point called? Say that this number is read negative 2. Continue the questioning to complete the scale as above.

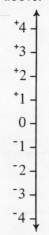

Observe with the children that the positive numbers are above 0 and the negative numbers are below 0.

If we wish to show a graph of an ordered pair of numbers, we can make a chart by placing two Integer Number Lines perpendicular to each other and select their point of intersection as 0.

To determine the location of an ordered pair of numbers, the first number of the ordered pair is read on the X–axis, we measure to the right of 0 if the first number of the pair is positive and to the left of 0 if the number is negative. Similarly, if the second number is positive, we measure above 0 on the Y–axis and, if negative, below 0. Locate the following points on the graph. Remember that the X–axis is read first.

a. ($^+$1, $^+$2)   b. ($^-$2, $^+$3)   c. ($^-$3, $^+$4)   d. ($^-$4, $^-$2)
e. ($^+$5, 0)   f. (0, $^+$5)   g. (0, $^-$4)

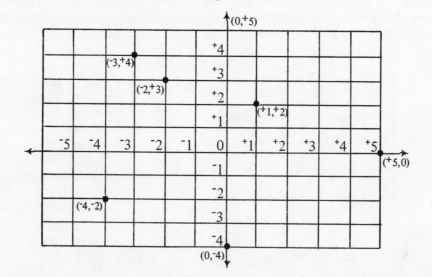

To develop facility with the graph and number pairs, children can use a similar chart and play a team game. The purpose of the game is to establish a pattern of 3, 4 or more points in a straight line. Who ever does this first wins the game.

Chapter Summary

Place value must be interpreted so that regrouping in subtraction will have meaning. Expanding numbers and reading numbers in several ways strengthen this concept.

1. **Use of sets:**
    a. One-to-one comparison

        ◯   How many are left?
        ◯ ◯   How many more or less?
        ◯ ◯
        ◯ ◯

    b. Removing sets

        ◯ ◯
        ◯ ◯   How many remain?
        ◯ → ◯   How many more or less?
        ◯ ⊠
        ◯ ⊠

    c. Determining the cardinality of sets

$$N \left\{ \begin{matrix} ◯ & ◯ & ◯ \\ ◯ & ◯ & ◯ \\ ◯ & ◯ & ◯ \end{matrix} \right\} - N \left\{ \begin{matrix} ◯ & ◯ & ◯ \\ ◯ & ◯ \end{matrix} \right\} = N \left\{ \begin{matrix} ◯ & ◯ \\ ◯ & ◯ \end{matrix} \right\}$$

$$9 \qquad - \qquad 5 \qquad = \qquad 4$$

2. **Relationship of addition to subtraction: learning the basic facts:**

    a.
    $$\begin{array}{c} 7 \\ +6 \\ \hline 13 \end{array} \longrightarrow \begin{array}{c} 13 \\ -6 \\ \hline 7 \end{array} \longrightarrow \begin{array}{c} 13 \\ -7 \\ \hline 6 \end{array}$$

    The sum becomes the minuend.
    The addends become subtrahends.
    Addition of subtrahend and difference is the minuend.

    b. The use of aids: whole number line

        0   1   2   3   4   5 $1 + 3 = 4$

                                $4 - 3 = 1$

3. **Subtraction without regrouping:**

    a. One-digit subtrahends

Place Value		Expanded Notation	
27	$2\,t + 7\,u$	27	$20 + 7$
$-\ 4 \longrightarrow$	$-\qquad 4\,u$	$-\ 4 \longrightarrow$	$-\qquad 4$
	$2\,t + 3\,u = 23$		$20 + 3 = 23$

<u>Common Algorism</u>

```
  27
-  4
  23
```

<u>Equation</u>

$$27 - 4 = (20 + 7) - 4 =$$
$$20 + (7 - 4) =$$
$$20 + \quad 3 \quad = 23$$

b. Two-digit subtraction

<u>Place Value</u>

```
  36        3 t + 6 u
- 20   →  - 2 t + 0 u
            1 t + 6 u = 16
```

<u>Expanded Notation</u>

```
  30 + 6
- 20 + 0
  10 + 6 = 16
```

<u>Common Algorism</u>

```
  36
- 20
  16
```

<u>Equation</u>

$$36 - 20 = (30 + 6) - 20 =$$
$$(30 - 20) + 6 =$$
$$10 \quad + 6 = 16$$

<u>Place Value</u>

```
  76        7 t + 6 u
- 45   →  - 4 t + 5 u
            3 t + 1 u = 31
```

<u>Expanded Notation</u>

```
  70 + 6
- 40 + 5
  30 + 1 = 31
```

<u>Common Algorism</u>

```
  76
- 45
  31
```

<u>Equation</u>

$$76 - 45 = (70 + 6) - (40 + 5) \quad \text{Renaming}$$
$$(70 - 40) + (6 - 5) =$$
$$30 \quad + \quad 1 \quad = 31$$

4. Subtraction with regrouping:

<u>Basic Fact</u>

```
  13        10 + 3
-  7   →  -    7              →
   6          3 + 3 = 6
```

$$13 - 7 = (10 + 3) - 7 =$$
$$(10 - 7) + 3 =$$
$$3 \quad + 3 = 6$$

<u>Place Value</u>

```
  53        5 t + 3 u      4 t + 13 u
- 27   →  - 2 t + 7 u  → - 2 t +  7 u
                          2 t +  6 u = 26
```

<u>Expanded Notation</u>

```
  85        80 + 5       70 + 15
- 49   →  - 40 + 9  → - 40 +  9
                       30 +  6 = 36
```

<u>Common Algorism</u>

```
  7 1
  8̸5̸
- 49
  36
```

Equation

$72 - 35 = (70 + 2) - (30 + 5) =$ Renaming

$(70 - 30) + (2 - 5) =$

$(60 - 30) + (12 - 5) =$ Regrouping

$30 \quad + \quad 7 \quad = 37$

Place Value

$$\begin{array}{l} 742 \\ -\,378 \end{array} \rightarrow \begin{array}{l} 7\,h + 4\,t + 2\,u \\ -\,3\,h + 7\,t + 8\,u \end{array} \rightarrow \begin{array}{l} 7\,h + 3\,t + 12\,u \\ -\,3\,h + 7\,t + 8\,u \end{array} \rightarrow \begin{array}{l} 6\,h + 13\,t + 12\,u \\ -\,3\,h + 7\,t + 8\,u \\ \hline 3\,h + 6\,t + 4\,u = 364 \end{array}$$

Expanded Notation

$$\begin{array}{l} 951 \\ -\,496 \end{array} \rightarrow \begin{array}{l} 900 + 50 + 1 \\ -\,400 + 90 + 6 \end{array} \rightarrow \begin{array}{l} 900 + 40 + 11 \\ -\,400 + 90 + 6 \end{array} \rightarrow \begin{array}{l} 800 + 140 + 11 \\ -\,400 + 90 + 6 \\ \hline 400 + 50 + 5 = 455 \end{array}$$

Equation

$\begin{array}{l} 576 \\ -\,289 \end{array}$ $576 - 289 = (500 + 70 + 6) - (200 + 80 + 9) \quad = $ Renaming

$(500 - 200) + (70 - 80) + (6 - 9) \quad =$

$(500 - 200) + (60 - 80) + (16 - 9) =$ Regrouping

$(400 - 200) + (160 - 80) + 16 - 9 \; =$ Regrouping

$200 \quad + \quad 80 \quad + \quad 7 \quad = 287$

5. **Developing skills:**

a. $\begin{array}{r} 23 \\ -\ 8 \end{array} \rightarrow \begin{array}{r} 10 + 13 \\ -\ 8 \\ \hline 10 + 5 = 15 \end{array}$ Using the basic fact

b. $\begin{array}{r} 46 \\ -\ 9 \end{array} \rightarrow \begin{array}{r} 10 + 36 \\ -\ 9 \\ \hline 1 + 36 = 37 \end{array}$ Subtracting from 10

c. $\begin{array}{r} 45 \\ -\ 6 \end{array} \rightarrow \begin{array}{r} 40 + 5 \\ -\ 6 \\ \hline 36 + 5 = 41 \end{array}$ Subtracting from tens

d. Renaming the subtrahend

$\begin{array}{r} 23 \\ -\ 7 \end{array}$ $23 - 7 = (20 + 3) - 7 = \quad$ Renaming 23

$(20 + 3) - (3 + 4) =$ Renaming 7

$20 + (3 - 3) - 4 \ =$

$20 + \quad 0 \quad - 4 \ =$

$20 \quad - 4 \ = 16$

Study Questions:

1. For every basic addition fact, there are two basic subtraction facts excluding the doubles. Illustrate what the statement means. What relationships are evident?

2. What basic subtraction fact must a child identify to complete the following example? How can you help him to identify this fact?

$$\begin{array}{r} 32 \\ -\ 15 \end{array}$$

3. Illustrate and explain this generalization: adding the same number to the minuend and the subtrahend does not change the difference.

4. What mathematical reasoning is behind the statement, "Add the subtrahend and the difference to check the correctness of the answer in subtraction"?

5. State several generalizations in subtraction. How can they be developed with children?

6. Illustrate the use of "expanded notation" in teaching regrouping in subtraction.

7. What will you do to correct the error if your class is solving the example as shown?

$$
\begin{array}{r}
43 \\
- 15 \\
\hline
32
\end{array}
$$

8. Solve the example 13 – 6 in four different ways. Suggest appropriate experiences for developing the algorisms presented.

9. You are to make a recommendation dealing with the method of subtraction to be used. Which method do you recommend? Why?

10. Check several arithmetic series for their presentation of subtraction.

Selected Text References

1. Banks, J. Houston, *Elementary School Mathematics*, Boston: Allyn and Bacon, Inc., 1966. Chapter 2.

2. Dwight, Leslie A., *Modern Mathematics for the Elementary Teacher*, New York: Holt, Rinehart and Winston, Inc., 1966. Chapters 8 and 9.

3. Hollister, George E., and Agnes G. Gunderson, *Teaching Arithmetic in the Primary Grades*, Boston: D. C. Heath and Company, 1964. Chapter 6.

4. Kramer, Klaas, *The Teaching of Elementary School Mathematics*, Boston: Allyn and Bacon, Inc., 1966. Chapter 11.

5. Shipp, Donald E., and Sam Adams, *Developing Arithmetic Concepts and Skills*, Englewood Cliffs, N.J.: Prentice–Hall, Inc., 1964. Chapters 3 and 4.

6. Spencer, Peter Lincoln, and Marguerite Brydegaard, *Building Mathematical Competence in the Elementary School*, New York: Holt, Rinehart and Winston, Inc., 1966. Chapters 7, 13 and 14.

7. Swenson, Esther, *Teaching Arithmetic to Children*, New York: The Macmillan Company, 1964. Chapters 7 and 8.

Selected Readings from the Arithmetic Teacher

1. Deans, Edwina, "Practice in Renaming Numbers—An Aid to Subtraction," *12:* 142, February, 1965.

2. Easterday, Kenneth, and Helen Easterday, "A Logical Method for Basic Subtraction," *13:* 404–406, May, 1966.

3. Grossnickle, Foster E., "Verbal Problem Solving," *11:* 12–17, January, 1961.

4. Hess, Marvel, "Second–Grade Children Solve Problems," *13:* 317–318, April, 1966.

5. Irwin, Evelyn S., "An Approach to Subtraction Using Easy Facts," *11:* 260–261, April, 1964.

6. Spross, Patricia, "Considerations in the Selection of Learning Aids," *11:* 350–353, May, 1964.

Chapter V

Multiplication of Whole Numbers

Multiplication of whole numbers may be thought of as finding the sum of two addends of equal size without adding. The processes of addition and multiplication are related in that knowing $4 + 4 + 4 = 12$, one can reason that $3 \times 4 = 12$.

In the modern mathematics programs, the two parts of a multiplication fact are simply called "factors." Factors are numbers that are multiplied to form a product; factors are also divisors of that product. To develop meanings beyond these statements, the terms multiplier and multiplicand are introduced and defined in order to develop a language which will aid teachers in presenting multiplication and for the learner to interpret the process. When understanding is evidenced by children, the terms multiplier and multiplicand can be dropped in favor of the term factors.

Multiplication is a binary operation since only two numbers are multiplied at a time. In the number sentence $4 \times 6 = 24$, 4 is the multiplier, 6 the multiplicand and 24 the product. The multiplier indicates the number of groups present; the multiplicand the number in each group. The language resulting from these definitions describes multiplication as repeated addition. The equation $3 \times 6 = 18$ can be read as 3 groups of $6 = 18$, 3 6's $= 18$ or 6 is to be added 3 times.

The basic properties and principles of multiplication are presented as a review for the reader. Understanding these laws is essential to the planning necessary for teaching multiplication to children. Such terms as "renaming" and "expanding" continue to be used to interpret numbers to children.

Properties of Multiplication

1. **Commutative property**: The order in which two numbers are multiplied does not change the product.

   $$\begin{array}{cc} 8 & 4 \\ \underline{\times 4} & \underline{\times 8} \\ 32 & 32 \end{array} \qquad 4 \times 8 = 8 \times 4$$

   The generalization can be stated: $(a \times b) = (b \times a)$

2. **Associative property**: The grouping of three or more factors in multiplication does not change the product.

   a. $6 \times 4 \times 8 =$
       $(6 \times 4) \times 8 = 192$ Associative property
       $6 \times (4 \times 8) = 192$ Associative property

   b. $12 \times 35 \times 26 =$
       $(12 \times 35) \times 26 = 10,920$ Associative property
       $12 \times (35 \times 26) = 10,920$ Associative property

   c. The generalization can be stated:
      $a \times b \times c = (a \times b) \times c = a \times (b \times c)$

3. **Distributive property**: If a number is expanded, given another name and each addend is multiplied by another number, the product is the sum of the partial products. Illustration:

   a. $4 \times 8 = 32$
      $4 \times (5 + 3) =$ (Think another name for 8)
      $(4 \times 5) + (4 \times 3) =$ (Multiply each addend by 4)
      $\ \ 20 \ \ + \ \ 12 \ \ = 32$ (Sum of partial products equals the product of 4×8)

   b. $24 \times 36 =$
      $24 \times (30 + 6) =$ Renaming 36
      $(24 \times 30) + (24 \times 6) =$ Distributive property
      $\ \ 720 \ \ + \ \ 144 \ \ = 864$

      $24 \times 36 =$
      $(20 + 4) \times (30 + 6) =$
      $(20 \times 30) + (20 \times 6) + (4 \times 30) + (4 \times 6) =$
      $\ \ 600 \ \ + \ \ 120 \ \ + \ \ 120 \ \ + \ \ 24 \ \ = 864$

   The generalization can be stated: For any three numbers represented by a, b, and c, $a \times (b + c) = (a \times b) + (a \times c)$.

4. **Zero and 1**: Zero and 1 are of special interest in multiplication. When 0 is a factor in multiplication, the product is always 0. If multiplication is applied to an equation such as 3×0, the product is 0. Because multiplication is commutative, 0×3 is also 0.

   Just as adding 0 to a number produced the number, we observe that multiplying by 1 produces the number. This important property, the identity element of multiplication, allows us to interpret any whole number as a fraction and permits us to rename fractions to simplify the operations of multiplication and division of fractions. We express these properties as:

   $1 \times N = N$ Any multiple of 1 is that multiple
   $1 \times 0 = 0$ Any multiple of 0 is 0

The Basic Facts in Multiplication

The basic multiplication facts consist of all the possible arrangements of two 1–place numbers from 0 through 9. A basic fact is the grouping and the answer ($3 \times 5 = 15$). See chart on page 85.

Presentation

Formal multiplication is usually begun in the third grade. When children approach arithmetic from the point of relationships, many pupils who cannot solve a problem by the multiplication method can solve the problem by addition. The relationship of addition to multiplication can be used as an excellent starting point in introducing the multiplication process.

Write several problems on the chalkboard, making them similar to the following and asking the children to solve them in any way that they can. Make no mention of multiplication.

1. How many wheels are needed to build 3 wagons if each wagon is to have 4 wheels?
2. In our room we have 2 rows of small chairs. If each row has 3 chairs, how many chairs are there in all?

THE MULTIPLICATION FACTS (Zero Omitted)

1	1	1	1	1	1	1	1	1
1	2	3	4	5	6	7	8	9
1	2	3	4	5	6	7	8	9

2	2	2	2	2	2	2	2	2
1	2	3	4	5	6	7	8	9
2	4	6	8	10	12	14	16	18

3	3	3	3	3	3	3	3	3
1	2	3	4	5	6	7	8	9
3	6	9	12	15	18	21	24	27

4	4	4	4	4	4	4	4	4
1	2	3	4	5	6	7	8	9
4	8	12	16	20	24	28	32	36

5	5	5	5	5	5	5	5	5
1	2	3	4	5	6	7	8	9
5	10	15	20	25	30	35	40	45

6	6	6	6	6	6	6	6	6
1	2	3	4	5	6	7	8	9
6	12	18	24	30	36	42	48	54

7	7	7	7	7	7	7	7	7
1	2	3	4	5	6	7	8	9
7	14	21	28	35	42	49	56	63

8	8	8	8	8	8	8	8	8
1	2	3	4	5	6	7	8	9
8	16	24	32	40	48	56	64	72

9	9	9	9	9	9	9	9	9
1	2	3	4	5	6	7	8	9
9	18	27	36	45	54	63	72	81

Solutions presented by the children will vary with background of experience and understanding of arithmetical concepts. Consider the following solutions to the first problem above:

1. Several children used sticks in the following manner:

    / / / /   4 sticks to represent 4 wheels

    / / / /   3 sets to represent 3 wagons

    / / / /   Answer 12, arrived at by counting

2. Several children drew circles to represent the wheels on each wagon:

The 3 sets represent the 3 wagons. The answer was arrived at by counting by ones and by twos.

3. Other solutions to look for are:

a. Addition (3 X 4 says that 4 is to be added 3 times)

```
  4 wheels
  4 wheels
+ 4 wheels
 12 wheels
```

```
  4 wheels
+ 4 wheels
  8 wheels
+ 4 wheels
 12 wheels
```

b. Use of the number line or a ruler

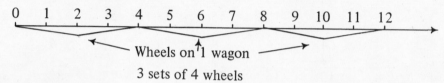

Wheels on 1 wagon

3 sets of 4 wheels

c. Multiplication

```
  4 wheels
X 3  ◄────── (Thinking of 3 sets of 4 wheels)
 12 wheels
```

The following questions are useful as a guide in discussing the various solutions:

1. What did you think as you solved the problem?
2. Does the solution show how you arrived at the answer?
3. What are the facts in the problem?
4. Do your drawings show the facts in the problem?
5. What solution is the best? Why?
6. What does your text tell about the solution we call multiplication?

With the help of the text, the children can identify the basic facts in the problem. For example: read the equation 3 X 4 = 12 as 3 sets of 4 is 12 or 3 groups of 4 is 12.

Rediscover through the use of concrete and semiconcrete materials number stories dealing with multiplication.

Divide 6 into two equal sets:

How many in each set? (3) How many sets? (2) What is the language which describes what you have shown? (2 sets of 3 is 6; 2 groups of 3 is 6) The verb is singular because 2 sets of 3 is another name for 6.

Divide 12 into two equal sets:

```
    * *          * *
    * *          * *
    * *          * *
```

How many stars in each set? How many sets?

Write the vertical and the equation forms:

```
    6                  2 X 6 = 12
  X 2
   12
```

Divide 8 into four equal sets:

How many sets? How many in each set?

Write the multiplication fact:

Vertical form	Equation form
2 X 4 ── 8	4 X 2 = 8

What is the language which describes what you have shown?

4 sets of 2 is 8

4 groups of 2 is 8

The following multiplication facts were discovered and stated orally while teaching the "families." Have the children illustrate each of the following facts using objects and drawing pictures. Continue to use addition as a way to solve each equation. This relates addition to multiplication.

2 X 1 = 2	3 X 1 = 3	4 X 1 = 4	5 X 1 = 5
2 X 2 = 4	3 X 2 = 6	4 X 2 = 8	5 X 2 = 10
2 X 3 = 6	3 X 3 = 9	4 X 3 = 12	5 X 3 = 15
2 X 4 = 8	3 X 4 = 12	4 X 4 = 16	
2 X 5 = 10	3 X 5 = 15		
2 X 6 = 12	3 X 6 = 18		
2 X 7 = 14			
2 X 8 = 16			
2 X 9 = 18			

6 X 1 = 6	7 X 1 = 7	8 X 1 = 8	9 X 1 = 9
6 X 2 = 12	7 X 2 = 14	8 X 2 = 16	9 X 2 = 18
6 X 3 = 18			

When the children have learned to find the product of two numbers, they can apply this understanding to finding one of the factors when one factor and the product are given. Analyze what is stated in each equation. Write the equation □ X 2 = 6. Ask, "How many sets of 2 are there in 6?" Help them to see that they can find the missing number by placing the blocks into sets of 2.

□ □   □ □   □ □

Then, 3 sets of 2 equal 6. Write the equation 3 X 2 = 6. Provide for practice with other equations with missing factors. This activity is readiness for measurement division.

Children can now be directed to discover what steps are necessary to solve an equation when the multiplier and the product are given. Write several equations on the chalkboard and ask the class to tell and demonstrate what must be done. In the early presentation, the term "multiplier" is more precise in meaning than "factor." Later, when children understand the multiplication equation, permit them to make their choice of usage. The teacher should recognize in this manipulation the readiness phase of partition division. Example:

$$3 \times \square = 6$$

What does the multiplier identify? Arrange the 6 into 3 sets. This may be done by putting 1 in each of 3 sets until none remain.

First distribution:

Second distribution:

How many blocks in each set? Write the equation, $3 \times 2 = 6$. Repeat this approach with similar equations.

Begin to compare equations with the expressed purpose of setting the stage for the development of the commutative property of multiplication. Because children have discovered commutivity with addition and have now been introduced to multiplication as repeated addition, they may recognize the property at once. Challenge the children to write equations for the following sets, using questions such as these:

Which equations have a common product?

Do the equations have the same numbers?

What property of multiplication have you identified?

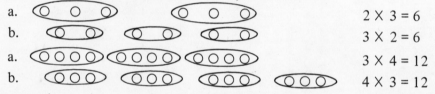

a. $2 \times 3 = 6$

b. $3 \times 2 = 6$

a. $3 \times 4 = 12$

b. $4 \times 3 = 12$

Arrays can be used as models for multiplication equations. Placed on cards, the models can be turned to the vertical or the horizontal position to express commutivity.

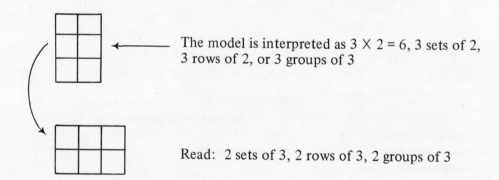

The model is interpreted as $3 \times 2 = 6$, 3 sets of 2, 3 rows of 2, or 3 groups of 3

Read: 2 sets of 3, 2 rows of 3, 2 groups of 3

Then, $3 \times 2 = 2 \times 3$. The order in which any pair of whole numbers is multiplied does not affect the product, ($a \times b = b \times a$). This is the commutative property of multiplication.

Perhaps the most important property of multiplication is a property which connects addition to multiplication. The distributive concept is illustrated below:

$\longrightarrow$ $3 \times 5 = 15$

$$3 \text{ sets of } 2 + 3 \text{ sets of } 3 = 3 \text{ sets of } 5$$
$$(3 \times 2) \quad + \quad (3 \times 3) = 3 \times 5$$
$$6 \quad + \quad 9 \quad = 15$$
$$15 \quad = 15$$

In the example, the number of elements in the total set was divided into a set of 2 and a set of 3 elements. Since there were three original sets of 5, each set of 2 and 3 is multiplied by 3. Therefore, $(3 \times 2) + (3 \times 3) = 6 + 9 = 15$. When the structure of tables is discussed, the distributive property is used to help children to see relationships and to learn the multiplication facts.

Important Ideas Begun

1. Addition and multiplication are related processes.
2. The multiplier always indicates the number of equal sets. (The number of addends.)
3. The multiplicand always indicates the number in each set.
4. The multiplier is the *first* digit on the left when the algorism is written as an equation: $(4 \times 3 = 12)$.
5. The multiplicand is the *second* digit when the algorism is written as an equation: $(4 \times 3 = 12)$.
6. Interpreting a basic multiplication fact.
7. The multiplication symbol $(\times)$ asks the question, "How many in all if the designated number of groups are combined?"
8. Meaning of the commutative and distributive properties.

The Multiplication Tables

Multiplication facts are usually presented in tables for convenience of record. The table of fours is developed to show the relationships within the structure of any table. The multiplier is the first number in the equation form and it tells how many sets of 4 are being considered. To avoid rote learning of the multiplication facts, the children are encouraged to find the products of the unknown facts by using known ideas. In order to do this, the language of the multiplier and the multiplicand is emphasized. In this instance, one can soon understand why an emphasis is placed upon these terms. Before beginning this activity, the teacher evaluates each child in his knowledge of the basic facts of 4. Let us assume she finds that this group of students knows the basic facts of 4 listed below. These facts, then, are used to discover the unknown facts.

$$1 \times 4 = 4$$
$$2 \times 4 = 8$$
$$3 \times 4 = 12$$
$$4 \times 4 = 16$$
$$10 \times 4 = 40$$

How can these five facts be used to structure the table of fours? What generalization can be developed?

1. $3 \times 4 = \square$. The box asks the question, "How many?"

    Since 1 four is 4 and 2 fours are 8,

    then 3 fours are $4 + 8 = 12$

    $$1 \times 4 = \ \ 4$$
    $$2 \times 4 = \ \ 8$$
    $$\overline{3 \times 4 = 12}$$

2. $4 \times 4 = \square$.

    There are 3 fours in 12. 1 four is 4.

    Then, 4 fours are $12 + 4 = 16$.

    $$3 \times 4 = 12$$
    $$1 \times 4 = \ \ 4$$
    $$\overline{4 \times 4 = 16}$$

    or

    2 fours are 8. 4 fours is double 2

    fours. Then, $4 \times 4 = 8 + 8 = 16$.

    $$2 \times 4 = \ \ 8$$
    $$2 \times 4 = \ \ 8$$
    $$\overline{4 \times 4 = 16}$$

3. $5 \times 4 = \square$

    $$3 \times 4 = 12$$
    $$2 \times 4 = \ \ 8$$
    $$\overline{5 \times 4 = 20}$$

    or

    $$1 \times 4 = \ \ 4$$
    $$4 \times 4 = 16$$
    $$\overline{5 \times 4 = 20}$$

    or

    Given: $10 \times 4 = 40$

    5 sets of 4 is one half of 10 sets of 4

    Then, $5 \times 4 = 20$

4. $6 \times 4 = \square$.

    Since 3 sets of $4 = 12$, then 6 sets of 4

    is twice 3 sets of 4. $6 \times 4 = 24$.

    $$3 \times 4 = 12$$
    $$3 \times 4 = 12$$
    $$\overline{6 \times 4 = 24}$$

    There are several ways to arrive at $6 \times 4 = \square$. Can you find them?

5. $7 \times 4 = \square$.

    3 sets of $4 = 12$

    3 sets of $4 = 12$

    1 set of $4 = \ \ 4$

    7 sets of $4 = 28$

    $7 \times 4 = 28$

    Can you find several ways to find 7×4?

6. $8 \times 4 = \square$.

    Since $4 \times 4 = 16$, then $8 \times 4 = 16 + 16$ or 2×16.

    $8 \times 4 = 32$

7. $9 \times 4 = \square$.

    Given: $10 \times 4 = 40$

    9 sets of 4 is 1 set of 4 less than 10 sets of 4, then $9 \times 4 = 40 - 4 = 36$

    Then, $9 \times 4 = 40 - 4 = 36$

    $9 \times 4 = 36$

Another approach to thinking through unknown multiplication facts is the use of the distributive property. The idea of renaming or expanding a number is not new to most children by this time. Ask the children to structure the following chart. Then, as an assignment, ask them to find the products for examples such as the following using the concept of renaming one of the factors. The distributive property permits students to use known facts to find unknown facts. To find 2 X 8, the child may use 2 X (3 + 5) as the key fact. Then, (2 X 3) + (2 X 5) = 16. Therefore, 2 X 8 = 16.

2 X 3 =	6 X 4 =
4 X 5 =	7 X 5 =
2 X 7 =	9 X 3 =
5 X 9 =	8 X 4 =

Multiplicand

X	1	2	3	4	5
1	1	2	3	4	5
2	2	4	6	6	10
3	3	6	9	12	15
4	4	8	12	16	20
5	5	10	15	20	25

(left margin, rotated) Multiplier

Do the children use other names for 7, 8 and 9? How many different combinations can they make?

2 X 7 =	2 X (5 + 2),	2 X (4 + 3)
3 X 8 =	3 X (5 + 3),	3 X (4 + 4)
3 X 9 =	3 X (5 + 4),	3 X (5 + 2 + 2)
6 X 4 =	(4 + 2) X 4,	(3 + 3) X 4,
7 X 5 =	(5 + 2) X 5,	(4 + 3) X 5
9 X 3 =	(5 + 4) X 3	

As children discover the use of the chart and can apply the principle of renaming a number orally in interpreting a basic fact, they can be introduced to writing the equations. Provide time and guidance so that children can think through the pattern.

1. 4 X 7 = ☐
   4 X (3 + 4) =   Renaming 7
   (4 X 3) + (4 X 4) = 4 times each addend (Distributive property)
       12 +   16 = 28   addition of partial products
   Then, 4 X 7 = 28
2. 6 X 4 = ☐
   (2 + 4) X 4 =   Renaming 6
   (2 X 4) + (4 X 4) = Each addend of the multiplier times each addend of the multiplicand (Distributive property)
       8   +   16 = 24
   Then, 6 X 4 = 24

3. $7 \times 8 = \square$

    $(3 + 4) \times (5 + 3) =$ Renaming 7 and 8

    $(3 \times 5) + (3 \times 3) + (4 \times 5) + (4 \times 3) =$ Distributive property

      $15 \quad + \quad 9 \quad + \quad 20 \quad + \quad 12 \quad = 56$

    Then, $7 \times 8 = 56$

4. Use of the verticle form

    $6 \times 8 = \square$ $5 + 3$ Renaming 8

                  $\times\ 2 + 4$ Renaming 6

                     12     $4 \times 3 = 12$

                     20     $4 \times 5 = 20$

                      6     $2 \times 3 = \ 6$

                     10     $2 \times 5 = 10$

                     48

Each child can be encouraged to construct a chart so that he can keep a record of the facts he is learning. As the chart is being completed, identify properties and patterns which help him to understand multiplication. What does the diagonal from upper left to lower right indicate? What appears on either side of the diagonal? What do 0 and 1 contribute to the chart? Can you apply the distributive property to the chart? The chart given here is completed so that the teacher can approach the structure of the basic multiplication facts through a study of its internal patterns.

X	0	1	2	3	4	5	6	7	8	9
0	0	0	0	0	0	0	0	0	0	0
1	0	1	2	3	4	5	6	7	8	9
2	0	2	4	6	8	10	12	14	16	18
3	0	3	6	9	12	15	18	21	24	27
4	0	4	8	12	16	20	24	28	32	36
5	0	5	10	15	20	25	30	35	40	45
6	0	6	12	18	24	30	36	42	48	54
7	0	7	14	21	28	35	42	49	56	63
8	0	8	16	24	32	40	48	56	64	72
9	0	9	18	27	36	45	54	63	72	81

As the children work on the structure of tables, stimulate interest by asking them to identify patterns in the tables. Examples:

	a.	b.	
1 × 6 =	6	6	
2 × 6 =	12	3	← Excess of nines, 12 – 3
3 × 6 =	18	9	← Excess of nines, 18 – 9 or 0
4 × 6 =	24	6	
5 × 6 =	30	3	
6 × 6 =	36	9	
7 × 6 =	42	6	
8 × 6 =	48	3	← Excess of nines
9 × 6 =	54	9	

In column a, the pattern is 6, 2, 8, 4, 0, 6, 2, 8, and 4. Will the pattern repeat in the teens? In any decade? The excess of 9's, column b, provides another pattern which repeats as 6, 3 and 9. An excellent assignment for homework for students would be to discover patterns in other tables. Why do some tables have similar patterns? Would common factors provide a clue?

The table of 9's provide some unusual patterns. Consider the following:

1 × 9 = 9   a. Units column: 9, 8, 7, 6, 5, 4, 3, 2, 1
2 × 9 = 18   b. Tens column: 1, 2, 3, 4, 5, 6, 7, 8
3 × 9 = 27   c. Reversals: 9 and 90
4 × 9 = 36   18 and 81
5 × 9 = 45   27 and 72, etc.
6 × 9 = 54   d. 2 × 9 = 18 Consider the 2 as 20, then subtract 2, 20 – 2 = 18
7 × 9 = 63   3 × 9 = 27 30 – 3 = 27
8 × 9 = 72   e. Add products diagonally: 9 + 1 = 10, 8 + 2 = 10, 7 + 3 = 10,
9 × 9 = 81   etc.
              0 + 8 = 8, 1 + 7 = 8, 2 + 6 = 8, etc.
              What number comes between 8 and 10?

One activity which will stimulate interest and practice in the basic multiplication facts is to use the fingers of the two hands to obtain products for the facts above the tables of fives. Before the activity is assigned, children must understand the basic meaning of multiplication. Presentations are determined by the background and understanding of the children.

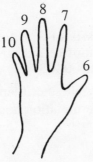

Left hand

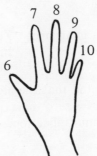

Right hand

The thumbs are always numbered 6. To multiply 7 X 8, place the finger tip of number ⑦ against the finger tip of number ⑧. Count the two fingers touching, that is, ⑦ and ⑧, and the fingers above, ⑥ on the left hand and

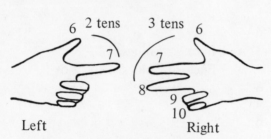

⑥ and ⑦ on the right hand. The number of fingers involved is 5. The number is always read as tens. Therefore, 5 tens = 50. The fingers folded in are multiplied—3 fingers on the left hand times the 2 fingers on the right hand—3 X 2 = 6. Then, 50 + 6 = 56. So, 7 X 8 = 56.

Left   Right

Perform the multiplication, 6 X 6:

a. How many tens? (Thumb against thumb—2 tens or 20)
b. How many fingers are folded in on each hand? 4. (4 X 4 = 16. Therefore, 20 + 16 = 36.) So, 6 X 6 = 36.

Perform the multiplication, 10 X 10:

a. What fingers are put together? (The little fingers.)
b. How many tens? (10 tens = 100.)
c. How many units to be multiplied? (None.)

Perform the multiplication, 9 X 6:

a. How many tens? (Thumb of the right hand against the number ⑨ finger of the left hand. Add the thumb, ⑨, on the left hand and fingers ⑥, ⑦, ⑧ and ⑨ on the right hand. (5 tens = 50.)
b. How many units? (1 X 4 = 4.)
c. 9 X 6 = 50 + 4 = 54

The Zero in Multiplication

The zero continues its two functions in multiplication, that of indicating that no units, tens, etc. are present and as a place holder. The meaning of zero is easy to demonstrate if the beginning language in multiplication is used for interpretation. The term "group" is used synonomously with "set." Examples:

$$\begin{array}{r} 4 \\ \times\ 3 \\ \hline 12 \end{array}$$ Language: 3 sets of 4; 3 groups of 4; 4 to be added 3 times. Therefore, 4 + 4 + 4 = 12.

$$\begin{array}{r} 0 \\ \times\ 3 \\ \hline 0 \end{array}$$ Language: 3 groups of 0; 3 sets of 0; 0 to be added 3 times. 0 + 0 + 0 = 0. Therefore, 3 X 0 = 0.

$$\begin{array}{r} 3 \\ \times\ 0 \\ \hline 0 \end{array}$$ Language: Zero groups of 3; zero sets of 3; 3 to be added 0 times. In this case, addition cannot be indicated. Since multiplication is commutative, then 0 X 3 = 0.

It is generally stated that the algorism 0 X 3 is not possible since there is no way to indicate the writing of 3 zero times. It is because of this interpretation that one considers but 90 basic facts in multiplication.

Multiplication with zero

Examples: a.   10
                    $\times$ 2
                    ─────
                      20

              Read: 2 groups of 0 = 0   1 ten
                     2 groups of 1 ten = 2 tens   + 1 ten
                                                        ─────
                                                        2 tens

              b.   60
                    $\times$ 4
                    ─────
                       0   4 groups of 0 = 0
                     240   4 groups of 6 tens = 24 tens
                    ─────   = 240
                     240
                              60 + 60 + 60 + 60 = 240

When children have learned several basic facts in multiplication, they are ready to use them in solving problems having a 2-digit multiplicand and a 1-digit multiplier. The two insights to be developed are:

1. The quantity given to the basic fact depends upon the position in the number.

      31   a. Ones times ones are ones. 2 ones times 1 one = 2 ones.
    $\times$ 2   b. Ones times tens are tens. 2 ones times 3 tens = 6 tens.
    ─────
      62

      43   a. Ones times ones are ones. 3 $\times$ 3 = 9.
    $\times$ 3   b. Ones times tens are tens. 3 ones times 4 tens = 12 tens.
    ─────   12 tens = 120. The 12 is written in the hundreds and tens
     129   place.

2. Identify the mechanics of multiplication.

      32   a. Knowledge of the sequence of steps. Generally, multiplica-
    $\times$ 3   tion is begun at the right, multiplying each digit in the multi-
    ─────   plicand by each digit in the multiplier. Each product is con-
                     sidered in the light of its place value.

Children can best learn to perform multiplication through the use of story problems. The children are asked to solve the problems in any way or in as many ways as possible for them. The solutions which they offer may not include each of the following patterns in the sequence. It will take time to advance to the use of the equation form for many. The teacher continually encourages the children to use various aids in solving their problems and then she guides them to write their solutions. There is no regrouping in this first approach to multiplication.

Problem: Mary has 4 boxes of pencils. In each box there are 10 pencils. How many pencils does she have? Each of these examples should be solved using aids which children have. Solutions:

   a. Addition
      10 pencils
      10 pencils
      10 pencils
      10 pencils
      ─────────
      40 pencils   (Can begin to generalize about zero)

b. The concept of ten

1 ten		1 ten	(1 set of 10)

1 ten

1 ten ———→ X 4   (4 such sets)

1 ten

1 ten

4 tens   (4 tens is 40)

c. Multiplication

10

X 4

40   (Thinking 4 sets of 10 is 40)

Problem: There are 12 buttons on each card. How many buttons does Jane have if she has 4 cards of buttons?

a. Addition

12 buttons

12 buttons

12 buttons

12 buttons

48 buttons

b. Guide children to discover that one really multiplies ones times ones as they did when learning the basic facts. Then help them to see that the second multiplication is ones times tens. Helping children to become aware of the position that the number holds is a key to understanding why the products are placed as they are.

Distributive property	Place value
10 + 2	1 ten + 2 ones
X 4	X 4
40 + 8 = 48	4 tens + 8 ones = 48

c. Use of partial products

12

X 4

8 ← 4 X 2

40 ← 4 X 10

48

d. Equation form

$4 \times 12 = 4 \times (10 + 2) =$ Expanded notation

$(4 \times 10) + (4 \times 2) =$ Distributive property

$40 \quad + \quad 8 \quad = 48$

The purpose in learning any basic fact is not to repeat it in any rote pattern but to help one to identify the fact in the solution of a problem. Merely stating or writing the facts in table form does not guarantee understanding or use. Asking children to structure problems using the known basic facts is an excellent procedure for developing understanding.

Two Place Multipliers

To teach 2–place multipliers, the teacher has two purposes in mind which she will help children discover. The first is the concept of multiplying by 10's (100, 1000) and the second, multiplying by a 2–digit number is multiplying by tens and ones. Ask children to solve several examples similar to the following in several ways or in as many ways as they can. The teacher always tries to anticipate what responses the children will make.

a.
$$\begin{array}{cccc} 10 & 30 & 23 & 43 \\ \times\ 10 & \times\ 20 & \times\ 10 & \times\ 20 \end{array}$$

What number appears in the units place each time addition is performed?
What is 10 × 10? Is the product always hundreds?
Are the products three digit numbers?
What generalization is discovered by the children?

b. Rewrite the example to illustrate the statement that whenever one multiplies by a 2–place number, one multiplies by ones and tens. Expand 12 to 10 + 2. The use of 10 and 2 as multipliers of 24 and then adding the partial products is an application of the distributive property of multiplication.

Expanding 12

$$\begin{array}{ccc} 24 & 24 & 24 \\ \times\ 12 \longrightarrow & \times\ 10 & \times\ 2 \\ & \overline{240}\quad + & \overline{48}\ =\ 288 \end{array}$$

Partial products

$$\begin{array}{lll} 24 & & \\ \times\ 12 & & \\ \hline 8 & \leftarrow & 2 \times 4 \\ 40 & \leftarrow & 2 \times 20 \\ 40 & \leftarrow & 10 \times 4 \\ 200 & \leftarrow & 10 \times 20 \\ \hline 288 & & \end{array}$$

Common algorism

$$\begin{array}{lll} 24 & & \\ \times\ 12 & & \\ \hline 48 & \leftarrow & 2 \times 24 \\ 240 & \leftarrow & 10 \times 24 \\ \hline 288 & & \end{array}$$

Expanding both the multiplier and the multiplicand may be introduced to some children who have a good understanding of the distributive property. Parentheses may be placed around an expanded number for clarity.

$$\begin{array}{ll} 32 & (30 + 2) \\ \times\ 23 \longrightarrow & \times\ (20 + 3) \\ & 90 + 6 \\ & \underline{600 + 40} \\ & 600 + 130 + 6 \\ & = 736 \end{array}$$

Units times units = units
Units times tens = tens
Tens times units = tens
Tens times tens = hundreds
Tens written under tens

23 × 32 = (20 + 3) × (30 + 2) =	Expanded notation
(20 × 30) + (20 × 2) + (3 × 30) + (3 × 2) =	Distributive property
600 + 40 + 90 + 6 = 736	
or 600 + (40 + 90) + 6 =	Associative property
600 + 130 + 6 = 736	

Many children soon reach a point when they will omit several steps in the algorism. They prefer to move to a mental level of computation.

During the early phase of teaching multiplication, think and speak in terms of place value. When we speak of units times units, units times tens, etc., we mean numbers holding these places. A number in the units place times a number in the tens place will always produce a number of tens. These tens are regrouped to hundreds and tens when written. When children are in doubt as to the name of the number in terms of place value, ask them to solve examples similar to the following.

$$\begin{array}{cccccc} 1 & 10 & 1 & 10 & 100 & 10 \\ \times\,1 & \times\,1 & \times\,10 & \times\,10 & \times\,10 & \times\,100 \end{array}$$

$$\begin{array}{r} 32 \\ \times\,13 \\ \hline 6 \\ 90 \\ 20 \\ 300 \\ \hline 416 \end{array}$$

Units times units equal units. $3 \times 2 = 6$. 6 is written in the units place.

Units times tens equal tens. $3 \times 3 = 9$. 9 is written in the tens place.

Partial products are indicated to emphasize each multiplication. The next action moves to 1 ten as a multiplier.

Ten times units equal tens. The commutative property of multiplication makes this true.

Units times tens = tens times units. The products are in terms of tens.

$1 \times 2 = 2$. 2 is written in the tens place.

Tens times tens equal hundreds.

$1 \times 3 = 3$. 3 is written in the hundreds place.

The distributive property is introduced to arrive at products of 10's, 100's and so on. An interesting exploration can be made at this point to discover how one can multiply such factors.

$30 \times 50 = (3 \times 10) \times 50 =$		Expanded notation
$3 \times (10 \times 50) =$		Associative property
$3 \times \quad 500 \quad = 1500$		
$30 \times 50 = (3 \times 10) \times (5 \times 10) \quad =$		Expanded notation
$(3 \times 5) \times (10 \times 10) \quad =$		Commutative and associative property
$15 \times \quad 100 \quad =$		1500
$40 \times 600 = (4 \times 10) \times (6 \times 100) \quad =$		Expanded notation
$(4 \times 6) \times (10 \times 100) \quad =$		Commutative and associative property
$24 \times \quad 1{,}000 \quad =$		24,000
$200 \times 700 = (2 \times 100) \times (7 \times 100) =$		
$(2 \times 7) \times (100 \times 100) =$		
$14 \times \quad 10{,}000 \quad =$		140,000

Regrouping in Multiplication

In the study of basic facts, the product is generally thought of as units. In $3 \times 4 = 12$, the 12 has two interpretations when spoken, that of 12 ungrouped things and a group of 1 ten and 2 ones. Whenever a number is written, for example 12, the number specifically indicates 1 ten and 2 ones. These interpretations are necessary in developing a clear-cut meaning of regrouping.

When the teacher moves into regrouping in multiplication, she can use a laboratory situation in which the children are guided to select aids of various kinds for illustrating the operation. The use of an adding machine, place value charts, and the abacus are useful for this activity. Following this experience, problems should be provided for the group to solve in several ways. The discussion of the various algorisms suggested by the pupils provide further insight into multiplication. The following sequence might be anticipated by the teacher. The algorism retained by the child because he feels secure with it may be one of the simpler forms such as addition or partial products.

Activities

Feed 14 into the calculator. How many times will one pull the handle to solve 3 × 14?

Indicate 3 × 14 on a place value chart.

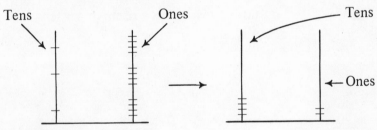

Place 3 × 14 on an abacus.

Examples

1. Partial products

```
   14
 × 3
 ─────
   12   ←  3 × 4
   30   ←  3 × 10
 ─────
   42
```

Expanded notation

```
   10 + 4
 ×      3
 ──────────
   30 + 12  =  42
```

Place value

```
   1 ten  +  4 ones
 ×              3
 ─────────────────────
   3 tens + 12 ones  =  42
```

Common algorism

```
    1
   14
 × 3
 ─────
   42
```

2. Partial products

```
   57
 × 8
 ─────
    56   ←  8 × 7
   400   ←  8 × 50
 ─────
   456
```

Place value

```
   5 tens +  7 ones
 ×              8
 ─────────────────────
   40 tens + 56 ones  =  456
   56 ones  =  56
   40 tens  =  400
```

Expanded notation   Common algorism

$$\begin{array}{r} 57 \\ \times\ 8 \\ \hline \end{array} \rightarrow \begin{array}{r} 50 + 7 \\ \times\qquad 8 \\ \hline 400 + 56\ =\ 456 \end{array} \qquad\qquad \begin{array}{r} {\scriptstyle 5} \\ 57 \\ \times\ 8 \\ \hline 456 \end{array}$$

Regrouping in Multiplication (2–digit multipliers)

The sequence which the teacher thinks through to prepare for teaching 2–place multipliers is reviewed below:

$$\begin{array}{r} 10 \\ \times 10 \\ \hline 100 \end{array} \quad \begin{array}{r} 12 \\ \times 10 \\ \hline 120 \end{array} \quad \begin{array}{r} 16 \\ \times 12 \\ \hline \end{array} \rightarrow \begin{array}{r} 16 \\ \times 10 \\ \hline 160 \end{array} + \begin{array}{r} 16 \\ \times\ 2 \\ \hline 32 \end{array} = 192 \rightarrow \begin{array}{r} 16 \\ \times 12 \\ \hline 12 \\ 20 \\ 60 \\ 100 \\ \hline 192 \end{array} \rightarrow \begin{array}{r} 16 \\ \times 12 \\ \hline 32 \\ 160 \\ \hline 192 \end{array}$$

Why should one start with 10×10 and 10×12?

Why is the multiplier expanded?

What insights does the partial products algorism provide?

Why is it good practice to ask children to state the place value as they multiply?

$$\begin{array}{r} 46 \\ \times 34 \\ \hline 24 \\ 160 \\ 180 \\ 1200 \\ \hline 1564 \end{array} \qquad \begin{array}{r} 40 + 6 \\ \times 30 + 4 \\ \hline 160 + 24 \\ 1200 + 180 \\ \hline 1200 + 340 + 24\ =\ 1564 \end{array} \qquad \text{Tens written under tens}$$

$$\begin{array}{r} 36 \\ \times 24 \\ \hline \end{array} \longrightarrow \begin{array}{r} 36 \\ \times 20 \\ \hline 720 \end{array} + \begin{array}{r} 36 \\ \times\ 4 \\ \hline 144 \end{array} \longrightarrow \begin{array}{r} 36 \\ \times 24 \\ \hline 144 \\ 72 \\ \hline 864 \end{array}$$
$$720 + 144\ =\ 864$$

$$\begin{array}{r} 48 \\ \times 37 \\ \hline 56 \\ 280 \\ 240 \\ 1200 \\ \hline 1776 \end{array}$$

$\leftarrow\ 7 \times 8 = 56 \quad \leftarrow$ Units times units = units.
   Regroup units.
$\leftarrow\ 7 \times 4 = 280 \quad \leftarrow$ Units times tens = tens.
   Regroup tens.
$\leftarrow\ 3 \times 8 = 240 \quad \leftarrow$ Tens times units = tens.
   Regroup tens.
$\leftarrow\ 3 \times 4 = 1200 \leftarrow$ Tens times tens = hundreds.

Note: Another name for 56 units is 5 tens and 6 ones. Another name for 28 tens is 2 hundreds plus 8 tens plus 0 ones. Another name for 24 tens is 2 hundreds plus 4 tens plus 0 ones. Tens times tens are hundreds.

Multiplication is rich in materials beyond the routine algorisms. The purpose of the activities at the close of several chapters is to bring the teacher into an awareness of the many possibilities to interest and challenge children to think for themselves and, consequently, discovering new insights and algorisms.

Many additional activities can be introduced as the teacher observes daily progress in children. She can make the students aware of the importance of observing patterns in numbers. Children should be permitted to guess and to estimate as a way to learn. For example, the number of digits in the product can be determined with some accuracy if one looks at a pattern in the tens place. When the multiplier and the multiplicand are 2–digit numbers, it does not necessarily mean that the product will be a 4–digit number, it can also be a 3–digit number. Knowing that tens times tens are hundreds or 10 tens, one can estimate the number of digits in the product.

$$\begin{array}{r} 35 \\ \times\ 26 \\ \hline 210 \\ 70 \\ \hline 910 \end{array}$$
The product of $2 \times 3 = 6$ hundreds. Since 6 hundreds is less than 10 hundreds, one can estimate the product to be at least 600, a 3–digit number. In completing the multiplication, the product is 910.

$$\begin{array}{r} 46 \\ \times\ 38 \\ \hline 368 \\ 138 \\ \hline 1748 \end{array}$$
The product of $3 \times 4 = 12$ hundreds. Because the number of hundreds is equal to or more than 10 hundreds or 1000, the estimated product is at least 1200. The product is 1748, a 4–digit number.

What are the estimated products for the following examples?

26 X	38	=	At least 600
38 X	53	=	At least 1500
36 X	284	=	At least 6000
56 X	347	=	At least 15,000
246 X	421	=	At least 80,000
457 X	834	=	At least 320,000

Discovery Opportunities

To broaden the activities with numbers while children are solving problems with 2–digit multipliers, the teacher can stimulate her group to observe what happens over and over when they multiply by 11. As she notes progress in understanding, she can introduce a challenge at any time by asking questions.

Do you see a pattern when multiplying a 2–digit number by 11? In your solution, can you omit the partial products and write just the product? Questions such as these make excellent homework assignments whether the children work individually or in groups.

If you can multiply by 11, what change or changes in your generalization for multiplying by 11 is necessary to multiply by 12, 13, 14 and so on through 19?

Observe the pattern in the partial products as you multiply a teen times a teen. Can you manipulate the numbers in the multiplicand and the multiplier and perform the operation as a mental activity?

Identify the pattern in the product as you square a 2–digit number ending in 5. How can you manipulate the numbers in the tens place to arrive at the correct product?

Checking the Product

Children can be led to realize that there are different ways to verify an answer. Because a few children use methods similar to those on the following page, others may become interested in new approaches, too.

1. Interchanging the multiplier and the multiplicand. This is an application of the commutative property.

```
   58              23
 X 23            X 58
  174             184
  116             115
 1334            1334
```

2. Casting nines. (Check Chapter III "Addition of Whole Numbers," for further details.)

```
     4628   →   4 + 6 + 2 + 8 = 20, excess is 2
   X 253    →   2 + 5 + 3 = 10, excess is 1
   13884
   23140
    9256
 1170884   →   1 + 1 + 7 + 0 + 8 + 8 + 4 = 29, excess is 2
```

 a. The excess of nines in the multiplicand is 2
 b. The excess of nines in the multiplier is 1
 c. Since this is multiplication, the two excesses are multiplied: $1 \times 2 = 2$
 d. The excess in the original product is 2
 e. Since the original product also has an excess of nines equal to 2, the product is probably correct

3. Patterns within the multiplier: If the multiplier is 36, the 6 is twice 3. Multiply by 3 (3 is in the tens place in this example) first and then multiply the partial product obtained by 2 since 6 is 2×3.

```
    648
  X  36
  19440        Multiply by 3 (30 X 648)
   3888   ←─── Then 2 X 1,944 = 3,888. The partial product 3,888 is the
  23328        same as if we had multiplied by 6. Note that 1,944 is 3 X 648.
```

Extending Multiplication

Insight into place value greatly simplifies multiplication. The following examples are generally termed difficult because of the zeros. Greater insight can be gained by asking the children to write the thinking process to the right side of the example.

```
   301
 X   7
     7   ↔   7 X 1 = 7.           One times ones are ones
    00   ↔   7 X 0 = 0.           Seven groups of 0 = 0
  2100   ↔   7 X 300 = 2,100.     Ones times hundreds are hundreds

 7 X 301 = 7 X (300 + 1)  =       Expanded notation
           (7 X 300) + (7 X 1) =  Distributive property
              2100   +    7   = 2,107
```

```
   357        Analyze the individual place value products as ones X ones, etc.
 X 204
  1428   ←   4 X 357 = 1,428
  0000   ←   0 X 357 = 0  (zero groups of 357 equal 0)
 71400   ←   200 X 357 = 71,400  (200 groups of 357)
 72828
```

$$
\begin{array}{r}
403 \\
\times\ 306 \\
\hline
2418 \\
0000 \\
120900 \\
\hline
123318
\end{array}
$$

Analyze the role of the zero:
    In the multiplier
    In the multiplicand
    In the second partial product
    The zeros encircled.

Expanding the multiplier: Distributive property

$$
\begin{array}{r}
426 \\
\times\ 253 \\
\hline
\end{array}
\rightarrow
\quad
\begin{array}{r}
426 \\
\times\ 200 \\
\hline
85,200
\end{array}
+
\begin{array}{r}
426 \\
\times\ 50 \\
\hline
22,300
\end{array}
+
\begin{array}{r}
426 \\
\times\ 3 \\
\hline
1,278
\end{array}
$$

Multiply by:
units, tens, hundreds

$$85,200 + 21,300 + 1,278 = 107,778$$

Equation form

$$253 \times 426 = (200 + 50 + 3) \times 426 =$$ Expanded notation

$$(200 \times 426) + (50 \times 426) + (3 \times 426) =$$ Distributive property

$$85,200 + 21,300 + 1,278 = 107,778.$$

Common algorism

$$
\begin{array}{r}
{}^{1} \\
426 \\
\times\ 253 \\
\hline
1278
\end{array}
$$
Multiplication by 3

$$
\begin{array}{r}
{}^{1\,3} \\
426 \\
\times\ 253 \\
\hline
1278 \\
21300
\end{array}
$$
Multiplication by 50

$$
\begin{array}{r}
{}^{1} \\
426 \\
\times\ 253 \\
\hline
1278 \\
21300 \\
85200 \\
\hline
107778
\end{array}
$$
Multiplication by 200

Whole Numbers: Primes, Composites, Factors and Multiples

Factors of a number are arranged in pairs. What are the pairs of factors in 12? The diagram below identifies the pairs.

$$1,\quad 2,\quad 3,\quad 4,\quad 6,\quad 12$$

The relationships which exist between primes, composites, factors and multiples open up for children an excellent approach to the study of fractions and a preparation for the new algorisms in multiplication and division.

1. **Prime number:** A number whose only factors are 1 and the number itself. One is not a prime number because it has only *one* factor. Examples:
   a. 3 → factors of 3 are 1 and 3.
   b. The first 8 primes are 2, 3, 5, 7, 11, 13, 17 and 19. Does the definition hold for each?

2. **Composite numbers**: Any whole number other than a prime. A composite number has factors other than 1 and itself and contains one set of prime factors. Examples:

a. 4 → factors are 1, 2 and 4 or the prime factors 2 and 2.

b. 12 → factors are 1, 2, 3, 4, 6 and 12 or the prime factors 3, 2 and 2.

3. **Factoring**: The process of writing a composite number as a product of two or more factors. When multiplication is first presented to children, the terms multiplier and multiplicand are developed because they are significant in interpreting the algorism. When meaning has been established, the term "factor" can be used.

Examples:

a. 16 → 2 X 8 = 16. 2 X 8 is called factorization of 16.

b. 24 → 3 X 8 = 24. Now express each factor as a prime number: 3 X 8 = 3 X 2 X 4 = 3 X 2 X 2 X 2 = 24. This is prime factorization.

The Fundamental Theorem of Arithmetic states that every composite number can be expressed as a product of primes in one and only one way except for the order of the prime factors. Examples:

(1) 60 = 2 X 2 X 3 X 5
        = 2 X 3 X 2 X 5
        = 2 X 5 X 3 X 2

These are all the same prime factors and the only difference is the order of the factors in the indicated product.

(2)

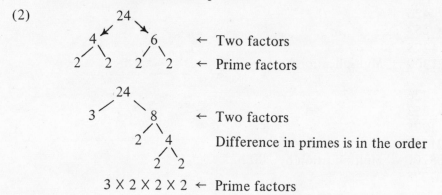

3 X 2 X 2 X 2 ← Prime factors

4. **Least common multiple**: The smallest nonzero whole number which two or more given whole numbers will divide evenly. Multiples correspond to the product in multiplication and the dividend in division. Examples:

a. Multiples of 12: 12, 24, 36, 48, 72, etc.
    1 X 12 = 12
    2 X 12 = 24
    3 X 12 = 36, etc.

b. Multiples of 18: 18, 36, 54, 72, 90, etc.
    1 X 18 = 18
    2 X 18 = 36
    3 X 18 = 54, etc.

Common multiples of 12 and 18 are: 36, 72, etc. The least common multiple of 12 and 18 is 36.

$36 \div 12 = 3$
$36 \div 18 = 2$ Divided evenly

Given the set of multiples for 12 and 18, find the lowest common multiple.

Set A $\{12, 24, 36, 48, 72 \ldots \}$

Set B $\{18, 36, 48, 72, 90 \ldots \}$

By observation, the number is 36.

5. **Greatest common divisor (highest common factor):** The largest whole number that is a common factor of two or more whole numbers.

a. 16 = 1, 2, 4, (8) 16
b. 24 = 1, 2, 3, 4, 6, (8) 12, 24

The greatest common divisor (g. c. d.) common to 16 and 24 is 8.

c. Given a set of factors for 16 and 24, find the greatest common divisor (greatest common factor).

Set A = $\{1, 2, 4, 8, 16 \}$

Set B = $\{1, 2, 3, 4, 8, 12 \}$

By observation, the greatest common divisor is 8.

The activities surrounding the development of the concepts of primes, composites, factors and multiples will add interest and understanding to the study of numbers. Examples:

1. $\begin{array}{r} 246 \\ \times\ 24 \\ \hline 984 \\ 492 \\ \hline 5904 \end{array}$ Factors of 24 are 4 and 6

$\begin{array}{r} 246 \\ \times\ 6 \\ \hline 1476 \end{array}$ Multiply by the factor 6

$\begin{array}{r} \times\ 4 \\ \hline 5904 \end{array}$ Multiply by the factor 4

2. $\begin{array}{r} 357 \\ \times\ 18 \\ \hline 2856 \\ 357 \\ \hline 6426 \end{array}$ Prime factors of 18 are 2, 3 and 3

$\begin{array}{r} 357 \\ \times\ 2 \\ \hline 714 \end{array}$ Multiply by the prime factor 2

$\begin{array}{r} \times\ 3 \\ \hline 2142 \end{array}$ Multiply by the prime factor 3

$\begin{array}{r} \times\ 3 \\ \hline 6426 \end{array}$ Multiply by the prime factor 3

Square Root

Finding the average of 2 factors is a convenient way to establish a square root. The method is less rigorous than the square root algorism. Before this approach can be developed with children, such mental activities as squaring a 2–digit number ending in 5 and multiplying teens times teens are established. The materials and activities at the close of several chapters provide for teachers a source of supplementary content. There are many concepts and relationships to be learned as children approach new materials. They must know their meaning and they must understand when and how they can be used.

1. $\sqrt{784}$ Estimate the square root by first establishing one of the factors.
$30 \times 30 = 900$.   The factor 30 is too large
$25 \times 25 = 625$.   The factor 25 is too small

The square root is somewhere between 25 and 30. Select one of the factors as a divisor and divide. The remainder can be dropped.

```
     31
25)784
    75
    34
    25
     9
```

Average the two factors

```
     25
   + 31
 2)56
   28   ←   the square root of 784
```

In this example, 28 is the exact square root.

2. $\sqrt{1158}$ Establish one of the factors. What number times itself (squared) is the number or close to the number 1158?
$30 \times 30 = 900$.   900 is below 1158
$35 \times 35 = 1225$. 1225 is above 1158

The square root is somewhere between 30 and 35, being closer to 35. Use 35 as a trial divisor.

```
      33
35)1158
   105
   108
   105
```

Average the two factors

```
     35
   + 33
 2)68
   34   ←   the approximate square root
```

In this example, the square root is 34^+.

Important Ideas Begun in Multiplication

1. The commutative, associative and distributive properties of multiplication.
2. The language of multiplication.
3. The relationships of addition and multiplication.
4. The structure of the multiplication table.
5. Multiplication by 1–digit multipliers.
6. Multiplication by 2–digit multipliers.
7. The zero in multiplication.
8. Multiplication by tens, hundreds, etc.
9. Place value in multiplication.

10. Regrouping.
11. Use of the equation in multiplication.
12. Several ways of multiplying.
13. Whole numbers: primes, composites, factors and multiples.
14. Square root: by the "average" method.

Activities to Broaden the Scope of Multiplication

Many of these activities are "discovery projects." By working several examples, at times as many as a dozen, children discover that certain patterns become evident in the solutions. Using these patterns as criteria for interpretation, a generalization can be stated which, in many cases, is applicable to mental calculation. Just one interpretation is presented here. Children will find others. It should be stressed that mental calculation is not the same as paper–pencil calculation. This activity is not meant for total class teaching. Much of this work can be assigned as research to students who indicate a good knowledge of arithmetic. This activity has a two–fold purpose: (1) to develop greater interest in arithmetic and (2) to provide for individual differences.

1. **To multiply any 2 digits by 11**

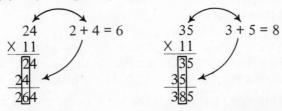

a. What recurring patterns do you see? Note that the sum of the tens digits in the partial product and the sum of the two digits in the multiplicand are the same. The two digits in the multiplicand become the hundreds place and the units place, respectively, because tens times tens are hundreds and ones times ones are ones. Therefore, one can merely add the digits in the multiplicand and write this sum between the same two digits to multiply by eleven.

b. What change in thinking is necessary in the following example?

$$
\begin{array}{r}
58 \\
\times\ 11 \\
\hline
58 \\
58 \\
\hline
638
\end{array}
\qquad
\begin{array}{r}
96 \\
\times\ 11 \\
\hline
96 \\
96 \\
\hline
1056
\end{array}
$$

2. **Multiply 3 or more digits by 11**

$$
\begin{array}{r}
763 \\
\times\ 11 \\
\hline
763 \\
763 \\
\hline
8393
\end{array}
$$

Steps:

a. $1 \times 3 = 3$ units $\times$ units.

b. $1 \times 6 = 6, 6 + 3 = 9$. 3 is in the tens place in the second partial product. It is also the number to the right of 6 in the multiplicand.

c. $1 \times 7 = 7, 7 + 6 = 13$. Write the 3 and carry the 1. 6 is in the hundreds place in the partial product. It is also the number to the right of 7 in the multiplicand.

d. $10 \times 700 = 7000$. 7 is in the fourth place in the partial product. 1000 is to be carried. $7 + 1 = 8$.

Generalization: To multiply by 11, multiply by 1 and add the digit to the right for each multiplication. The addition of the digit to the right is made because of the multiplication by 10. The last multiplication is made by the 1 ten.

3. **Practice in writing numerals.** To practice fours, multiply by 4×9 or 36. To write sevens, multiply by 7×9 or 72. Why is 8 omitted? Multiply with 8 in the sequence.

$$\begin{array}{r} 12,345,679 \\ \times\ 36 \\ \hline 444,444,444 \end{array}$$

4. **To multiply a teen times a teen**

Observe the pattern in the partial products

$$\begin{array}{r} 14 \\ \times\ 12 \\ \hline 8 \\ 20 \\ 40 \\ 100 \\ \hline \end{array}$$

The numbers in the block are 2, 4 and 10. The sum of these numbers is 16. Each number in the block is, however, 20, 40 and 100, a total of 160. ($10 \times 16 = 160$)

How can one account for the 8 in the partial product? $2 \times 4 = 8$

Then, $160 + 8 = 168$

What numbers in the multiplicand and the multiplier can be manipulated to get a sum of 16? $14 + 2 = 16$. Multiplication by 10, $10 \times 16 = 160$

$2 \times 4 = 8$

Then, $160 + 8 = 168$

$$\begin{array}{r} 17 \\ \times\ 16 \\ \hline 42 \\ 60 \\ 70 \\ 100 \\ \hline 272 \end{array}$$

The numbers in the block are 6, 7 and 10.

$17 + 6\ = 23$

$10 \times 23 = 230$

$6 \times 7 = 42$

$230 + 42 = 272$

Generalization: To multiply teens, add the multiplicand to the units digit in the multiplier and multiply by 10. To this number add the product of the unit digits.

5. **To square a 2-digit number ending in 5**

To establish a pattern, students are encouraged to multiply several 2-digit numbers ending in 5.

What repeating pattern is evident in each example?

Can this pattern be accepted as a part of the solution? What are the digits in the units and tens place each time?

How many digits will there be in each product? This is determined as one looks at the original example.

How can the digits in the multiplier and the multiplicand be combined to get the digits in the hundreds and thousands place? These can be determined by squaring the number in the tens place and adding 1 factor or raising a factor by 1 and multiplying by the original factor.

$$
\begin{array}{r}
65 \\
\times\ 65 \\
\hline
325 \\
390 \\
\hline
4225
\end{array}
\qquad
\begin{array}{r}
65 \\
\times\ 65 \\
\hline
4225
\end{array}
$$

steps

a 4–digit product

square $5 \to 25$

$(6 \times 6) + 6 = 42$ or

$6 \times 7 = 42$ (Tens times tens equal

$4200 + 25 = 4225$ hundreds)

6. **To multiply 2–digit numbers ending in 5**

What repeating pattern is evident in each multiplication?

What digits repeat in the units and tens place?

How many digits will there be in the product?

To identify the pattern in this example, the tens digits add to an even number.
$7 + 5 = 12$

How can numbers be manipulated to arrive at the digits in the hundreds and thousands position?

$$
\begin{array}{r}
75 \\
\times\ 55 \\
\hline
375 \\
375 \\
\hline
4125
\end{array}
\qquad
\begin{array}{r}
75 \\
\times\ 55 \\
\hline
4125
\end{array}
$$

steps

square $5 \to 25$

$(5 \times 7) + \dfrac{(7 + 5)}{2} = 35 + 6 = 41$

$4100 + 25 = 4125$

Manipulate the following: 35×55, 45×85, 75×95

7. **The complement method of multiplication**

The complement of a number is the difference between the number and 10 or a power of 10.

$$
\begin{array}{r}
8 \\
\times\ 7 \\
\end{array}
\begin{array}{l}
2 \\
3
\end{array}
\qquad
\begin{array}{l}
10 - 8 = 2,\ \text{the complement} \\
10 - 7 = 3,\ \text{the complement}
\end{array}
$$

The complement is subtracted from the number diagonally placed to obtain the number of tens.

$7 - 2 = 5$
$8 - 3 = 5$ interpreted to be 5 tens or 50

The complements are multiplied to obtain the number of units.
$3 \times 2 = 6$

Then, $50 + 6 = 56$

Equation: $(10 - 2) \times (10 - 3) = 100 - 50 + 6 = 56$

$(10 - 2)$ and $(10 - 3)$ are other names for 8 and 7

$$96 \quad\nwarrow\quad\nearrow\quad 4 \qquad 100 - 94 = 4$$
$$\times\ 88 \quad\swarrow\quad\searrow\quad 12 \qquad 100 - 12 = 88$$

$$88 - 4\ = 84 \qquad \text{interpreted to be } 8400\ (10 \times 10 = 100)$$
$$96 - 12 = 84 \qquad \text{note that the product must be a 4–digit number}$$

The complements are multiplied to obtain the number of units.

$$12 \times 4 = 48$$

Then, $8400 + 48 = 8448$

Equation: $(100 - 12) \times (100 - 4) = 10,000 - 1600 + 48$
$$= 8448$$

8. **Multiply any number by a teen**

```
  2857
X   16
 17142
  2857
 45712
```

Review multiplication by 11's.

How will this multiplication differ? Instead of the unit being 1, it is 6.

Multiply each number in the multiplicand by 6. As each number is multiplied, add the number to the right and any digit to be carried. The number to the right is added because a multiplication by 10 must be satisfied. Observe the partial products to substantiate your manipulation.

After each number in the multiplicand has been multiplied by 6, the last multiplication is 1×2 (10×2000) and any digit carried added. Then, $(1 \times 2) + 2 = 4$, the digit in the 10,000 position.

9. **Place multiplication**

```
  36
X 23
```

a. What numbers multiplied are ones?
Ones times ones are ones. $3 \times 6 = 18$.
Write the 8 and carry the 1 ten.

b. What numbers multiplied are tens? Tens are the next place to fill.
Ones times tens and tens times ones are tens.
$3 \times 3 = 9$ tens and $2 \times 6 = 12$ tens.
9 tens + 12 tens + the 1 ten carried = 22 tens. (220)
Write 2 in the tens place and carry 2 hundreds.

c. What numbers multiplied are hundreds? Hundreds are the next place to fill.
Tens times tens = hundreds.
2 tens times 3 tens = 6 hundreds.
6 hundreds + 2 hundreds (carried) = 8 hundreds.
The product is 828.

```
   574
X  326
186924
```

One times ones = ones

Ones times tens and tens times ones = tens.

Ones times hundreds, hundreds times ones and tens times tens = hundreds.

Tens times hundreds and hundreds times tens = thousands.

Hundreds times hundreds = tens thousands or hundred thousands. Because 3 × 5 is more than 10, the product will have 6 digits.

This algorism can be thought through by many children in the fifth and sixth grades. Encourage them to think in place value.

10. **Lattice method of multiplication:**

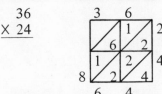

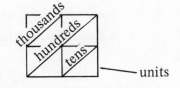

$$\begin{array}{r} 36 \\ \times\ 24 \end{array}$$

2 × 6 = 12
2 × 3 = 6
4 × 6 = 24
4 × 3 = 12

Add diagonally; read answer left to right: 864.

11. **Multiplying numbers using the distributive property:**

57 × 57 =

(50 + 7) × (50 + 7) = 3249.

Steps: a. 50 × 50 = 2500
        b. 50 × 7 = 350
        c. 7 × 50 = 350
        d. 7 × 7 =   49
                    3249

12. **Renaming numbers:**

53 × 47 =

(50 – 3)   Another name for 47

(50 + 3)   Another name for 53

(50 + 3) × (50 – 3) =

2500 – 150 + 150 – 9 =

Then, 2500 – 9 = 2491

13. **Use 10 clothespins and a wire coathanger as a device for multiplying two 1–digit numbers above 5:**

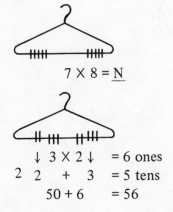

7 × 8 = <u>N</u>

↓ 3 × 2 ↓   = 6 ones
2 2 + 3   = 5 tens
   50 + 6   = 56

a. Clothespins grouped in fives.

b. Find the complement of each factor. Example: 7 × 8 = □. The complement of 7, (10 – 7), = 3, the complement of 8, (10 – 8), = 2.

c. Using the complements 3 and 2, turn down 3 and 2 clothespins. The clothespins which are turned down are multiplied; 3 × 2 = 6 units. The clothespins which remain up are added and make the tens ; 2 + 3 = 5 tens. Then, 50 + 6 = 56. Therefore, 7 × 8 = 56.

14. **Sequence of algorisms:** These are suggested steps because each teacher must develop the sequence of teaching as she best sees and understands the properties and concepts of multiplication.

a. Relate addition to multiplication

$$
\begin{array}{r} 4 \\ 4 \\ +\,4 \\ \hline 12 \end{array} \longrightarrow \begin{array}{r} 4 \\ \times\,3 \\ \hline 12 \end{array}
$$

3 sets of 4, 3 groups of 4, 4 to be added 3 times.

b. A single digit multiplier times 2– or 3–digit multiplicands

$$
\begin{array}{r} 10 \\ \times\,3 \\ \hline \end{array} \longrightarrow \begin{array}{r} 1\ \text{ten} \\ \times\,3 \\ \hline 3\ \text{tens} \end{array}
$$

Place value   Renaming 12

$$
\begin{array}{r} 12 \\ \times\ 4 \\ \hline \end{array} \longrightarrow \begin{array}{r} 1\ \text{ten} + 2\ \text{ones} \\ \times\ 4 \\ \hline 4\ \text{tens} + 8\ \text{ones} = 48 \end{array} \longrightarrow \begin{array}{r} 10 + 2 \\ \times\ 4 \\ \hline 40 + 8 = 48 \end{array}
$$

Equation

$$
4 \times 12 = 4 \times (10 + 2) = \text{Renaming 12}
$$
$$
(4 \times 10) + (4 \times 2) = \text{Distributive property}
$$
$$
40 \quad + \quad 8 \quad = 48
$$

Place value   Expanded notation

$$
\begin{array}{r} 312 \\ \times\ 3 \\ \hline \end{array} \longrightarrow \begin{array}{r} 3\,h + 1\,t + 2\,u \\ \times\ 3 \\ \hline 9\,h + 3\,t + 6\,u = 936 \end{array} \longrightarrow \begin{array}{r} 300 + 10 + 2 \\ \times\ 3 \\ \hline 900 + 30 + 6 = 936 \end{array}
$$

Equation

$$
3 \times 312 = 3 \times (300 + 10 + 2) = \text{Expanded notation}
$$
$$
(3 \times 300) + (3 \times 10) + (3 \times 2) = \text{Distributive property}
$$
$$
900 \quad + \quad 30 \quad + \quad 6 \quad = 936
$$

c. Two–digit multipliers (no regrouping). Use addition to establish the generalization when multiplying by 10.

$$
\begin{array}{r} 10 \\ \times\,10 \\ \hline \end{array} \qquad \begin{array}{r} 12 \\ \times\,10 \\ \hline \end{array} \qquad \begin{array}{r} 32 \\ \times\,20 \\ \hline \end{array}
$$

Rename multiplier   Place value

$$
\begin{array}{r} 21 \\ \times\,12 \\ \hline \end{array} \longrightarrow \begin{array}{r} 21 \\ \times\,10 \\ \hline 210 \end{array} \ + \ \begin{array}{r} 21 \\ \times\ 2 \\ \hline 42 \end{array} = 252
$$

$$
\begin{array}{r} 2\,t + 1\,u \\ 1\,t + 2\,u \\ \hline 4\,t + 2\,u \\ 2\,h + 1\,t \\ \hline 2h + 5\,t + 2\,u = 252 \end{array}
$$

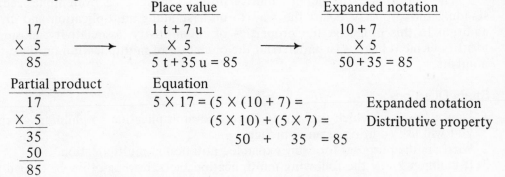

Expanded notation

$$
\begin{array}{r}
20 + 1 \\
\times\ 10 + 2 \\
\hline
40 + 2 \\
200 + 10 \\
\hline
200 + 50 + 2\ =\ 252
\end{array}
$$

Equation

$12 \times 21 = (10 + 2) \times 21 =$ Expanded notation

$(10 \times 21) + (2 \times 21)$ $=$ Distributive property

$210\ \ +\ \ 42\ \ =\ 252$

d. Regrouping

	Place value		Expanded notation

$$
\begin{array}{r}
17 \\
\times\ 5 \\
\hline
85
\end{array}
\quad\longrightarrow\quad
\begin{array}{r}
1\,t + 7\,u \\
\times\ 5 \\
\hline
5\,t + 35\,u = 85
\end{array}
\quad\longrightarrow\quad
\begin{array}{r}
10 + 7 \\
\times\ 5 \\
\hline
50 + 35 = 85
\end{array}
$$

Partial product

$$
\begin{array}{r}
17 \\
\times\ 5 \\
\hline
35 \\
50 \\
\hline
85
\end{array}
$$

Equation

$5 \times 17 = (5 \times (10 + 7) =$ Expanded notation

$(5 \times 10) + (5 \times 7) =$ Distributive property

$50\ +\ \ 35\ \ = 85$

Expanding multiplier

$$
\begin{array}{r}
24 \\
\times\ 16
\end{array}
\longrightarrow
\begin{array}{r}
24 \\
\times\ 10 \\
\hline
240
\end{array}
\ +\
\begin{array}{r}
24 \\
\times\ 6 \\
\hline
144
\end{array}
= 384
$$

Partial products

$$
\begin{array}{r}
24 \\
\times\ 16 \\
\hline
24 \\
120 \\
40 \\
200 \\
\hline
384
\end{array}
$$

Common algorism

$$
\begin{array}{r}
\overset{2}{24} \\
\times\ 16 \\
\hline
144 \\
24 \\
\hline
384
\end{array}
$$

Equation

$16 \times 24 = (10 + 6) \times (20 + 4) =$ Expanded notation

$= (10 \times 20) + (10 + 4) + (6 \times 20) + (6 \times 4) =$ Distributive property

$200\ +\ \ 40\ +\ 120\ +\ 24\ \ = 384$

Summary

The teacher who wants to develop a successful airthmetic program must first evaluate the child's experiences. Children come to school with different abilities and backgrounds and these experiences must be known before an intelligent program can be planned. The teacher's first job then is one of appraisal of the interests and abilities of the children.

It is essential that each child build an arithmetic vocabulary. Familiar names should be reviewed by means of concrete objects and explained in their arithmetical sense. It is important to help them to use these terms in their proper setting.

   Incidental number situations in the classroom offer excellent opportunities for
teaching arithmetic. Experiences in rational counting, one–to–one correspondence, comparison and problem solving are within the daily activities of a classroom.

   The understanding of a number involves many concepts. Each number can transmit
many ideas and these ideas contribute to the building of broader meanings, skills and understandings. With the use of concrete materials, and a language, children can gain real insight and a lasting interest in arithmetic.

   The importance of the distributive property cannot be overemphasized. Understanding this property opens the way to understanding multiplication and division. In
addition to this property, the properties of commutivity, associativity, closure and the
identity element help us to understand the operation of multiplication on the set of whole
numbers.

Study Questions

1. Plan a lesson in which you are to introduce multiplication to children. Explain how
   you will use addition as an approach.
2. What are the purposes for using expanded notation in multiplication?
3. If children know the following multiplication facts, how can they be helped to ration-
   alize the balance of the facts?

     $1 \times 6 = 6$

     $2 \times 6 = 12$

     $3 \times 6 = 18$

     $10 \times 6 = 60$

4. How can one use the following table to arrive at the product for 3×7, 4×9 and 6×8?
   What mathematical law is involved?

X	0	1	2	3	4	5
0	0	0	0	0	0	0
1	0	1	2	3	4	5
2	0	2	4	6	8	10
3	0	3	6	9	12	15
4	0	4	8	12	16	20
5	0	5	10	15	20	25

5. What are the factors of 18 and 24? What are the prime factors of 18 and 24? What
   is the lowest common multiple of 18 and 24?
6. Multiply 37×43 in four different ways. Explain why the algorisms that you use work.
7. Describe how you will teach the use of 1 and 0 when they are factors in multiplication.
8. Show in five ways how you can find the answer to 4×16. Explain each algorism.
9. It is often stated that there are only 90 multiplication facts. What are the bases for this
   assertion?

10. Give several examples in which the properties of commutivity, associativity and distributivity are applied.
11. Prepare several arrays which illustrate the distributive property of multiplication.
12. Check several arithmetic series for their presentation of multiplication.

Selected Text References

1. Banks, J. Houston, *Elementary School Mathematics*, Boston: Allyn and Bacon, Inc., 1966. Chapter 3.
2. Dutton, W. H., and L. J. Adams, *Arithmetic for Teachers*, Englewood Cliffs, N. J.: Prentice-Hall, Inc., 1961. Chapter 4.
3. Dwight, Leslie A., *Modern Mathematics for the Elementary Teacher*, New York: Holt, Rinehart and Winston, Inc., 1966. Chapter 10 and 11.
4. Kramer, Klaas, *The Teaching of Elementary School Mathematics*, Boston: Allyn and Bacon, Inc., 1966. Chapters 5, 12 and 20.
5. Meserve, Brucke E., and Max Sobel, *Introduction to Mathematics*, Englewood Cliffs, N. J.: Prentice–Hall, Inc., 1964. Chapter 1.
6. Spencer, Peter Lincoln, and Marguerite Brydegaard, *Building Mathematical Competence in the Elementary School*, New York: Holt, Rinehart and Winston, Inc., 1966. Chapters 7 and 8.
7. Swenson, Esther, *Teaching Children Arithmetic*, New York: The Macmillan Company, 1964. Chapters 9 and 10.

Selected Readings from the Arithmetic Teacher

1. Coon, Lewis H., "Number Line Multiplication for Negative Numbers," *13:* 213–217, March, 1966.
2. Deans, Edwina, "Independent Work in Arithmetic," *8:* 77–80, February, 1961.
3. Flournoy, Frances, "Applying Basic Mathematical Ideas in Arithmetic," *11:* 104–108, February, 1964.
4. Hannon, Herbert, "A New Look at Basic Principles of Multiplication with Whole Numbers," *7:* 357–361, November, 1960.
5. Jackson, Humphrey C., "Tables and Structures," *7:* 71–76, February, 1960.
6. Oesterle, Robert A., "What About Those Zero Facts?" *6:* 109–111, March, 1959.
7. Peterson, John A., and Joseph Hashisaki, "Patterns in Arithmetic," *13:* 209–212, March, 1966.

Chapter VI

Division of Whole Numbers

Division and subtraction are processes in which groups of specific quantities are subtracted from an original group. We have explained subtraction in terms of addition by saying that subtraction undoes addition. It is also important to explain division in terms of multiplication in presenting the process to elementary children. Multiplication and division are related in knowing that 4 X 6 = 24, one can reason that 24 ÷ 6 = 4. In algebraic language, a divided by b is a number c such that b X c = a. Division can be defined, then, as the process of finding the second factor when the product and one factor is given. The quotient is the missing factor. As an illustration, 5 X □ = 45, then, 45 ÷ 5 = 9.

The dividend is not always a multiple of the divisor. Children have discovered that some numbers cannot be divided into two equal groups. In this situation, they stated the result in terms of a remainder as 1 left over. As children progress, they will observe that the remainder may be expressed as a fraction and written in the quotient. In the example 29 ÷ 4, the result of the division may be stated as 7 and a remainder of 1 or 7¼.

What are several relationships between multiplication and division?

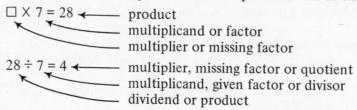

1. The product in multiplication is the dividend in division. These terms indicate the total number of things one has.
2. The divisor and quotient are the factors of a multiplication statement.
3. When the product and one factor is given, one divides to find the missing factor.

Properties of Division

The commutative and associative properties do not apply to division. Neither is the set of whole numbers closed to division. Some of the properties of division are:

1. Any number divided by 1 is the number. Example: 12 ÷ 1 = 12. For any number x, x ÷ 1 = x since x times 1 = x.
2. Distributive property of division with respect to addition: When the sum of two whole numbers is to be divided by a given nonzero number, one can divide each of the addends by the given number and the partial quotients added. Example: 35 ÷ 7 = (21 + 14) ÷ 7 = (21 ÷ 7) + (14 ÷ 7) = 3 + 2 = 5. If a, b and c are whole numbers with c ≠ (not equal to) 0, then (a + b) ÷ c = (a ÷ c) + (b ÷ c).
3. Compensation: Multiplying or dividing the divisor and the dividend by the same nonzero number does not change the quotient. Examples: 36 ÷ 4 = (3 X 36) ÷ (3 X 4) = 108 ÷ 12 = 9. 72 ÷ 12 = (72 ÷ 4) ÷ (12 ÷ 4) = 18 ÷ 3 = 6.

Presentation of Division

Division is the inverse operation of multiplication. In Chapter V, "Multiplication of Whole Numbers," a language was developed to show that equal groups are combined and to describe what actually happens in the process. The same language is applicable to division. In the example $27 \div 9 = \square$, these questions are asked:

What number times 9 is 27?
How many nines in 27?
How many groups of 9 in 27?
How many sets of 9 in 27?

In learning the multiplication facts, children have had experience finding the product and the missing factor. As they were learning the basic addition facts, many multiplication facts were discovered. When 12 was divided into two equal groups using manipulative material, $2 \times 6 = 12$ was identified orally and later written. Division is involved when a missing factor is present. In introducing division, the multiplication equation with the missing multiplier should be used. This will permit the students to think in terms of the measurement concept. With the multiplicand given, they have an opportunity to think about the size of each group. In the example $\square \times 4 = 12$, children can manipulate various objects in finding how many groups of 4 there are in 12. What solutions do they discover?

Count as many groups of 4 objects as possible. How many groups of 4 are there in 12?

☐ ☐　　☐ ☐　　☐ ☐
☐ ☐　　☐ ☐　　☐ ☐

How many times can a group of 4 be added?
    $4 + 4 = 8, 8 + 4 = 12$. Four is added 3 times.

How many groups of 4 can be subtracted from 12?
    $12 - 4 = 8, 8 - 4 = 4, 4 - 4 = 0$. Four is subtracted 3 times.

Counting groups on the number line.

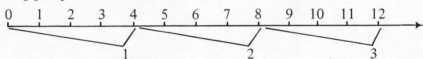

Three groups of 4 can be counted.

As children demonstrate their insight in finding the missing factor using such solutions as indicated above, the division algorism is introduced as a way of solving examples. Developing the concept of division is facilitated by the use of the subtractive algorism in which the divisor is subtracted one group at a time from the dividend or by a multiple of the divisor.

Problem: Mary has 18 pieces of candy. She wishes to put 6 pieces of candy in each sack. How many sacks does she need?

What is given in the problem?
Is a product given? (18 pieces of candy)
Is a multiplier or a multiplicand given?
(The multiplicand, 6 pieces of candy)

$$\square \times 6 = 18 \longrightarrow 18 \div 6 = \square$$

$$
\begin{array}{r}
6 \overline{)\,18} \\
-6 \qquad 1 \qquad (1 \times 6) \\
\hline
12 \\
-6 \qquad 1 \\
\hline
6 \\
-6 \qquad 1 \\
\hline
3 \qquad \text{3 sacks are needed}
\end{array}
$$

$$3 \times 6 = 18 \qquad 18 \div 6 = 3$$

Problem: There are 45 boys out for baseball. If each team has 9 players, how many teams does the school have?

Analyze what is given in the problem.

$$
\begin{array}{r}
9 \overline{)\,45} \\
-9 \qquad 1 \\
\hline
36 \\
-18 \qquad 2 \\
\hline
18 \\
-18 \qquad 2 \\
\hline
5 \qquad \text{the school has 5 teams}
\end{array}
$$

$$5 \times 9 = 45 \qquad 45 \div 9 = 5$$

Example: $\square \times 4 = 20 \qquad 20 \div 4 = \square$

$$
\begin{array}{r}
4 \overline{)\,20} \\
-4 \qquad 1 \\
\hline
16 \\
-4 \qquad 1 \\
\hline
12 \\
-4 \qquad 1 \\
\hline
8 \\
-8 \qquad 2 \\
\hline
5 \qquad \text{5 groups of 4 in 20}
\end{array}
$$

$$20 \div 4 = 5 \qquad 5 \times 4 = 20$$

The structure of the 90 basic division facts provides several generalizations helpful in establishing the quotient. The children should not be required to use any one approach in learning these facts but rather to use a combination of methods discovered during the learning period. It has been emphasized that there is "no one correct procedure" for solving problems. Many techniques will be discovered and many children will find success in the more simple solutions.

The teacher has the task of selecting various activities which will place before children opportunities to discover and observe generalizations about the basic division facts. The following generalizations are common to division.

The 9 Zero Facts

The zero facts are not encountered in division until the introduction of 2–digit dividends other than the basic facts; therefore, it seems reasonable that a thorough study of the zero facts be postponed until there is a need for them.

DIVISION FACTS (90)

quotient	0	1	2	3	4	5	6	7	8	9
1)	0	1	2	3	4	5	6	7	8	9
2)	0	2	4	6	8	10	12	14	16	18
3)	0	3	6	9	12	15	18	21	24	27
4)	0	4	8	12	16	20	24	28	32	36
5)	0	5	10	15	20	25	30	35	40	45
6)	0	6	12	18	24	30	36	42	48	54
7)	0	7	14	21	28	35	42	49	56	63
8)	0	8	16	24	32	40	48	56	64	72
9)	0	9	18	27	36	45	54	63	72	81

In arithmetic, the example $4 \div 0$ is not possible. This is true because there is no number which, when multiplied by zero, will give a product of 4. In statements written as $a \div b$, we are reminded that b cannot be zero. A review of the zero multiplication facts are necessary at this time as an explanation why zero cannot be a divisor.

$0 \times 4 = \square$

Can 4 be written zero times? Cannot be proven by addition.

$4 \div 0 = \square$

How many zeros in 4? $0)\overline{4}$ not possible
Zero times what number is 4?

The multiplication fact cannot be written. There is no number times zero which will give a product of 4.

Rewrite the basic fact placing the 4 as the multiplier.

$4 \times 0 = \square$
4 groups of zero
Zero is to be added 4 times. $0 + 0 + 0 + 0 = 0$

$0 \div 4 = \square$
4 times what number is zero? 0
How many fours in zero? $4)\overline{0}$
Then, $0 \div 4 = 0$ $\underline{0}$

The generalization which children will discover is: if zero is divided by a nonzero number, the quotient is zero.

$$\begin{array}{cccccccccc} & 0 & & 0 & & 0 & & 0 & & 0 & & 0 & & 0 & & 0 & & 0 \\ 1\overline{)0} & & 2\overline{)0} & & 3\overline{)0} & & 4\overline{)0} & & 5\overline{)0} & & 6\overline{)0} & & 7\overline{)0} & & 8\overline{)0} & & 9\overline{)0} \end{array}$$

The 9 Ones Facts (One as a Divisor)

It may be that this generalization was introduced as early as the first grade when children were dividing in developing concepts of numbers. What happens to 4 if it is divided into two groups? What happens to 4 if it is separated into groups of 1 each? The generalization for one is: when dividing any number by 1, the quotient is the number.

Problem: Jack has 3 apples. If he places 1 apple in each sack, how many sacks will he need?

$$1\text{ apple}\,\overline{)\,3\text{ apples}}^{\,3\text{ sacks}} \qquad \text{One apple in each group}$$

$$\begin{array}{ll} 1\overline{)3}^{\,3} & N \times 1 = 3 \\ \quad \underline{3} & 3 \times 1 = 3 \end{array}$$

$$\begin{array}{ccccccccc} & 1 & & 2 & & 3 & & 4 & & 5 & & 6 & & 7 & & 8 & & 9 \\ 1\overline{)1} & & 1\overline{)2} & & 1\overline{)3} & & 1\overline{)4} & & 1\overline{)5} & & 1\overline{)6} & & 1\overline{)7} & & 1\overline{)8} & & 1\overline{)9} \end{array}$$

Dividing a Number by Itself (8)

The generalization is: when dividing a number by itself, the quotient is always 1.

$$\begin{array}{cccccccc} & 1 & & 1 & & 1 & & 1 & & 1 & & 1 & & 1 & & 1 \\ 2\overline{)2} & & 3\overline{)3} & & 4\overline{)4} & & 5\overline{)5} & & 6\overline{)6} & & 7\overline{)7} & & 8\overline{)8} & & 9\overline{)9} \end{array}$$

($1\overline{)1}^{\,1}$ is considered in the examples having divisors of 1.)

The 8 Squares

Squaring is multiplying a number by itself. There is no generalization applicable to the squares. They are listed here to account for the structure of the 90 facts.

$$\begin{array}{cccccccc} & 2 & & 3 & & 4 & & 5 & & 6 & & 7 & & 8 & & 9 \\ 2\overline{)4} & & 3\overline{)9} & & 4\overline{)16} & & 5\overline{)25} & & 6\overline{)36} & & 7\overline{)49} & & 8\overline{)64} & & 9\overline{)81} \end{array}$$

($1\overline{)1}^{\,1}$ is considered in the examples having divisors of 1.)

The 28 Related Pairs

Fifty–six of the 90 division facts are related by pairs. In knowing that $56 \div 8 = 7$, one can reason that $56 \div 7 = 8$. The generalization for the related pairs is: from each division fact, $48 \div 8 = 6$, another division fact can be made by interchanging the divisor and the quotient, $48 \div 6 = 8$. Examples:

$$\begin{array}{cccc} 9 & 4 & 8 & 3 \\ 4\overline{)36} & 9\overline{)36} & 3\overline{)24} & 8\overline{)24} \end{array}$$

The above generalizations are not to be memorized as rules, but should be developed with the children as their experiences help them to discover the patterns in the basic facts.

The relationship between multiplication and division is emphasized in the following table. Note how products and quotients are found. Children can construct a similar chart which they will complete as they learn the basic facts.

THE BASIC 81 MULTIPLICATION and DIVISION FACTS

X ÷	1	2	3	4	5	6	7	8	9
1	1	2	3	4	5	6	7	8	9
2	2	4	6	8	10	12	14	16	18
3	3	6	9	12	15	18	21	24	27
4	4	8	12	16	20	24	28	32	36
5	5	10	15	20	25	30	35	40	45
6	6	12	18	24	30	36	42	48	54
7	7	14	21	28	35	42	49	56	63
8	8	16	24	32	40	48	56	64	72
9	9	18	27	36	45	54	63	72	81

How to use the chart:

To multiply 6 × 4: Find 6 in the left column. Move the finger to the column marked 4. The answer is 24.

To divide 24 by 6: Find 24 in the horizontal channel to the right of 6. Move the finger from 24 up to 4. The answer is 4.

Every division includes the number in a total group and the number of things in a small group or the number of small groups. Students have been made aware of the importance of a language which will help them to define the terms of the multiplication equation. In the learning stage, multiplier and multiplicand are used to convey a specific meaning to the divisor. It is this meaning of the divisor, whether it is a multiplier or a multiplicand, which will help clarify the meaning for each of the two types of division.

1. Measurement division: The product and the multiplicand are given. We are to find the number of groups.

Problem: I have 24 wheels. If I put 4 wheels on each wagon, how many wagons can I build?

Given: $\square \times 4 = 24 \longrightarrow 24 \div 4 = \square$

$$
\begin{array}{r}
4)\overline{24} \\
\underline{4} \qquad 1 \\
20 \\
\underline{8} \qquad 2 \\
12 \\
\underline{4} \qquad 1 \\
8 \\
\underline{8} \qquad \underline{2} \\
6 \qquad \text{I can build 6 wagons.}
\end{array}
$$

General patterns in measurement division.
  a. Divisor and dividend are labeled alike. (Wheels and wheels)
  b. The quotient is in terms of the question asked in the problem. (Wagons)
  c. One can count, add and subtract to find the quotient.
  d. Language: How many groups of 4 in 24? How many fours in 24? What number times 4 is 24?

2. Partition division: The product and the multiplier are given. We are to find the number in each group.

Problem: Mary has 42 pieces of candy. If she wishes to put the candy in 7 baskets, how many pieces will she have for each basket?

Given: $7 \times \square = 42 \longrightarrow 42 \div 7 = \square$

In partition division, the dividend and the multiplier are not labelled the same. The divisor states that the dividend is to be divided into 7 equal groups. How can this division be illustrated?

Place 1 piece of candy in each of 7 baskets.

O O O O O O O

Repeat the distribution. Place 1 piece of candy in each of the 7 baskets until no candy remains. When this has been done, count the number of pieces of candy in each basket. This is the quotient.

O O O O O O O
O O O O O O O
O O O O O O O
O O O O O O O
O O O O O O O
O O O O O O O

Subtractive algorism

```
7)42
   7        1
  35
  14        2
  21
   7        1
  14
  14        2
            ─
   6    Six pieces of candy in each basket.
```

General patterns in partition division.
  a. Dividend and quotient are labeled alike.
  b. The divisor states the number of groups.
  c. We are to find the number in each group.
  d. Counting, addition and subtraction are not applicable.

Important Ideas Begun

1. Division is a process of subtracting groups of the same size.
2. Multiplication and division are inverse processes.
3. The dividend indicates the total quantity in the group.
4. The divisor can indicate the size of a group. (Measurement.)
5. The divisor can indicate the number of groups. (Partition.)
6. The quotient is in terms of "how many groups" or "how many in a group?"
7. For each multiplication fact there are 2 division facts.
8. The language of division is related to multiplication.
9. Measurement and partition as division types.
10. The divisor times the quotient equals the dividend.
11. Generalizations concerning the division facts.

When insight has been developed, one soon discovers that in the actual manipulation of numbers, it is immaterial whether the problem is called measurement or partition because one operates on numbers and not on labels. The terms "measurement" and "partition" are not operations in division but ways of thinking through a problem. When a problem is stated in its abstract form, there is no way for one to know which of these divisions is meant. In the example $56 \div 8 = \square$, we do not know whether 8 is a multiplier or a multiplicand. This does not affect the quotient. In the examples $\square \times 9 = 63$ and $9 \times \square = 63$, dividing by 9 results in 7 in each situation. Children will find that in knowing the meaning of these two divisions problem solving is simplified.

Continue to discover the basic facts in division from known basic facts in multiplication. Guide the children to see that for each multiplication fact except for the squares, that there are two basic facts for division. Challenge the children to use the generalizations identified about the division facts; encourage them to use concrete materials, drawings, the number line and the subtractive algorism in arriving at the basic facts.

Using the Basic Facts

When children have learned several basic facts in division, they are ready to divide 2 and 3–digit numbers by a 1–digit divisor. Introducing the tens as dividends is a good starting point. This will prepare children for a sequential development in rewriting the dividend in an expanded form. The common algorism is not taught until children understand the subtractive form and this may be as late as the fifth grade for many. However, it is included here to complete the sequence in the teaching of division.

One-Digit Divisors

Problem: Jim has 20 marbles which he wants to divide into 2 groups. How many marbles will there be in each group? Solutions:

1. Use of the counting frame

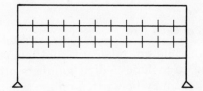

Two groups of ten
Ten in each group

2. Subtractive method

$$2\overline{)20}\text{ marbles}$$
$$\underline{-10}\qquad\qquad 5\qquad(5\times2)$$
$$10$$
$$\underline{-\ 6}\qquad\qquad 3\qquad(3\times2)$$
$$4$$
$$\underline{-\ 4}\qquad\qquad \underline{2}\qquad(2\times2)$$

10 marbles in each group

$$2\overline{)20}$$
$$\underline{-20}\qquad\qquad 10\qquad(2\times10)$$

10 marbles in each group

3. Common algorism

$$\begin{array}{r}10\\2\overline{)20}\\\underline{20}\end{array}$$
Language: 2 × what number is 20?
Divide 20 into 2 groups
How many in each group?

Problem: The school purchased 30 plants. The children will plant the flowers in 3 rows. How many plants will there be in each row? Solutions:

1. Divide the plants into three groups by placing 1 plant at a time in each of three groups. (Partition.)

Group 1	Group 2	Group 3
X	X	X
X	X	X
X	X	X
X	X	X
X	X	X
X	X	X
X	X	X
X	X	X
X	X	X
X	X	X

How many in each group? (10)

2. $3\overline{)30}$ plants
$$\underline{-\ 9}\qquad\qquad 3\qquad(3\times3)$$
$$21$$
$$\underline{-\ 9}\qquad\qquad 3$$
$$12$$
$$\underline{-12}\qquad\qquad \underline{4}$$
10 plants in each row

As these examples are discussed with children, relate the multiplication of a 1–digit multiplier times 10. Extend the dividend to include 2–digit numbers other than 10. In expanding the dividend, the partial quotients may be written on the side as in subtractive division or above the dividend. The subtractive algorism should be the form to stress until children indicate a good understanding of division.

```
2)24        ⟶      2)20        +      2)4
  20    10         20     10          4    2
   4                                  4
   4     2
        12                        10 + 2 = 12
```

In expanding 24, note that the division becomes a familiar pattern. The dividend is 20 in one part and a basic fact in the second part. The distributive property permits us to rename the dividend so that tens and ones are divided. Observe the pattern in the following examples:

```
4)48        ⟶      4)40        +      4)8

3)69        ⟶      3)60        +      3)9
```

To emphasize the importance of looking at the dividend as tens and ones, the examples 42 ÷ 3 and 192 ÷ 8 are solved by using groups of tens and ones and groups of hundreds, tens and ones.

Example: 3)42

The example calls for the division of 42 into 3 groups. Place 1 ten in each of three groups. One ten remains.

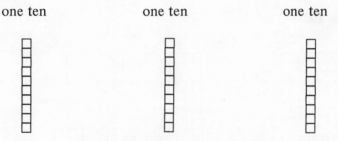

Substitute 10 ones for the 1 ten remaining. Add the 2 ones. (10 + 2 = 12.)

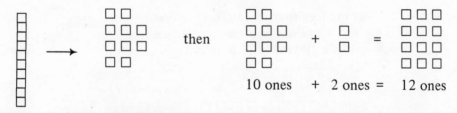

Divide the units into 3 groups and place 1 group with each 10. When 42 is divided into 3 groups, there are 14 in each group, 1 ten and 4 ones.

Expanding:

$$3\overline{)42} \longrightarrow \overset{10}{3\overline{)30}} + \overset{4}{3\overline{)12}} \qquad 10 + 4 = 14$$

Each group is 14

Other examples:

$$2\overline{)32} \longrightarrow 2\overline{)20} + 2\overline{)12}$$

$$4\overline{)64} \longrightarrow 4\overline{)40} + 4\overline{)24}$$

$$3\overline{)69} \longrightarrow 3\overline{)30} + 3\overline{)30} + 3\overline{)9}$$

$$3\overline{)30} + 3\overline{)30} + 3\overline{)9}$$
$$\underline{30} \quad 10 \qquad \underline{30} \quad 10 \qquad \underline{9} \quad 3$$

$$10 + 10 + 3 = 23$$

$$3\overline{)60} + 3\overline{)9}$$
$$\underline{60} \quad 20 \qquad \underline{9} \quad 3$$

$$20 + 3 = 23$$

Example:

$$8\overline{)192}$$

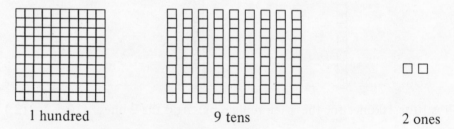

1 hundred   9 tens   2 ones

$8\overline{)192}$ What number times 8 equals 1? None.
8 is not contained in 1 group of 1 hundred.
Substitute 10 tens for 1 hundred.
Think 19 tens.

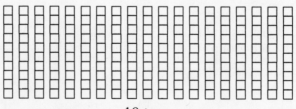

19 tens

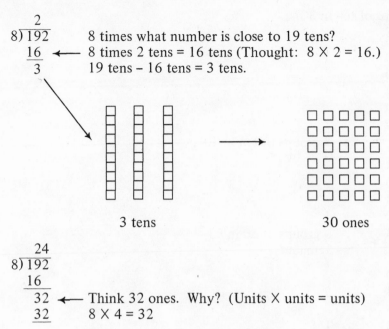

$$\begin{array}{r} 2 \\ 8\overline{)192} \\ \underline{16} \\ 3 \end{array}$$
8 times what number is close to 19 tens?
8 times 2 tens = 16 tens (Thought: 8 × 2 = 16.)
19 tens − 16 tens = 3 tens.

3 tens   30 ones

$$\begin{array}{r} 24 \\ 8\overline{)192} \\ \underline{16} \\ 32 \\ \underline{32} \end{array}$$
Think 32 ones. Why? (Units × units = units)
8 × 4 = 32

The multiplication statement is 8 × 24 = 192

In the previous examples one can see the importance of thinking place value; the common algorism is simplified when emphasis is given to place value.

The subtractive algorism is a more natural approach to division because it uses directly multiplication by 100s, 10s and 1s.

$$\begin{array}{r} 3\overline{)42} \\ \underline{30} \\ 12 \\ \underline{12} \\ 14 \end{array}$$
Are there as many as ten groups of 3 in 42?
10

4

$$\begin{array}{r} 8\overline{)192} \\ \underline{160} \\ 32 \\ \underline{32} \\ 24 \end{array}$$
Are there as many as ten groups of 8 in 192? More?
20

4

The concept of division as successive subtraction continues with 2 and 3–digit divisors. From the pupil's first introduction to division, he is encouraged and directed to see the relationship of the process to subtraction and multiplication. The previous illustrations are typical of the meaningful approach which the subtractive algorism has given to division.

Skills gained in the use of tens and multiples of tens in multiplication are essential to progress with 2 and 3–digit divisors. Each skill previously learned finds a place as progress is made in arithmetic.

How many groups of ten in 30?

```
10)30
   10        1
   20
   10        1
   10
   10        1
             3 groups of ten in 30
```

```
30)93
   60        2
   33
   30        1
    3  ←     3 groups of 30 in 93
             remainder
```

```
12)60
   24        2
   36
   12        1
   24
   24        2
             5 groups of 12 in 60
```

```
21)147                   How many groups of 21 in 147?
   42        2           What number times 21 is 147?
  105
   42        2
   63
   63        3
             7
```

In expanding the dividend, the division becomes tens and units. To estimate the quotient, ten is used first as a multiplier and then 1, 2, 3, 4 or 5. Is 144 as much as ten groups of 12?

```
12)144    ⟶     12)120        +       12)24
   120    10       120    10             24    2
    24
    24     2               10 + 2 = 12
          12
```

```
14)168    ⟶     14)140        +       14)28
                   140    10             28    2
                           10 + 2 = 12
```

```
15)195    ⟶     15)150        +       15)45
                   150    10             45    3
                           10 + 3 = 13
```

$$24\overline{)384} \longrightarrow 24\overline{)240} \qquad + \qquad 24\overline{)144}$$

	240	10	120	5
			24	
			24	1
				6

$$10 + 6 = 16$$

$36\overline{)936}$

360	10	Is 936 as much as ten groups of 36?
576		
360	10	Is 576 as much as ten groups of 36?
216		
180	5	As much as ten groups? One-half of ten groups?
36		
36	1	
26		

Review multiplication by tens, hundreds and thousands and ask the students to re-call the generalization learned about annexing zeros. The division of 2 and 3–digit numbers are made easy by the use of tens and powers of tens as trial quotients. Of the several approaches to estimating the trial quotient, the most reasonable and logical is the use of tens and powers of tens. In the development of the subtractive algorism, the emphasis has been upon the choice of a partial quotient which is easy for the child to use. This same reasoning should accompany the choice of a trial quotient in any algorism used in division. The questions which are asked about divisors with respect to the dividend can always be in terms of ten or powers of ten and 1, 2, 3, 4 or 5. One soon finds that the numbers 6, 7, 8 and 9 are seldom used as trial quotients. There is no need for them when one can think in terms of ten, one-half of ten or 1, 2, 3 and 4.

$37\overline{)5376}$

3700	100	Is 5376 as much as 100 × 37?
1676		Is 1676 as much as 50? No.
370	10	Is it as much as 10?
1306		
1110	30	Is it as much as 30?
196		Is it as much as 10? No.
185	5	Is it as much as 5?
11	145	
	remainder	

$326\overline{)57875}$

32600	100	Is the trial quotient as much as 100?
25275		
18300	50	Is the trial quotient as much as 50?
6975		
3260	10	Is the trial quotient as much as 10?
3715		
3260	10	
455		
326	1	Is the trial quotient as much as 5? No.
129	171	
	remainder	

Estimating the Quotient

Estimating quotients requires mental computation with numbers. Skill in estimating is a help to the student in checking the reasonableness of sums, differences, products and quotients. Practice in estimating begins early in the grades; the child may state that the door is 7 feet high, the room is 20 feet long and so on. Later he begins to look at numbers with a view to establishing a reasonable answer. In multiplication, we discovered a method of estimating number of digits in the product and a rounding off of the product which was based upon place value. In division, several approaches are possible. It has already been stated that the use of the subtractive algorism develops skill in estimating the quotient through the use of the partial quotients. It is this concept which we wish to develop further.

In addition to the partial quotient approach is the method of rounding the divisor up to the next decade or down to ten in the present decade and using this number as the trial divisor.

The examples presented below are solved using the subtractive concept of division. The quotients or the partial quotients are written above the dividend. The use of the partial quotient idea will almost eliminate the need for students to erase his work because he was not fortunate the first time to establish the true quotient.

```
          4
      31)176
          124      (4 X 31)
           52
```

When the partial dividend (52) is larger than the divisor, it should indicate to children that *not enough groups of 31 were taken out* by using 4 as the first quotient number. Comparing 31 and 52, one finds that another group of 31 can be taken out. Instead of erasing and starting over with 5 in the quotient, merely place a 1 above the 4 and write 31 below 52 and subtract. The quotient is 4 + 1 = 5, with a remainder of 21.

```
          1
          4
      31)176
          124
           52
           31      (1 X 31)
           21
```

The subtractive method has stressed the fact that a partial quotient and not the true quotient is a good starting point. This eliminates erasers, and develops insight into division.

```
          20
      76)2812
          152      (20 X 76)
          129
```

Not having to extract the true quotient on the first try eases the operation. The partial dividend, 129, is larger than the divisor, 76. This indicates that at least 10 more groups of 76 can be subtracted.

```
          1
          2
      76)2812
          152      (20 X 76)
          129
           76      (10 X 76)
           53
```

Indicates that at least another 10 groups of 76 can be subtracted. The partial quotient at this time is 30. (20 + 10)

```
      11
      26                  The true quotient is 37 (26 + 11.)
  76) 2812
      152      (20 X 76)
      129
       76      (10 X 76)
      532                 Bring down the 2. (Partial dividend is 532)
      456                 6 X 76 = 456
       76   ◄——————— Indicates that another group of 76 can be subtracted.
       76
```

```
        1
       71                 The true quotient is 81
  582) 47223
      4074      (70 X 582)
       648   ◄——————— Indicates that more groups of 582 can be subtracted
       582      (10 X 582)
       663
       582      (1 X 582)
        81                 Remainder
```

In each of the examples above, the estimated quotient was too small. What might happen if the quotient is too large? What might be the thought process? Can a quantity be put back if it has been taken out?

Step 1.

```
                            3
                            4̸
                        76) 2812
                            304      (40 X 76)
            76              ⁻23
          - 23   ◄————      76       (10 X 76)
            53              53
```

Estimate: How many 70's are there in 2800? (4.) The child multiplies and discovers that 304 (3040) is larger than the 281 (2812). What should he do? If he subtracts the smaller from the larger number (as 304 – 281 =⁻23), the remainder is that number which tells *how much too much* was taken out when 4 was used as the quotient. A negative sign is placed in front of the number to help think of it in a special way. To balance the operation, replace 10 groups of 76 and subtract the 23 from 76.   The 4 in the quotient is reduced by 1.   53 is the difference if one had started with 3 in the quotient.

Step 2.

```
                            3
                            4̸7              The quotient is 37
                        76) 2812
                            304
                          - 23              Bring down the 2. The partial dividend is 532.
                            76              Estimated quotient:  7 X 7 = 49
                            532             7 X 76
                            532
```

Trial quotient too small

$$
\begin{array}{r}
2\ 2 \\
633 \\
768\overline{)641280} \\
4608 \\
\hline
1804 \\
1536 \\
\hline
2688 \\
2304 \\
\hline
3840 \\
2304 \\
\hline
1536 \\
1536 \\
\hline
\end{array}
$$

The quotient is 835

600 × 768

200 × 768

30 × 768

3 × 768

2 × 768

Trial quotient too large

$$
\begin{array}{r}
71 \\
857 \\
368\overline{)282650} \\
2944 \\
\hline
{}^-118 \\
368 \\
\hline
2505 \\
1840 \\
\hline
665 \\
368 \\
\hline
2970 \\
2944 \\
\hline
26 \\
\end{array}
$$

The quotient is 767

800 × 368

Too much taken out
Replace 100 groups of 368

50 × 368

10 × 368

7 × 368

Remainder

$$
\begin{array}{r}
368 \\
-\ 118 \\
\hline
250 \\
\end{array}
$$
←——→

Earlier it was stated that one can round off the divisor as an aid to estimating the trial quotient. To be a learning situation, students must observe as he solves examples what is happening. The teacher helps them to generalize about the observations they have made.

1. Rounding off the divisor or the dividend, or both:

$$37\overline{)793} \longrightarrow 40\overline{)800}$$

The trial quotient is 20. (20 × 37 = 749)

2. Rule 1: If the units digit is 5 or less in the divisor, use the tens digit as the trial divisor.

$$
\text{Tens digit} \longrightarrow 25\overline{)76} \begin{array}{r} 3 \\ \\ 75 \\ \hline 1 \end{array}
$$

The trial divisor is 2
How many twos in 7?
The trial quotient is 3

In using 2 as a trial divisor, one has rounded off 25 to 20. The trial quotient is the true quotient.

3. Rule 2:   If the units digit in the divisor is 6 or more, raise the tens digit by 1. Try rounding tens digit up when the unit digit is 5 or 7.

$$\begin{array}{r} 2 \\ \text{Tens digit} \longrightarrow 27\overline{)\,71} \\ \underline{54} \\ 17 \end{array}$$

The trial divisor is 3
How many threes in 7?
The trial quotient is 2

In thinking about the 2 as a 3, one is really rounding off 27 to 30. How many 30's are in 71? The trial quotient is the true quotient.

In using these rules, children may have to try more than once to arrive at the correct quotient figure. Sometimes the trial quotient is too small; sometimes it is too large. By analyzing what is being done in division, additional groups can be taken out if the quotient is too small; if the quotient is too large, groups may be replaced.

Remainders

Children first identify remainders when they learn about the subgroups within the odd numbers. Dividing 7 into two groups produced two groups of 3 and 1 left over.

$$\begin{array}{ccc} 0\ 0\ 0 & 0\ 0\ 0 & 0 \qquad \longleftarrow \text{left over} \\ 3 & 3 & 1 \end{array}$$

Their generalization was: there is always a remainder of 1 when an uneven (odd) number is divided by 2.

What are the remainders?

$17 \div 2 = ?$

$425 \div 2 = ?$

$37,899 \div 2 = ?$

Types of Remainders (based upon an Analysis of the Problem to be Solved)

1. Written as a remainder;

Problem: Bill has 21 marbles. He divides them among his 4 friends. How many marbles will each friend receive?

$$\begin{array}{r} 5 \text{ marbles for each friend} \\ 4\overline{)\,21 \text{ marbles}} \\ \underline{20} \\ 1 \text{ marble remainder} \end{array}$$

Interpretation:

What is the question asked?
Would a fractional part of a marble be useful?
Is it immaterial where the remainder is written? (Yes.)
Is the remainder a part of the quotient? (No.)

2. Written as a fraction:

Problem: The school has a rope 23 feet long. What is the length of each piece of rope if it is divided into 3 pieces?

$$\begin{array}{r} 7 \longrightarrow \quad 7\ 2/3 \text{ feet} \\ 3\overline{)\,23 \text{ feet}} \\ \underline{21} \\ 2 \end{array}$$

Interpretation:

What does the remainder of 2 tell? (2 feet left over.)

The 2 feet left over is divided into how many parts? (3.)

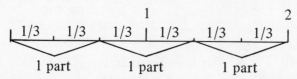

Each part is 2/3 of a foot long. When the remainder is written as a fraction, is it a part of the quotient? (Yes.)

3. Quotient rounded off:

Problem: The school policy states that 5 children can ride in one car. How many cars are needed to transport 27 children?

$$\begin{array}{r} 5 \text{ cars} \\ 5 \text{ children)} \overline{27 \text{ children}} \\ \underline{25} \\ 2 \text{ children left over} \end{array}$$

The quotient is rounded off to 6 cars to care for the remaining 2 children.

Problem: How many skirts can be made from 7 yards of cloth if it takes 2 yards for each skirt?

$$\begin{array}{r} 3 \text{ skirts} \\ 2 \text{ yds.)} \overline{7 \text{ yds.}} \\ \underline{6} \\ 1 \text{ yd. left over} \end{array}$$

Interpretation:

The quotient is stated as 3 skirts. The 1 yd. of material left over may be discussed in terms of what can be done with it. It is not a part of the quotient in this instance.

Comparing the Common and the Subtractive Algorisms

Example: $42 \div 3 = \square$

a.

$$\begin{array}{r} 1 \\ 3)\overline{42} \\ \underline{3} \\ 1 \end{array} \quad\begin{array}{l} \longleftarrow \text{ 3 } \times \text{ 1 ten} \longrightarrow \\ \longleftarrow \text{ 4 tens – 3 tens} \\ \quad 42 - 30 = 12 \longrightarrow \end{array} \quad \begin{array}{r} 10 \\ 3)\overline{42} \\ \underline{30} \\ 12 \\ \\ 4 \end{array}$$

b.

$$\begin{array}{r} 14 \\ 3)\overline{42} \\ \underline{3} \\ 12 \\ \underline{12} \end{array} \quad\begin{array}{l} \longleftarrow \text{ bring down the 2 units} \\ \longleftarrow \text{ units } \times \text{ units = units} \longrightarrow \end{array} \quad \begin{array}{r} 10 \\ 3)\overline{42} \\ \underline{30} \\ 12 \\ \underline{12} \end{array}$$

$$10 + 4 = 14, \text{ the quotient}$$

Example: 3568 ÷ 47 = □

```
                                                               5
         2                                                    20
        55                                                    50
    47)3568                                               47)3568
       235    ←───────── 50 × 47 ─────────→               2350
       121                                                1218
        94    ←───────── 20 × 47 ─────────→                940
       278                                                 278
       245    ←───────── 5 × 47 ──────────→                245
        33              remainder                           33
```

50 + 20 + 5 = 75, the quotient

It is no more difficult to divide by a 3-digit divisor than by a 2-digit divisor because concepts remain unchanged. Addition and subtraction may still be used to introduce 3-digit divisors. Children will generally choose to use the partial quotient method and to remove several groups of the divisor at one time. Pupils can be helped in finding the quotient figure by structuring a table before division is begun.

```
         67
   381)25545              1 × 381 =  381
      2286                2 × 381 =  762
      2685                3 × 381 = 1143
      2667                4 × 381 = 1524
        18 (Remainder)    5 × 381 = 1905
                          6 × 381 = 2286
                          7 × 381 = 2667
```

Example: 25,545 ÷ 381 = □

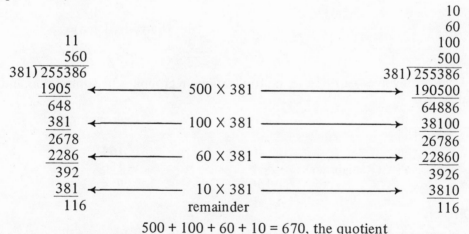

```
                                                             10
                                                             60
        11                                                  100
       560                                                  500
   381)255386                                          381)255386
      1905    ←────────── 500 × 381 ─────────→           190500
       648                                                64886
       381    ←────────── 100 × 381 ─────────→            38100
      2678                                                26786
      2286    ←────────── 60 × 381 ──────────→            22860
       392                                                 3926
       381    ←────────── 10 × 381 ──────────→             3810
       116              remainder                           116
```

500 + 100 + 60 + 10 = 670, the quotient

Advantages of the subtractive algorism

a. The exact quotient does not need to be found immediately.
b. The total dividend is considered in each subtraction.
c. No number needs to be "brought down."
d. Forgetting zero in the quotient is lessened.

Range of Difficulty in Division

In developing any presentation with children, one should be aware of the specific steps which are determined by the inclusiveness of the process. The following illustrations present a sequence which is built step by step upon the addition of one new idea in each step. If a child cannot perform for a given level in division, the failure should indicate to the teacher that the child must have more opportunity to learn about the process which is causing him difficulty. The sequence demonstrates clearly that children must understand the operations of subtraction and multiplication before division can be taught to them.

1. The dividend is an equal multiple of the divisor:

$$\begin{array}{r} 3 \\ 4\overline{)12} \\ 12 \end{array} \qquad\qquad \begin{array}{r} 2 \\ 21\overline{)42} \\ 42 \end{array}$$

2. The division involves a remainder:

$$\begin{array}{r} 3 \\ 5\overline{)17} \\ 15 \\ \hline 2 \end{array} \text{ (Remainder)} \qquad\qquad \begin{array}{r} 2 \\ 23\overline{)48} \\ 46 \\ \hline 2 \end{array} \text{ (Remainder)}$$

3. The subtraction involves regrouping (borrowing) and a remainder:

$$\begin{array}{r} 2 \\ 34\overline{)80} \\ 68 \\ \hline 12 \end{array} \text{ (Remainder)} \qquad\qquad \begin{array}{r} {}^{7}{}^{1} \\ 80 \\ 68 \\ \hline 12 \end{array}$$

4. The division involves carrying in the multiplication:

$$\begin{array}{r} 3 \\ 24\overline{)72} \\ 72 \end{array} \qquad\qquad \begin{array}{r} {}^{1} \\ 24 \\ \times\ 3 \\ \hline 72 \end{array} \text{ (Carrying 1 ten)}$$

5. Division involves carrying in multiplication, regrouping in subtraction and a remainder:

$$\begin{array}{r} 6 \\ 26\overline{)164} \\ 156 \\ \hline 8 \end{array} \text{ (Remainder)}$$

Carrying
$$\begin{array}{r} {}^{3} \\ 26 \\ \times\ 6 \\ \hline 156 \end{array}$$

Regrouping
$$\begin{array}{r} {}^{5}{}^{1} \\ 164 \\ -156 \\ \hline 8 \end{array}$$

Short Division

Division carried on as a mental process is generally thought of as short division.

Example: Steps taken mentally:

$$\begin{array}{r} 24 \\ 36\overline{)864} \end{array}$$

$2 \times 36 = 72$
$86 - 72 = 14.$ Think: partial dividend, 144
How many 36's in 144?
$4 \times 36 = 144$
$144 - 144 = 0$
Quotient is 24

Example: Old form for short division:

$$24\overline{)288}$$
$$12$$

Steps taken mentally:

How many 24's in 28?
Write 1 in the tens place
Subtract 24 from 28
Think 48
How many 24's in 48?
$2 \times 24 = 48$
$48 - 48 = 0$
The quotient is 12

Checks for Division

1. Addition:

$$37\overline{)148}$$
$$\underline{148}$$
$$4$$

The quotient tells that there are 4 groups of 37

37
37
37
+ 37
148

$$64\overline{)898}$$
$$\underline{64}$$
$$258$$
$$\underline{256}$$
$$2 \quad \text{(Remainder)}$$
$$14$$

Think: 10 groups of 64 = 640. Then, add 4 groups of 64 to 640

640
64
64
64
+ 64
896
+ 2 (Remainder)
898

2. Multiplication:

$$21\overline{)907}$$
$$\underline{84}$$
$$67$$
$$\underline{63}$$
$$4 \quad \text{(Remainder)}$$
$$43$$

Think: Divisor times quotient plus the remainder

43
× 21
43
86
903
+ 4 (Remainder)
907

$$21\overline{)907}$$
$$\underline{84}$$
$$67$$
$$\underline{63}$$
$$4$$
$$43$$

Think: Quotient times the divisor plus the remainder

21
× 43
63
84
903
+ 4 (Remainder)
907

3. Items to be considered in checking a problem for accuracy are:

> The multiplication facts involved
> Writing the wrong number
> Failure to bring down a number
> The use of zero (place value)
> The remainder is larger than the divisor

Patterns Which Indicate Divisibility

As children learn the concepts of division, they discover basic patterns in numbers which can be used in analyzing the division of a number into equal parts. Some of these patterns follow:

1. Any number ending in 0, 2, 4, 6 or 8 is divisible by 2. Examples: 10, 14, 36, 98, 378.
2. Any number ending in two digits which are divisible by 4 is divisible by 4. (Reasoning: 100 is divisible by 4.) Examples: 2356, 33332
3. Any number ending in 5 or 0 is divisible by 5. Examples: 20, 35, 160, 265.
4. If the sum of the digits in any number is divisible by 3, then the number is divisible by 3. This is sometimes stated that if the excess of nines in any number is divisible by 3 the number is divisible by 3. Examples: 654, 7,626, 48, 561.
5. Any number divisible by 2 and 3 is also divisible by 6. Examples: 618, 1,614, 13,608.
6. If the last 3 digits in any number are divisible by 8, then the number is divisible by 8. (Reasoning: 1000 is divisible by 8.) Examples: 4,328, 26,008, 83,936. 328 is divisible by 8; therefore, 4,328 is divisible by 8.
7. If the sum of the digits in a number is divisible by 9, then the number is divisible by 9. This generalization is sometimes stated that if the excess of nines in any number is zero the number is divisible by 9. Examples: 2,115, 12,690, 21,762.

Basic Ideas Begun

1. Meaning of division.
2. Measurement division.
3. Partition division.
4. Relationship of division to:
   a. Counting
   b. Addition
   c. Subtraction
   d. Multiplication
5. The language of division.
6. The basic facts in division.
7. The zero in division.
8. Generalizations based on the structure of the division facts.
9. Interpretation of remainders.
10. Two basic division facts are derived from one multiplication fact.
11. One–digit division.
12. Place value in division.
13. Expanding the dividend.
14. Estimating a quotient.
15. Two–digit division.

16. Structuring a multiplication table as an aid to finding the quotient number.
17. Steps in thinking through division from simple to complex solutions.
18. Performing division mentally.
19. Checks for division.
20. Patterns which indicate divisibility.

Activities to Broaden the Scope of Division

The following activities are not required of all children. As basic concepts are learned, permit children to study these approaches as research and share these experiences with their classmates.

1. Casting nines   (excess of nines)

```
      103
34) 3524
      34
     124
     102
      22
```

The excess of nines in the quotient, 103, is 4
Excess of nines in the divisor, 34, is 7
Excess of nines in the remainder, 22, is 4
Then, $(7 \times 4) + 4 = 32$
The excess of nines in 32 is 5
The excess of nines in the dividend, 3524, is 5.

Compare the excess of nines in the divisor, quotient and the remainder with the excess of nines in the dividend. If the excess of nines is the same, the quotient is probably correct. What would be the excess of nines if the quotient were written 301?

2. Factoring the divisor

```
15) 357
```

The factors of 15 are 3 and 5

Step 1.

```
      119
3) 357
    3
    5
    3
   27
   27
```

The quotient of the first factor

Step 2.   The quotient of the first factor becomes the dividend

```
      23
5) 119
   10
   19
   15
    4
```

To equate the remainder of 4 in terms of the original divisor 15, multiply 4/5 times the original divisor, 15

$$4/5 \times 15 = 12$$

The quotient is 23 with a remainder of 12

72)3186   The factors of 72 are 8 and 9

Step 1.

```
      398
    8)3186
      24
      78
      72
       66
       64
        2
```
First remainder. This remainder is added to the equated reminder

Step 2.

```
      44
    9)398
      36
      38
      36
       2
```

To equate the remainder of 2, in terms of the original divisor, multiply 2/9 times the original divisor, 72

$$2/9 \times 72 = 16$$

Then, 16 + 2 = 18, the remainder

The quotient is 44 with a remainder of 18

```
       33
    42)1386
```

Step 1.

```
        231
      6)1386
        12
        18
        18
         6
         6
```

Step 2:

```
        33
      7)231
        21
        21
        21
```

The second quotient obtained is the quotient of 1386 ÷ 42

3. A short division form: emphasis on place value

Form: 7968 ←— (dividend)   215 (quotient written to the right)

37 ←— (divisor rewritten for each quotient figure)

Step 1.   1   Step 2.   15
         7968   2   7968
         37   37   2 (Quotient)

How many 37's are there in 79? (2.) Multiply 2 × 3 (3 in 37), subtract 6 from 7 and write the difference, 1, above 7. Cross out 3 and 7 to indicate the completed thought process. Multiply 2 × 7 (7 in 37), subtract 14 from 19 and write the difference, 5, above 9. Cross out the 7 and the 19 to indicate the completed thought process. Partial dividend is 568.

Procedure:

    30 × 200 = 6000   7000 − 6000 = 1000
     7 × 200 = 1400   1900 − 1400 = 500

Step 3. The process to this point in one operation:

   X5
   7968   2 (Partial quotient)
   37
    37

Rewrite the divisor 37 as shown. The partial dividend is 568.

   1
   2
  189
  7968   21
  37
   37

How many 37's are there in 56? (1.) Write the 1 in the quotient. Multiply 1 × 3, subtract 3 from 5 and write the difference, 2, above the 5. Cross out 3 and 5. Multiply 1 × 7, subtract 7 from 26 and write the difference 19, above 26. Cross out 7 and 26. The partial dividend now is 198.

Procedure:

    30 × 10 = 300   500 − 300 = 200
     7 × 10 = 70   290 − 70 = 190

The partial dividend is 198.

Step 4.

   1
   24
  189
  7968   215
  37
   37
    37

How many 37's are there in 198? Write the 5 in the quotient. Multiply 5 × 3, subtract 15 from 19 and write the difference, 4, above the 9. Cross out 3 and 19. (48 is the partial dividend now.)

Procedure:

    30 × 5 = 150   198 − 150 = 48

Step 5.

   11
   24
  1893
  7968   215
  37
   37
    37

Multiply 5 × 7, subtract 35 from 48 and write the difference, 13, above 48. Cross out 7 and 48.

Procedure:

$7 \times 5 = 35$ $48 - 35 = 13$

The quotient is 215 with 13 as a remainder.

4. Complement approach

To divide 6357 by 97:

Think: $100 - 97 = 3$ (complement of 97 is 3).

Step 1.

$$\begin{array}{r} 6 \\ 100 - 3\overline{)6357} \\ 600 \\ \hline 35 \\ + \ 18 \\ \hline 53 \end{array}$$

How many 100's in 635? (6.)
Then, $6 \times 100 = 600$

$635 - 600 = 35$
Multiply the quotient 6 and the complement 3.
$6 \times 3 = 18$
Add 18 and 35 to compensate for dividing by 100.

Step 2.

$$\begin{array}{r} 65 \\ 100 - 3\overline{)6457} \\ 600 \\ \hline 35 \\ + \ 18 \\ \hline 537 \\ 500 \\ \hline 37 \\ + \ 15 \\ \hline 52 \end{array}$$

Bring down 7. The partial dividend is 537

How many 100's in 537? (5.)
Then, $5 \times 100 = 500$
$537 - 500 = 37$

Multiply the 5 in the quotient and the complement 3
$5 \times 3 = 15$.   Add 15 to 37 to compensate for dividing by 100

The quotient is 65 and a remainder of 52. Divide the common way and compare steps:

Procedure: To eliminate subtraction by hundreds:

$$\begin{array}{r} 6 \\ 100 - 3\overline{)6357} \\ + \ 18 \\ \hline 53 \end{array}$$

Think: $6 \times 100 = 600$
                $635 - 600 = 35$
Compensate: $6 \times 3 = 18$
                            $35 + 18 = 53$

$$\begin{array}{r} 65 \\ 100 - 3\overline{)6357} \\ + \ 18 \\ \hline 537 \\ + \ 15 \\ \hline 52 \end{array}$$

Bring down 7
Think: $5 \times 100 = 500$
               $537 - 500 = 37$
Compensate: $5 \times 3 = 15$
                            $37 + 15 = 52$

The quotient is 65 and a remainder of 52.

Divide 6897 by 94:

$$
\begin{array}{r}
1 \\
63 \\
100 - 6 \overline{)6897} \\
+\ 36 \\
\hline
125 \\
+\ 6 \\
\hline
317 \\
+\ 18 \\
\hline
35
\end{array}
$$

Think: $6 \times 100 = 600$. $689 - 600 = 89$.

$6 \times 6 = 36$.
$89 + 36 = 125$.

In this example, the first partial difference is larger than 100.

Therefore, write the 1 above the 6 in the quotient.
$(125 - 100 = 25)$
Multiply the 1×6 and add to 25
$25 + 6 = 31$. Bring down 7

Think: 300. Write 3 in the quotient

$3 \times 6 = 18$. Add $17 + 18 = 35$.

The quotient is 73 and the remainder is 35. Divide the common way and compare the steps.

Principle of Compensation

If the dividend and the divisor are both multiplied or divided by the same number, zero omitted, the quotient is not changed. Compensation shortens the process of division. In this example, the division is completed with a 1–digit divisor.

$$
\begin{array}{r}
15 \\
35 \overline{)525} \\
35 \\
\hline
175 \\
175 \\
\hline
\end{array}
$$

Principle: Divide the dividend and the divisor by the same nonzero number. The quotient does not change. The divisor is reduced to a single digit.

$$
\begin{array}{r}
15 \\
5 \overline{)75} \\
5 \\
\hline
25 \\
25 \\
\hline
\end{array}
$$

$$
\frac{525}{7} \div \frac{35}{7} = 75 \div 5 = 15
$$

$$
\begin{array}{r}
64 \\
25 \overline{)1623} \\
150 \\
\hline
123 \\
100 \\
\hline
23
\end{array}
$$
(Remainder)

Principle: Multiply both the divisor and the dividend by the same nonzero number. The quotient does not change. The divisor becomes 100. It is easy to divide by 100.

$$(4 \times 1623) \div (4 \times 25) = 6492 \div 100 = 64 \text{ and a remainder of } 92$$

$$
\begin{array}{r}
64 \\
100 \overline{)6492} \\
600 \\
\hline
492 \\
400 \\
\hline
92
\end{array}
$$

92/100 reduces to 23/25. (Remainder of 23.)

The principles of multiplication and division in the process of division is introduced to children when they are dividing by 1–digit numbers. These principles are an explanation for changing fractions to higher and lower terms and to division of decimals. Examples:

$$\overset{3}{4)\overline{12}} \rightarrow \overset{}{3 \times 4)\overline{3 \times 12}} \rightarrow \overset{3}{12)\overline{36}}$$

$$72 \div 12 = 6 \rightarrow (72 \div 6) \div (12 \div 6) =$$
$$ 12 \div 2 = 6$$

Sequence of Algorisms in Division

$\square \times 6 = 24 \qquad 24 \div 6 = \square$

$5 \times \square = 35 \qquad 35 \div 5 = \square$

$20 \div 5 = \square \qquad \square \times 5 = 20$

Subtractive approach

```
5)20                               4)40
  5    1 set of 5 subtracted         8   2 sets of 4 subtracted
 15                                 32
  5    1                            20   5 sets of 4 subtracted
 10                                 12
  5    1                            12   3 sets of 4 subtracted
       4 sets of 5 in 20                 10 sets of 4 in 40
       4 X 5 = 20                        10 X 4 = 40
       20 ÷ 5 = 4                        40 ÷ 4 = 10
```

Distributive property

```
4)68 ──→ 4)40    +   4)28
           12  3       16   4
           28          12            Partial quotients
           16  4       12   3
           12           7
           12  3
           10

                10 + 7 = 17
                68 ÷ 4 = 17
```

```
                                                                         86
3)258 ──→ 3)210    +   3)30    +   3)18  ──→  3)258
  120  40    60  20     12  4      15  5       24
  138       150         18          3          18
  120  40    60  20     15  5       3  1       18
   18        90          3          6
   18   6    90         30  30      1
        86   70  70      3          10
                         3
                         70  +   10  +   6  =  86
```

Subtractive algorism to the common algorism

```
                                                                    12
10) 40                    20) 240                              20) 240
    10    1                  100    5        ⟶                    20
    30                       140                                  40
    10    1                  100    5                             40
    20                        40
    10    1                   40    2
    10                              12
    10    1
          4
                          240 ÷ 20 = 12
                           20 × 12 = 240
    40 ÷ 10 = 4
    10 × 4  = 40
```

```
                                                                    36
12) 48                    24) 864                              24) 864
    12    1                   240   10                             72
    36                        624                                 144
    12    1                   240   10        ⟶                  144
    24                        384
    12    1                   240   10
    12                        144
    12    1                   120    5
          4                    24
                               24    1
                                    36
    48 ÷ 12 = 4
     4 × 12 = 48
```

```
64) 3968                           243) 70068
    640    10                           24300   100
    3328                                45768
    3200    50                          24300   100
    128                                 21468
    128     2                           12150    50
            62                           9318
                                         7290    30
                                         2028
                                         1215     5
                                          813
                                          729     3
                                           84    288
```

Estimating the quotient

```
      1
     74    ⟶   84
52) 4368
    364
     72
     52
    208
    208
```

```
       12
      254    ⟶   374
216) 80784
     432
     375
     216
    1598
    1080
     528
     432
     864
     864
```

Knowing that division means subtracting groups of the divisor from the minuend, one can reason that divisors can be rounded off and compensation applied. In the example below, 98 is rounded to 100 and, with each multiplication, compensation is allowed.

$$100 - 98 = 2$$

```
       1
     779          780
98) 76453
    700
     64
   +14            (7 × 2) Compensation
    785
    700
     85
   +14
    993
    900
     93
   +18
    111          111 > 100   Remove another group
    100
     11
   + 2
     13   Remainder
```

Summary

It is said that division is the most difficult operation to teach. However, if one considers its structure carefully, this does not have to be so. Knowing the properties and concepts of addition, subtraction and multiplication should only challenge the children to approach division with the view of analyzing its structure in terms of these operations. From this point of view, division should be the easiest operation to teach.

Division is concerned with finding the number of sets of a given quantity or the number in each set. We call the first measurement division and the second, partition division. In the public schools, we are concerned with these meanings of division because they help us to solve problems. The mathematician is only concerned with finding the missing factor.

The four fundamental operations of addition, subtraction, multiplication and division are related to each other as shown in the chart below. Division is defined as finding the missing factor when the product and a factor are given. This immediately relates it to multiplication as its inverse operation.

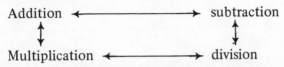

The distributive property of division permits renaming the dividend so that large numbers can be separated into convenient parts for the operation. The known factor is the common divisor for each partial dividend.

$$6 \overline{)84} \longrightarrow 6 \overline{)60} + 6 \overline{)24}$$

Division is not always written $36 \div 4 = N$. Because division and multiplication are related, we can write mathematical statements such as the following which also tell us to divide.

$$4 \times N = 36 \qquad N \times 9 = 36 \qquad 36 = N \times 9$$

One of the many challenges for children in division is the choice of partial quotients. When the quotient number is too small, it merely indicates that more groups can be removed. This approach helps children to see what is taking place as one divides, that is, the subtracting of 1 or more groups of the divisor at a time, and that the quotient is the sum of all the partial quotients. Finding the true quotient before one can begin to divide is distracting and almost impossible for many children.

Study Questions

1. Solve the following problem by counting, addition, subtraction and multiplication:

    Problem: Jack has 75¢ to spend each week. If he spends 15¢ each day, how many days will it take him to spend his money?

2. Why can zero not be used as a divisor?
3. Illustrate the use of the subtractive method of division in solving the following example. Compare with the common algorism:

    $$24 \overline{)867}$$

4. How can one tell that a number is evenly divided by a single digit? Example: $1232 \div 4$.
5. A principle states that multiplying or dividing the dividend and the divisor by the same nonzero number does not change the quotient. Illustrate the principle.
6. Why is it not necessary "to erase and start over again" at this point in the following example?

    $$
    \begin{array}{r}
    3 \\
    17 \overline{)799} \\
    \underline{51} \\
    28
    \end{array}
    $$

7. Illustrate the distributive property in division. How is the property used in presenting division?
8. Discuss the two meanings of division. Illustrate each.

9. Interpret the 3 possible meanings of a remainder.
10. Divide the following numbers in base 5:

3)421   Answer: 122.   4)2012   Answer: 224, remainder of 1.

11. Use aids described in the chapter to provide insight into place value in division. Prepare a lesson on regrouping.
12. Examine several arithmetic series used in the elementary school for their presentation of division.

Selected Text References

1. Dwight, Leslie A., *Modern Mathematics for the Elementary Teacher*, New York: Holt, Rinehart and Winston, Inc., 1966. Chapters 10 and 11.
2. Flournoy, Frances, *Elementary School Mathematics*, New York: The Center for Applied Research in Education, Inc., 1964. Chapters 2 and 5.
3. Grossnickle, Foster E., and Leo J. Brueckner, *Discovering Meanings in Elementary School Mathematics*, New York: Holt, Rinehart and Winston, Inc., 1963. Chapters 8 and 9.
4. Kramer, Klaas, *The Teaching of Elementary School Mathematics*, Boston: Allyn and Bacon, Inc., 1966. Chapters 13, 18 and 19.
5. Marks, John L., C. Richard Purdy, and Lucien B. Kinney, *Teaching Elementary School Mathematics for Understanding*, New York: McGraw-Hill Book Company, 1966. Chapter 7.
6. Swain, Robert L. and Eugene D. Nichols, *Understanding Arithmetic*, New York: Holt, Rinehart and Winston, Inc., 1965. Chapter 6.
7. Swenson, Esther, *Teaching Children Arithmetic*, New York: The Macmillan Company, 1964. Chapters 10 and 11.

Selected Readings from the Arithmetic Teacher

1. Bender, Marvin L., "Dividing by Zero," *8:* 176–179, April, 1961.
2. Capps, Lelon R., "Making Division Meaningful and Logical," *9:* 198–202, April, 1962.
3. Hilaire, Paul A., "Let's Take a Look at Division," *8:* 220–225, May, 1961.
4. Ruddell, Arden K., "Levels of Difficulty in Division," *6:* 97–99, March, 1959.
5. Zweng, Marilyn J., "Division Problems and the Concept of Rate," *11:* 547–556, December, 1964.
6. Spooner, George, "Divisibility and the Base-Ten Numeration System," *11:* 563–568, December, 1964.

Chapter VII

Numeration Systems and Bases

A very elaborate and extensive invention of man is his numeration system. Down through the centuries, man's development of some system of numbers was based on need, which grew out of the problems of expanding civilization, and on novelty, because of his interest in numbers.

Suppose one imagines himself back in the time when man did not have a system of numeration. It is most probable that all number systems grew out of the concept of a one-to-one correspondence between the elements of two sets. Suppose a man were a chief of a tribe or headman of a village. Since he needed to record the members of his group, it would be possible to do so by a matching process. He could place a pebble in a bag for each member of the group, cut a notch in a stick of wood or use any such scheme which would set up a one-to-one correspondence. This was the way that man kept record of his sheep, cattle or any other collection of things.

At this point in the development of numbers, he was considering two sets which had the same number property, that is, had the same number of objects in each set. By this scheme, primitive man could tell whether the set of objects had decreased, increased or had remained the same. He assured himself of his belongings by this simple one-to-one matching.

As civilization grew more and more complex, man was forced to improve his system for recording his possessions. This expansion of his system was the beginning of numerations systems which had two basic characteristics, symbols and a grouping scheme. Eventually, with the addition of a third characteristic, place value, he had the main elements for the Hindu–Arabic system.

The Egyptian, Greek and the Roman systems are presented for some detailed discussion. At this point students have completed the four operations in the set of whole numbers. They have discovered properties, concepts and generalizations which govern the set. The purpose of this unit in arithmetic is to guide the students to discover that in any numeration system certain characteristics such as symbols and rules for using the symbols are present. In addition to this purpose, it is the intention of the writer to stimulate interest and excitement in the study of numbers.

The symbols for each system are studied. If the children wish, they can involve the Greek letters in their study instead of the letters of our alphabet. The materials are presented as an aid to the teacher in building for her a historical background. The teacher will help the students to discover characteristics in the systems which make them work and then relate their findings to the Hindu–Arabic system.

One of the familiar aids to children is the abacus. Direct them to check their written work using the aid. Questions which will be common to the study of each system are:
1. Write the symbols from 1 to 100.
2. What are the rules for writing the numbers above 100?

3. Perform the operations. Is there a choice of algorisms?
4. Complete charts for the operations addition and multiplication. Are patterns present?
5. What principles are evident?
6. What characteristics does each system present?
7. Would printers like to use this system?
8. What new understanding of our decimal system have you discovered?

Egyptian Numeration System

The ancient Egyptians provide us with one of the oldest systems of notation. Imagine oneself living 5000 years ago. What were the symbols used? How were they used? Were they easy to manipulate in problem solving?

The Egyptian notation places emphasis on grouping and on 10. The characteristic of 10 shows up in moving from group to group (units to tens to hundreds, etc.). Seven symbols structure the scheme of notation:

Name	Symbol	Hindu Numbers
Tally mark	1	1
Heel bone or handle	∩	10
Scroll or coiled rope	ꝰ	100
Lotus flower	⚘	1,000
Reed or pointing finger	(	10,000
Fish	⌁	100,000
Man in astonishment	⚹	1,000,000

The first 40 numerals in the Egyptian notation are:

1	1			11	∩ 1		
2	1 1			12	∩ 1 1		
3	1 1 1			13	∩ 1 1 1		
4	1 1 1 1			14	∩ 1 1 1	1	
5	1 1 1	1 1		15	∩ 1 1 1	1 1	
6	1 1 1	1 1 1		16	∩ 1 1 1	1 1 1	
7	1 1 1	1 1 1	1	17	∩ 1 1 1	1 1 1	1
8	1 1 1	1 1 1	1 1	18	∩ 1 1 1	1 1 1	1 1
9	1 1 1	1 1 1	1 1 1	19	∩ 1 1 1	1 1 1	1 1 1
10	∩			20	∩ ∩		

21	∩∩ 1		31	∩∩∩ 1	
22	∩∩ 1 1		32	∩∩∩ 1 1	
23	∩∩ 1 1 1		33	∩∩∩ 1 1 1	
24	∩∩ 1 1 1	1	34	∩∩∩ 1 1 1	1
25	∩∩ 1 1 1	1 1	35	∩∩∩ 1 1 1	1 1
26	∩∩ 1 1 1	1 1 1	36	∩∩∩ 1 1 1	1 1 1
27	∩∩ 1 1 1	1 1 1 1	37	∩∩∩ 1 1 1	1 1 1 1
28	∩∩ 1 1 1	1 1 1 1 1	38	∩∩∩ 1 1 1	1 1 1 1 1
29	∩∩ 1 1 1	1 1 1 1 1 1	39	∩∩∩ 1 1 1	1 1 1 1 1 1
30	∩∩∩		40	∩∩∩∩	

The Egyptians used the principles of repetition and addition in writing numbers. Examples:

Hindu–Arabic	Egyptian
7	1 1 1 1 1 1 1 (Grouped for ease in reading)
13	∩ 1 1 1
268	ᗧᗧ ∩∩∩∩∩∩ 1 1 1 1 1 1 1 1
	or ᗧᗧ ∩∩∩ 1 1 1 1 / ∩∩∩ 1 1 1 1
3,245	⚱⚱⚱ ᗧᗧ ∩∩ 1 1 / ∩∩ 1 1 1
21,214	⟮⟮ ⚱ ᗧᗧ ∩ 1 1 1 1
132,642	⌒ ⟮⟮ ⚱⚱ ᗧᗧᗧ/ᗧᗧᗧ ∩∩/∩∩ 1 1
2,123,122	⚲⚲ ⌒ ⟮⟮ ⚱⚱⚱⚱ᗧ ∩/∩ 1 1

The Egyptian system did not lend itself to manipulation within the fundamental processes because of the necessity in repeating each symbol. The abacus was used as the instrument for calculating. In grouping, 10 tally marks make a heelbone, 10 heelbones make a scroll, etc. Examples:

1. Addition:

```
  321      ᗧᗧᗧ   ∩∩    1
+ 245       ᗧᗧ   ∩∩    1 1 1
  566   +         ∩∩    1 1
         ᗧᗧᗧ   ∩∩∩ 1 1 1
          ᗧᗧ   ∩∩∩ 1 1 1
```

Hundreds   Tens   Units

2. Subtraction: use of cancellation

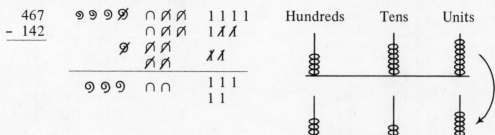

3. Multiplication: In solving the following exercises in multiplication have the children compare the algorisms in terms of place value, regrouping, the number of symbols and ease of manipulation with the Hindu–Arabic operation in multiplication. To what conclusion do they come?

The principle of compensation using division and multiplication by two was, perhaps, a method used by Egyptians to multiply. The product was found by adding the multiplicands which appeared above the multipliers which were odd numbers. Examples:

a.   16 $(2 \times 16) = 32$ $(2 \times 32) = 64$ $(2 \times 64) = 128$
    $\times 14$ → $(14 \div 2) = 7$ → $(7 \div 2) = 3$ → $(3 \div 2) = 1$

The odd multipliers are 7, 3 and 1. Therefore, the product is $32 + 64 + 128 = 224$.

b.   32 $(2 \times 32) = 64$ 128   256   512
    $\times 18$ → $(18 \div 2) = 9$ →   4 →   2 →   1

(Note: the fraction is not considered)

The odd multipliers are 9 and 1. The number appearing above 9 is 64, and above 1 is 512.

        512
      + 64
      576, the product of 18×32

c. Multiplication using Egyptian symbols:

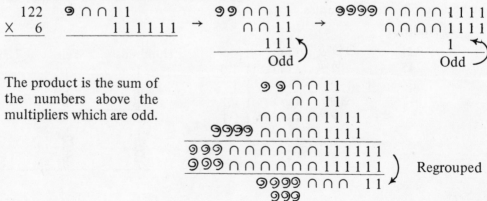

The product is the sum of the numbers above the multipliers which are odd.

Is this multiplication easy to perform? What have you learned from this exercise? Find the answer to the example below using an abacus. Is it easier to solve?

d. Multiplication using our algorism. Recall the use of place value in multiplication.

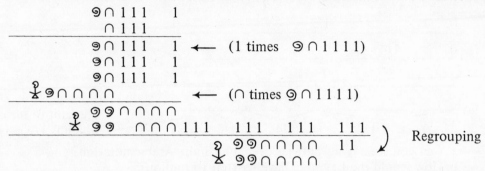

The Egyptians extended their notation to include fractions. With one exception, two–thirds, all fractions had numerators of 1.

Egyptian fractions:

1/2   = [

1/3   = ⟨▯⟩ ←The only fractions to have different forms in writing

2/3   = ⟨▱⟩

1/4   = ⟨▱⟩   An oval and four tally marks

1/5   = ⟨▱⟩   An oval and five tally marks

1/10   = ⟨▱⟩   An oval and a heel bone

1/100 = ⟨▱⟩   An oval and a scroll

1/1000 = ⟨▱⟩   An oval and a lotus flower

Combining fractions: Interest the children in constructing the following units of measure.

Our notation: 1/2 + 1/3 = 5/6.

Egyptian: [+ ⟨▯⟩ (No symbol for 5/6). Our plus sign is used here to simplify the notation.

The sum was probably found by constructing a unit of measure which combined 1/2 and 1/3.

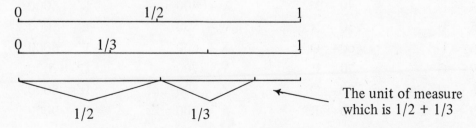

The unit of measure which is 1/2 + 1/3

1/2 + 1/4 + 1/6

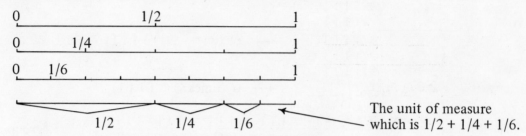

Egyptian notation:

Construct a unit of measure which combines each of these fractions.

The unit of measure which is 1/2 + 1/4 + 1/6.

a. Can you see any advantages over the Hindu–Arabic notation?
b. How would the Egyptian have written 15 million?
c. Why was the zero not necessary in the Egyptian notation?
d. Does the order in which the numerals are written effect the sum?

How many symbols does it take to write each of the following numbers in Egyptian notation? Compare with the Hindu–Arabic notation.

Hindu–Arabic	Egyptian	Number of symbols the Egyptians Used
19	∩ 1 1 1 1 1 1 1 1 1	10
99	∩ ∩ ∩ ∩ ∩ 1 1 1 1 ∩ ∩ ∩ ∩ 1 1 1 1 1	18
999	?	?
9,999	?	?
99,999	?	?

Greek Numeration System (about 400 B.C.)

One of the most cumbersome systems of notation was used by the Greeks. The 24 letters of their alphabet and three additional symbols were used to represent the numerals. These were combined using the principles of addition and multiplication.

To give recognition to the structure, our own letters of the alphabet are used:

1 - A	10 - J	S - 100	A' - 1000
2 - B	20 - K	T - 200	B' - 2000
3 - C	30 - L	U - 300	C' - 3000
4 - D	40 - M	V - 400	D' - 4000
5 - E	50 - N	W - 500	E' - 5000
6 - F	60 - O	X - 600	F' - 6000
7 - G	70 - P	Y - 700	G' - 7000
8 - H	80 - Q	Z - 800	H' - 8000
9 - I	90 - R	# - 900	I' - 9000

When numbers above 1,000 were written, a symbol was used to multiply a number by 10,000. The symbol π is used in this instance to multiply by 10,000.

B^π = 2 × 10,000 = 20,000

M^π = 40 × 10,000 = 400,000

S^π = 100 × 10,000 = 1,000,000

To write to 100, 19 different symbols were used; to write to 1,000, 28 different symbols were used. Numbers within a story were identified by drawing a line above the number. A' H O E. As with the Egyptian notation, the abacus was used for calculating.

Children will find it interesting to find the sum of the letters in their names. They may wish to compare the sums of several names.

1. Does the order in which the numerals are written affect the sum?
2. What advantages does the system of notation have over the Hindu–Arabic?
3. To choose a friend, Tarah must find someone whose name has the same sum as hers. What is the sum of her name? Which person can she choose as a friend: Dick, Billy or Tom?

Roman Numeration System

At one time in Europe, the Roman numeration system had the most popular advantage in the commercial world. By the turn of the 15th century, it was in competition with the Hindu–Arabic numerals for supremacy in world trade. With the invention of the printing press, the Hindu–Arabic numerals were stablilized in form and, with the ease of manipulation, were subsequently accepted as the system of notation throughout the world.

The seven symbols are spaced in a five–two pattern and involve the principle of repetition, addition, subtraction and multiplication.

I   C   (2 × 50)

V   (5 × 1)   D   (5 × 100)
X   (2 × 5)
L   (5 × 10)   M   (2 × 500)

Principles:

3	1 1 1	–	Repetition and addition
30	XXX	–	Repetition and addition
4	IV	–	Subtraction (1 from V)
90	XC	–	Subtraction (X from C = XC)
20,000	$\overline{XX}$	–	The bar indicates a multiplication by 1,000
40,013	$\overline{XL}$XIII	–	The bar over $\overline{XL}$ indicates a multiplication by 1,000.

The purpose of any of these activities is to give children an opportunity to relate known concepts and principles to new situations as well as identifying new elements. Such concepts as regrouping and renaming can be easily identified. Ask the children to identify the following ideas as they work with the Roman numerals.

1. Are all symbols lined up according to value?
2. Are similar symbols combined or cancelled?
3. Can VIII + IV be interpreted as V + V + II? Is this renaming?

4. In the example XL + XIII, is the X in XL subtracted? Is the X in XIII additive? Can they be cancelled as addition is performed? XL + XIII = L + III = LIII
5. What principle is illustrated: VII + IX = (V + II) + (V + IV) = (V + V) + (II + IV).

Compare the Roman numerals with the Egyptian numerals.

Operations:

1. Addition with Roman numerals

547	DXLVII	
+ 296	+ CCXCVI	
13	III	Addition of 1's
130	X	Addition of V's
700	CXXX	Addition of XL and XC
843	DCC	Addition of D and CC
	DCCCXXXXIII	
	DCCCXLIII	Combined

2. Subtraction with Roman numerals

635	DCXXXV	
− 357	− CCCLVII	
8	III	Subtract II from V
70	V	Subtract V from X
200	LXX	Subtract L from C, add XX
278	CC	Subtract CCC from D
	CCLXXVIII	

3. Multiplication with Roman numerals

36	XXXVI	
× 24	× XXIV	
24	IV	Multiply IV times 1
120	XX	Multiply IV times V
120	XL	Multiply IV times X
600	XL	Multiply IV times X
864	XL	Multiply IV times X
	X	Multiply X times 1
	L	Multiply X times V
	C	Multiply X times X
	C	Multiply X times X
	C	Multiply X times X
	X	Multiply X times 1
	L	Multiply X times V
	C	Multiply X times X
	C	Multiply X times X
	C	Multiply X times X
	DCCCLXIV	

The process can be shortened: for example,

```
    XXXVI
     XXIV
     XXIV        IV times VI
      CXX        IV times XXX
      CXX        XX times VI
   DC            XX times XXX
 DCCCLXIV
```

4. Division with Roman numerals

24)864		XXIV) DCCCLXIV	
240	10	CCXL	X
624		DCXXIV	
240	10	CCXL	X
384		CCCLXXXIV	
240	10	CCXL	X
144		CXLIV	
144	6	CXLIV	VI
36		(Quotient) – XXXVI	

Process shortened:

```
XXIV) DCCCLXIV
       DCCXX        XXX
       CXLIV
       CXLIV          VI
                    XXXVI
```

Fractions

1/12 = –		7/12 = S–	
2/12 = =		8/12 = S=	
3/12 = = –		9/12 = S= –	
4/12 = = =		10/12 = S= =	
5/12 = = = –		11/12 = S= = –	
6/12 = S		12/12 = 1 whole	

The S is the first letter of the Latin word *semis* which means one–half. 7/12 = 1/2 + 1/12.

1. Did the Romans need a symbol for zero? Explain.
2. How did the Romans write large numbers?
3. The principle of subtraction is attributed to the clockmakers of Europe, and was seldom used by the Romans. Write the following numbers in Roman notation:
   a. 14   b. 41   c. 93   d. 444.

Bases Other than 10

A numeration system is a scheme for naming numbers. Every numeration system consists of basic numerals and a set of rules for combining them to make other numerals. The Greeks, without a place system, had to memorize 27 different symbols just to write numbers from 1 to 999. Each numeral in 777 was different: *psi* (700 → X), *omicron*

$(70 \rightarrow 0)$, *zeta* $(7 \rightarrow Z)$. In contrast, while the Romans used few symbols, they had to keep repeating them: 777 was DCCLXXVII. In both of these ancient systems, multiplication and division were too difficult to be done without the abacus.

The earliest known ancestors of the symbols that we use today came from South Asia. At some point in the early history of India, the numerals were arranged in a "place system." It is this "place system" that makes the number system so simple to use. The Hindu system, our system today, was built around the base 10 probably because they had 10 fingers and counted on their fingers. With these 10 symbols, 0, 1, 2, 3, 4, 5, 6, 7, 8, 9, and the place system, one can express any number, no matter how large or how small.

The base which the Hindu chose could have been any number other than 10. The rules for operations in base 10 hold for any base.

Base 10

Basic Symbols: 0, 1, 2, 3, 4, 5, 6, 7, 8, 9.

PLACE VALUE CHART

1000	100	10	1

1.

a. How many groups of ten? Symbol, 10. Read: One group of ten and no ones.

b. How many left over? Symbol, 2. $10 + 2 = 12$.

c. 12 is one group of ten and two more. In base 10, we have a name for one group of ten and two more. It is twelve.

2.

a. How many groups of ten? Symbol, 20. Read: Two groups of ten and no ones.

b. How many left over? Symbol, 4. $20 + 4 = 24$.

3.

a. How many groups of ten? Twelve groups of ten.

b. Ten groups of ten is one group of one hundred. Symbol, 100. Read: One group of one hundred, no tens, no ones.

c. How many groups of ten left over? Symbol, 20. $100 + 20 = 120$.

4. Examples:

a. $8 + 7 =$ ○○○○ ○○○○ + ○○○ ○○○ = ○○○○○ ○○○○○ ○○○○○ = 15

The base or grouping → $10\overline{)15}$ ← The total

$$
\begin{array}{r}
1 \\
10\overline{)15} \\
10 \\
\hline
5
\end{array}
$$

Group of ten

Left over   15

b.   8   +   7   =

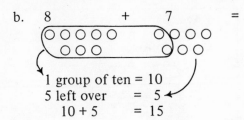

1 group of ten = 10
5 left over   = 5
10 + 5   = 15

Compensation: Add a number to one
addend, subtract the number from the
second addend.

$(8 + 2) + (7 - 2) = 10 + 5 = 15$

5. Expanded notation: Shows the meaning of place value

$$437 = 400 + 30 + 7$$
$$= (4 \times 100) + (3 \times 10) + (7 \times 1)$$
$$= (4 \times 10 \times 10) + (3 \times 10) + (7 \times 1)$$
$$= (4 \times 10^2) + (3 \times 10^1) + (7 \times 10^0)$$
Ten to the zero power is one

One way to gain understanding of our decimal system is to study a number system
with a different base. There are many possible systems to choose; base 5, base 2 and base
12 are presented here for study. Materials which one can use will be similar to those already developed and used in our decimal system. The following activities are to be used
by children for each base to be studied.

1. Make an abacus for each base. Think through each operation using the abacus.
2. Move to working examples using paper and pencil. Several students may prefer to
   solve examples mentally.
3. Structure charts for the four operations similar to those made in the decimal system. Identify patterns present in the chart.
4. Challenge the children to convert numbers from one base to another.
5. Illustrate number properties in each of the bases.
6. Summarize the insights used. What concepts of our decimal system have been
   strengthened?

Base 5

Because we group objects by tens, we call our numeration system a base 10 system.
When we group objects by another number, for example, 5, we call our numeration system base 5. To identify bases other than 10, a subscript is placed to the lower right of the
number, as 12_5. 12_5 is read: one, two, base 5, or 1 group of 5 and 2 ones.

BASE 10	BASE 5
Group by tens	Group by fives
1 ten and 2 ones In base 10, we write: 12. In base 10, we say: twelve.	2 fives and 2 ones In base 5, we write 22_5. In base 5, we read: 2 groups of five and two ones, or two, two, base 5.

BASE 10	BASE 5
Group by tens	Group by fives

3 tens and 2 ones
In base 10, we write 32.

Five squared, one five and two ones.
In base 5, we write 112_5.
Read: One group twenty–five, one group five and two ones or one, one, two, base 5.

PLACE VALUE CHART, BASE 5

	One Hundred Twenty-five $(5 \times 5 \times 5)$	Twenty-five (5×5)	Fives (5×1)	Units
			3	2
		1	1	2
	2	1	3	4

$32_5 = (3 \times 5) + (2 \times 1) = 15 + 2 = 17_{10}$

$112_5 = 25 + 5 + 2 = 32$. Read as base 10 when subscript is omitted

$2134_5 = (2 \times 125) + (1 \times 25) + (3 \times 5) + (4 \times 1) =$
$\qquad\quad 250 \;+\; 25 \;+\; 15 \;+\; 4 \quad = 294$

Number Line

$4_5 + 3_5 = N_5$

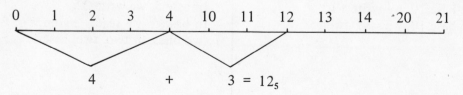

$\qquad\qquad 4 \qquad\qquad + \qquad\quad 3 = 12_5$

Abacus

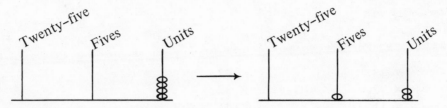

When 3_5 is added to 4_5, a group of 5 is carried to the second place.

$$4_5 + 3_5 = 10_5 + 2_5 = 12_5$$

Addition and Subtraction Table, Base 5

+ −	1	2	3	4	10
1	2	3	4	10	11
2	3	4	10	11	12
3	4	10	11	12	13
4	10	11	12	13	14
10	11	12	13	14	20

Check table for patterns similar to base 10 table.

How many basic facts make up the family of 10_5?

4	1	2	3
1	4	3	2
10_5	10_5	10_5	10_5

Examples:

$$\begin{array}{r} 4 \\ + 3 \\ \hline \end{array} \longrightarrow \begin{array}{r} 4 + 1 = 10 \\ 3 - 1 = \underline{2} \\ 12_5 \end{array} \qquad \begin{array}{r} 24_5 \\ + 32_5 \\ \hline 111_5 \end{array} \longrightarrow \begin{array}{r} 20 + 4 \\ 30 + 2 \\ \hline 100 + 11 = 111_5 \end{array} \qquad \begin{array}{r} 323_5 \\ + 432_5 \\ \hline 1310_5 \end{array}$$

$$\begin{array}{r} 12_5 \\ - \ 4 \\ \hline 3 \end{array} \qquad \begin{array}{r} 43_5 \\ - 14_5 \\ \hline 24_5 \end{array} \longrightarrow \begin{array}{r} 30 + 13 \\ - 10 + \ 4 \\ \hline 20 + \ 4 = 24_5 \end{array} \qquad \begin{array}{r} 31_5 \\ - 13_5 \\ \hline 13_5 \end{array} \longrightarrow \begin{array}{r} 13_5 \\ + 13_5 \\ \hline 31_5 \end{array}$$

Multiplication and Division Table, Base 5

× ÷	1	2	3	4	10
1	1	2	3	4	10
2	2	4	11	13	20
3	3	11	14	22	30
4	4	13	22	31	40
10	10	20	30	40	100

Can you discover several patterns?

$3 \times 3 = 9$, base 10

$9 \div 5 = 1$ group of 5
    and 4 left over $\rightarrow 14_5$

$4 \times 4 = 16$, base 10

$16 \div 5 = 3$ groups of 5
    and 1 left over $\rightarrow 31_5$

Then $31_5 \div 4 = 4$

Examples:

$$\begin{array}{r} 3 \\ \times\ 2 \\ \hline \end{array} \rightarrow \begin{array}{r} 3 \\ +\ 3 \\ \hline 11_5 \end{array} \qquad \begin{array}{r} 10_5 \\ \times\ \ 2 \\ \hline 20_5 \end{array} \qquad \begin{array}{r} 12_5 \\ \times\ \ 2 \\ \hline 24_5 \end{array} \qquad \begin{array}{r} 23_5 \\ \times\ \ 3 \\ \hline 124_5 \end{array} \rightarrow \begin{array}{r} ^1 \\ 23_5 \\ 23_5 \\ +\ 23_5 \\ \hline 124_5 \end{array}$$

$$\begin{array}{r} 43_5 \\ \times\ 32_5 \\ \hline 11 \\ 130 \\ 140 \\ 2200 \\ \hline 3031_5 \end{array} \qquad\qquad \begin{array}{r} 43_5 \\ \times\ 32_5 \\ \hline 141 \\ 234 \\ \hline 3031_5 \end{array}$$

$$\begin{array}{r} 4\overline{)413_5} \\ 400 \\ \hline 13 \\ 13 \\ \hline \end{array} \quad \begin{array}{r} 100_5 \\ 2 \\ \hline 102_5 \end{array} \qquad\qquad \begin{array}{r} 102_5 \\ \times\ \ 4 \\ \hline 413_5 \end{array}$$

$$\begin{array}{r} 34_5\overline{)4131_5} \\ 3400 \\ \hline 231 \\ 212 \\ \hline 14 \end{array} \quad \begin{array}{r} 100 \\ 3 \\ \hline 103_5 \end{array} \rightarrow \begin{array}{r} 103_5 \\ \times\ 34_5 \\ \hline 422 \\ 314 \\ \hline 4112 \\ +\ \ 14 \\ \hline 4131_5 \end{array}$$

Converting Base 5 To Base 10

$$3243_5 = (3 \times 125) + (2 \times 25) + (4 \times 5) + (3 \times 1) =$$
$$\quad\ 375 \quad + \quad 50 \ + \ 20 \ + \quad 3 \quad = 448$$

Convert the following numbers to base 10 using the chart.

PLACE VALUE CHART, BASE 5

125	25	5	1
		2	3
	3	1	4
3	2	3	1

$$23_5 = (2 \times 5) + (3 \times 1) = 10 + 3 = 13$$
$$314_5 = (3 \times 25) + (1 \times 5) + (4 \times 1) = 75 + 5 + 4 = 84$$
$$3231_5 = (3 \times 125) + (2 \times 25) + (3 \times 5) + (1 \times 1) = 375 + 50 + 15 + 1 = 441$$

Converting Base 10 To Base 5

348 to base 5:

Divide by the base and record the remainders:

$$5)\overline{348}$$
$$5)\overline{69} \qquad 3 \text{ remainder}$$
$$5)\overline{13} \qquad 4 \text{ remainder}$$
$$5)\overline{2} \qquad 3 \text{ remainder}$$
$$0 \qquad 2 \text{ remainder}$$

Read from the bottom up to arrive at the number in base 5: 2343_5

Proof: $(2 \times 125) + (3 \times 25) + (4 \times 5) + (3 \times 1) = 348$

Summary

1. Grouping by 5 is like grouping by 10.
2. Numbers in base 5 can be expanded.
3. The fundamental laws hold for base 5. Examples:

Commutative:
$3_5 + 4_5 = 4_5 + 3_5, 12_5 \times 23_5 = 23_5 \times 12_5$

Associative:
$(4 + 11_5) + 23_5 = 4 + (11_5 + 23_5)$
$(2 \times 12_5) \times 4 = 2 \times (12_5 \times 4)$

Distributive:
$4 \times 12_5 = (4 \times 10_5) + (4 \times 2)$

Base 2

Binary numerals are based on groups of twos, just as our decimal system is based on tens.

Comparing Base 10 and Base 2 (Binary Symbols, 0, 1)

Base 10 Notation	Binary Grouping	Binary Notation
1	○	1
2	⬭	10_2
3	⬭ ○	11_2
4	⬭ ⬭	100_2
5	⬭ ⬭ ○	101_2
6	⬭ ⬭ ⬭	110_2
7	⬭ ⬭ ⬭ ○	111_2
8	⬭ ⬭ ⬭ ⬭	1000_2
9	⬭ ⬭ ⬭ ⬭ ○	1001_2
10	⬭ ⬭ ⬭ ⬭ ⬭	1010_2

PLACE VALUE CHART, BASE 2

8 (2 × 2 × 2)	4 (2 × 2)	2 (2 × 1)	1	Base 10 Notations
		1	1	2 + 1 = 3
	1	0	1	4 + 0 + 1 = 5
1	1	0	1	8 + 4 + 0 + 1 = 13
1	1	1	1	8 + 4 + 2 + 1 = 15

Basic Addition and Multiplication Facts

Addition

$$\begin{array}{cccc} 0 & 0 & 1 & 1 \\ +\,0 & +\,1 & +\,0 & +\,1 \\ \hline 0 & 1 & 1 & 10_2 \end{array}$$

Multiplication

$$\begin{array}{cccc} 0 & 1 & 0 & 1 \\ \times\,0 & \times\,0 & \times\,1 & \times\,1 \\ \hline 0 & 0 & 0 & 1 \end{array}$$

Addition Table

+	0	1
0	0	1
1	1	10

Multiplication Table

×	0	1
0	0	0
1	0	1

Study these examples to see how base 10 ideas are used in base 2.

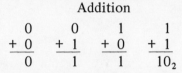

$$\begin{array}{c} 1 \\ +\,1 \\ \hline 10_2 \end{array} \qquad \begin{array}{c} 11_2 \\ +\,\ 1 \\ \hline 100_2 \end{array} \qquad \begin{array}{c} {}^{1\,1} \\ 101_2 \\ +\,\ 11_2 \\ \hline 1,000_2 \end{array} \qquad \begin{array}{c} {}^{1} \\ 10,011_2 \\ +\,11,010_2 \\ \hline 101,101_2 \end{array}$$

$$\begin{array}{c} 1 \\ \times\,1 \\ \hline 1 \end{array} \qquad \begin{array}{c} 10_2 \\ \times\,10_2 \\ \hline 100_2 \end{array} \longrightarrow \begin{array}{c} 2 \\ \times\,2 \\ \hline 4_{10} \end{array} \quad \text{See chart for place value of 4}$$

$$\begin{array}{c} 101_2 \\ \times\ \ 11_2 \\ \hline 101 \\ 101\ \ \\ \hline 1,111_2 \end{array} \qquad \begin{array}{c} 1,011_2 \\ \times\ \ \ 101_2 \\ \hline 1,011 \\ 1,01\ 1\ \ \\ \hline 110,111_2 \end{array}$$

$$\begin{array}{c} 1 \\ -\,1 \\ \hline 0 \end{array} \quad \begin{array}{c} 10_2 \\ -\,\ 1 \\ \hline 1 \end{array} \quad \begin{array}{c} 11_2 \\ -\,10_2 \\ \hline 1 \end{array} \quad \begin{array}{c} 101_2 \\ -\,\ 10_2 \\ \hline 11_2 \end{array} \quad \begin{array}{c} 1,101_2 \\ -\,\ 110_2 \\ \hline 111_2 \end{array}$$

$$10_2\,\overline{)\,11_2} \\ \underline{10} \\ 1 \text{ (Remainder)}$$

$$\begin{array}{r} 101_2 \\ 10_2\,\overline{)\,1,010_2} \\ \underline{1\ 0} \\ 10 \\ \underline{10} \\ 0 \end{array}$$

$$\begin{array}{r} 110_2 \\ 101_2\,\overline{)\,11,110_2} \\ \underline{10\ 1} \\ 101 \\ \underline{101} \\ 0 \end{array}$$

$$\begin{array}{r} 1,010 \\ 110\,\overline{)\,111,111} \\ \underline{110} \\ 111 \\ \underline{110} \\ 11 \text{ (Remainder)} \end{array}$$

In each of the processes, note that the digits are all zero or one. In multiplication, because you multiply by one, you never have a "carry" number.

Converting Base 2 To Base 10 (Check the Place Value Chart)

$1101_2 = (1 \times 8) + (1 \times 4) + (0 \times 2) + (1 \times 1) = 13$

Converting Base 10 To Base 2

$2\overline{)\,13}$
$\quad 2\overline{)\,6} \qquad$ 1 remainder
$\quad 2\overline{)\,3} \qquad$ 0 remainder
$\quad 2\overline{)\,1} \qquad$ 1 remainder
$\qquad 0 \qquad$ 1 remainder

13 base 10 = 1101 base 2

Base 12: Numeration with the Dozen System

You have seen that it is possible to use a numeration system other than base 10. We have set up numeration systems using bases less than 10. Consider now a base which is greater than 10.

Base 12, sometimes called the "dozen system," has been a controversial issue for many years. The advocates of the "dozen system" believe that it would be more convenient than our base 10 because it is related to our units of measure such as 12 inches in a foot, 12 hours on our clocks, 60 minutes in an hour, 12 eggs in a dozen, etc. They also favor this base because it would provide more even divisors when working with fractions.

The "dozen system" is more accurately called the duodecimal system. Duodecimal is another name for twelve. Two new symbols must be added to our base 10 to complete the set of numerals. The symbols usually used are T for ten and E for eleven. Base 12 forms groups of twelve (dozens), twelve–twelves (gross) and so on.

Comparing Base 10 and Base 12

Base Ten Notation	Dozen Grouping	Base Twelve Notation
1	○	1
2	○ ○	2
3	○ ○ ○	3
4	○ ○ ○ ○	4
5	○ ○ ○ ○ ○	5
6	○ ○ ○ ○ ○ ○	6
7	○ ○ ○ ○ ○ ○ ○	7
8	○ ○ ○ ○ ○ ○ ○ ○	8
9	○ ○ ○ ○ ○ ○ ○ ○ ○	9
10	○ ○ ○ ○ ○ ○ ○ ○ ○ ○	T New symbol
11	○ ○ ○ ○ ○ ○ ○ ○ ○ ○ ○	E New symbol
12	○ ○ ○ ○ ○ ○ ○ ○ ○ ○ ○ ○	10 1 dozen or 1 do

The egg carton makes a convenient means of grouping by dozens. After nine eggs have been placed in the carton, one needs a new symbol for one more than nine and another symbol for two more than nine. These symbols and their names may be invented. One complete dozen will be represented by 10_{12} which is read as "onedo" for one dozen, or merely "one zero." The number 26_{12} may be read as "twodo six" or as two, six base 12. The two refers to two groups of a dozen each and six more.

EGG CARTON

①	②	③	④
⑤	⑥	⑦	⑧
⑨	Ⓣ	Ⓔ	⑩

ADDITION–SUBTRACTION TABLE, BASE 12

$\begin{array}{c}+\\-\end{array}$	1	2	3	4	5	6	7	8	9	T	E	10
1	2	3	4	5	6	7	8	9	T	E	10	11
2	3	4	5	6	7	8	9	T	E	10	11	12
3	4	5	6	7	8	9	T	E	10	11	12	13
4	5	6	7	8	9	T	E	10	11	12	13	14
5	6	7	8	9	T	E	10	11	12	13	14	15
6	7	8	9	T	E	10	11	12	13	14	15	16
7	8	9	T	E	10	11	12	13	14	15	16	17
8	9	T	E	10	11	12	13	14	15	16	17	18
9	T	E	10	11	12	13	14	15	16	17	18	19
T	E	10	11	12	13	14	15	16	17	18	19	1T
E	10	11	12	13	14	15	16	17	18	19	1T	1E
10	11	12	13	14	15	16	17	18	19	1T	1E	20

PLACE VALUE CHART, BASE 12

Twelve^3 (12 × 12 × 12) or Great Gross	Twelve^2 (12 × 12) or Gross	Twelves (12 × 1) or Dozen	Ones or Units
		3	3
	4	3	T
2	1	E	E

$33_{12} = (3 \times 12) + 3 = 39$, base 10

$43T_{12} = (4 \times 12 \times 12) + (3 \times 12) + (T \times 1) = 622_{10}$

$21EE_{12} = (2 \times 12 \times 12 \times 12) + (1 \times 12 \times 12) + (11 \times 12) + (11 \times 1) = 3743_{10}$

Addition and Subtraction in the "Dozen" System

$$\begin{array}{c} 7 \\ + T \\ \hline 15 \end{array} \rightarrow \begin{array}{c} 7 - 2 = 5 \\ T + 2 = 10_{12} \\ \hline 15_{12} \end{array} \quad \begin{array}{c} E \\ + T \\ \hline 19_{12} \end{array} \rightarrow \begin{array}{c} 10 \\ + 11 \\ \hline 21 \end{array} \quad \begin{array}{c} 1 \\ 12\overline{)21} \\ 12 \\ \hline 9 \end{array} = 19_{12} \quad \begin{array}{c} 36_{12} \\ + 24_{12} \\ \hline 5T_{12} \end{array}$$

$$\begin{array}{c} {\scriptstyle 1\ 1} \\ 8\,E5_{12} \\ + T\,47_{12} \\ \hline 1740_{12} \end{array} \rightarrow \begin{array}{l} 7 + 5 = 12, \quad 12 \div 12 = 10 \\ 4 + E + 1 = 16, 16 \div 12 = 14 \\ T + 8 + 1 = 19, 19 \div 12 = 17 \end{array} \quad \begin{array}{c} 46_{12} \\ 65_{12} \\ \hline TE_{12} \end{array}$$

If one knows that $7 + T = 15_{12}$, then $15_{12} - T = 7$ and $15_{12} - 7 = T$. One can use addition–subtraction facts chart until one can think in base 12.

Examples:

$$\begin{array}{c} 9 \\ -6 \\ \hline 3 \end{array} \qquad \begin{array}{c} 14_{12} \\ -7 \\ \hline 9 \end{array} \longrightarrow \quad \text{Regroup:} \quad \begin{array}{l} 12 + 4 = 16 \\ 16 - 7 = 9 \end{array}$$

$$\begin{array}{c} 4E_{12} \\ - 18_{12} \\ \hline 33_{12} \end{array} \qquad \begin{array}{c} 315_{12} \\ - 1E8_{12} \\ \hline 119_{12} \end{array} \qquad \begin{array}{c} {\scriptstyle T10} \\ \cancel{E0T}_{12} \\ - 7TT_{12} \\ \hline 320_{12} \end{array}$$

DUODECIMAL NUMBER LINE

0 1 2 3 4 5 6 7 8 9 T E 10 11 12 13 14 15 16 17 18 19 1T 1E 20

7 + 9 = 14_{12}

0 1 2 3 4 5 6 7 8 9 T E 10 11 12 13 14 15 16 17 18 19 1T 1E 20

−8

13 − 8 = 7

Multiplication and Division in the Duodecimal System

$$
\begin{array}{r} 4 \\ \times\ 3 \\ \hline 10_{12} \end{array}
\longrightarrow
\begin{array}{r} 4 \\ 4 \\ +\ 4 \\ \hline 10_{12} \end{array}
\qquad
\begin{array}{r} 10_{12} \\ \times\ \ 6 \\ \hline 60_{12} \end{array}
\qquad
\begin{array}{r} 12_{12} \\ \times\ \ 6 \end{array}
\longrightarrow
\begin{array}{c} 10_{12}\ \ +\ \ 2 \\ \times\ 6 \\ \hline 60_{12}\ \ +\ \ 10_{12}\ =\ 70_{12} \end{array}
$$

$$
\begin{array}{r} 416_{12} \\ \times\ \ 5T_{12} \\ \hline 3530 \\ 1876 \\ \hline 20090_{12} \end{array}
$$

T × 6 = 60,   60 ÷ 12 = 5 groups of 12 and no ones = 50, write 0, carry 5.

(T × 1) + 5 = 15,   15 ÷ 12 = 1 group of 12 and 3 units = 13, write 3, carry 1.

(T × 4) + 1 = 41,   41 ÷ 12 = 35.

5 × 6 = 30,   30 ÷ 12 = 2 groups of 12 and 6 units = 26, write 6, carry 2

(5 × 1) + 2 = 7

5 × 4 = 20,   20 ÷ 12 = 1 group of 12 and 8 units = 18.

Remember: group by twelves.

$$
\begin{array}{r} 3E5_{12} \\ \times\ \ \ 4 \\ \hline 18 \\ 38 \\ 10 \\ \hline 1398_{12} \end{array}
\longrightarrow
\begin{array}{r} 3E5_{12} \\ 4)\overline{1398_{12}} \\ \underline{10} \\ 39 \\ \underline{38} \\ 18 \\ \underline{18} \end{array}
$$

(3 × 4 = 12,   12 ÷ 12 = 10_{12})

(E × 4 = 44,   44 ÷ 12 = 38_{12})

(5 × 4 = 20,   20 ÷ 12 = 18_{12})

$$
\begin{array}{r} 4T6_{12} \\ \times\ \ 47_{12} \\ \hline 2T16 \\ 1760 \\ \hline 1T416_{12} \end{array}
\longrightarrow
\begin{array}{r} 4T6_{12} \\ 47_{12})\overline{1T416_{12}} \\ \underline{164} \\ 401 \\ \underline{39T} \\ 236 \\ \underline{236} \end{array}
$$

(4 × 47 = 164_{12})

(T × 47 = 39T_{12})

(6 × 47 = 236_{12})

$$
\begin{array}{r} E8T4_{12} \\ \times\ \ \ \ 7 \\ \hline 24 \\ 5T \\ 48 \\ 65 \\ \hline 6T204_{12} \end{array}
\longrightarrow
\begin{array}{r} E8T4_{12} \\ 7)\overline{6T204_{12}} \\ \underline{65} \\ 52 \\ \underline{48} \\ 60 \\ \underline{5T} \\ 24 \\ \underline{24} \end{array}
$$

(E × 7 = 65_{12})

(8 × 7 = 48_{12})

(T × 7 = 5T_{12})

(4 × 7 = 24_{12})

MULTIPLICATION–DIVISION TABLE, BASE 12

X ÷	0	1	2	3	4	5	6	7	8	9	T	E	10
0	0	0	0	0	0	0	0	0	0	0	0	0	0
1	0	1	2	3	4	5	6	7	8	9	T	E	10
2	0	2	4	6	8	T	10	12	14	16	18	1T	20
3	0	3	6	9	10	13	16	19	20	23	26	29	30
4	0	4	8	10	14	18	20	24	28	30	34	38	40
5	0	5	T	13	18	21	26	2E	34	39	43	47	50
6	0	6	10	16	20	26	30	36	40	46	50	56	60
7	0	7	12	19	24	2E	36	41	48	53	5T	65	70
8	0	8	14	20	28	34	40	48	54	60	68	74	80
9	0	9	16	23	30	39	46	53	60	69	76	83	90
T	0	T	18	26	34	42	50	5T	68	76	84	92	T0
E	0	E	1T	29	38	47	56	65	74	83	92	T1	E0
10	0	10	20	30	40	50	60	70	80	90	T0	E0	100

Converting Base 12 To Base 10 (Check the Place Value Chart)

$$43T_{12} = (4 \times 144) + (3 \times 12) + (T \times 1) =$$
$$= (4 \times 12 \times 12) + (3 \times 12) + T \times 1 =$$
$$= (4 \times 12^2) + (3 \times 12^1) + (T \times 12^0) =$$
$$= 576 + 36 + 10 = 622_{10}$$

$$
\begin{array}{r}
576 \\
36 \\
+ \quad 10 \\
\hline
622_{10}
\end{array}
$$

Converting Base 10 To Base 12 (Divide by the Base)

```
12)622
 12)51      T
  12)4      3
    0       4
```

Base 12 = $43T_{12}$

One finds when working in other bases that they present striking parallels to many of the difficulties children have in base 10. One of the purposes behind the study of bases in the elementary school is to help children to identify these difficulties and to analyze the errors made. Examples:

BASE 10

$$\begin{array}{rl} 7 & 7+3=10 \\ +\ 6 \longrightarrow & 6-3=\underline{\ \ 3} \\ & 13_{10} \end{array}$$

Then, $6 + 7 = 13_{10}$

$$\begin{array}{rl} 14_{10} & 14 \\ \underline{\times\ \ 3}\longrightarrow & 14 \\ & \underline{14} \\ & 42_{10} \end{array}$$

$$\begin{array}{r} 24_{10} \\ \underline{\times\ \ 3} \\ 12 \\ \underline{60} \\ 72_{10} \end{array}$$

BASE 5

$$\begin{array}{rl} 4 & 4+1=10 \\ +\ 3 \longrightarrow & 3-1=\underline{\ \ 2} \\ & 12_5 \end{array}$$

Then, $3 + 4 = 12_5$

$$\begin{array}{rl} 14_5 & \overset{2}{14_5} \\ \underline{\times\ \ 3}\longrightarrow & 14_5 \\ & \underline{14_5} \\ & 102_5 \end{array}$$

$$\begin{array}{r} 24_5 \\ \underline{\times\ \ 3} \\ 22 \\ \underline{110} \\ 132_5 \end{array}$$

Enrichment activities discovered during the study of whole numbers are applicable to the study of bases.

1. Make a set of Napier's bones to be used in base 5.
2. Add from left to right in any base that you choose.
3. Identify patterns which will help you to do mental arithmetic.

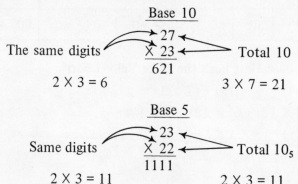

Base 10

The same digits $\qquad$ 27 $\qquad$
$\times$ 23 $\qquad$ Total 10
621

$2 \times 3 = 6$ $\qquad$ $3 \times 7 = 21$

Base 5

Same digits $\qquad$ 23 $\qquad$
$\times$ 22 $\qquad$ Total 10_5
1111

$2 \times 3 = 11$ $\qquad$ $2 \times 3 = 11$

4. Make a slide for addition and subtraction in any base.

A	0	1	2	3	4	10	11	12	13	
B	0	1	2	3	4	10	11	12	13	14	20

To add 3 and 4, slide the A scale so that the zero on A is above the 3 on the B scale. Then the numeral on the B scale below 4 on the A scale is the sum.

$$3 + 4 = 12_5$$

5. Count by 2, 3, etc. in a base of your choice.

The Wosy System (Quinary Base)*

To break away from the constant use of the Hindu–Arabic symbols, use the following set of symbols for a base 5 system. Names were given to each place so that the numbers could be read in a way similar to our decimal system.

	Symbols	
0	□	Zo
1	Φ	Wo
2	∀	To
3	△	Tro
4	⚠	Fo

PLACE VALUE CHART

125's (Woserds)	25's (Wosens)	5's (Woseys)	1's (Wos)
		3	0
		2	3
	1	3	1
	4	0	0
3	1	2	2

30	=	△ □	= Trosey
23	=	∀ △	= Tosey Tro
131	=	Φ △ Φ	= Wosen Trosey Wo
3124	=	△ Φ ∀ △	= Troserd Wosen Tosey Fo

Examples:

$$
\begin{array}{r} 12_5 \\ + 22_5 \\ \hline 34_5 \end{array}
\rightarrow
\begin{array}{r} \Phi\ \forall \\ + \forall\ \forall \\ \hline \triangle\ ⚠ \end{array}
\qquad
\begin{array}{r} 314_5 \\ + 132_5 \\ \hline 1001_5 \end{array}
\rightarrow
\begin{array}{r} \triangle\ \Phi\ ⚠ \\ + \Phi\ \triangle\ \forall \\ \hline \Phi\ \square\ \square\ \Phi \end{array}
$$

$$
\begin{array}{r} \triangle\ \Phi\ ⚠ \\ + \Phi\ \triangle\ \forall \\ \hline \Phi\ \square\ \square\ \Phi \end{array}
\qquad\leftarrow
$$

Read: Trosen Wosey Fo
Wosen Trosey To
Woserd Zosen Zosey Wo or Woserd Wo

Reversing 3–digit numbers. Note that the pattern in the Wosey System adds up to 4.

431	⚠ △ Φ	341	△ ⚠ Φ	← Trosen Fosey Wo
− 134	− Φ △ ⚠	− 143	− Φ ⚠ △	← Wosen Fosey Tro
242	∀ △ ∀	143	Φ △ △	← Wosen Tosey Tro

*The Wosey System was developed by Mrs. Margaret Anderson, Mrs. Laverne Holton, Mrs. Beverly Kanewski and Mrs. Mary McCuiston. The examples used here with permission of the originators.

Chapter Summary

The history of numeration is the history of man's progress down through the ages. It is the writer's purpose to use this chapter as a means for stimulating interest in our number system and to strengthen the concepts and generalizations which students have studied relating them to other numeration systems and bases.

Arithmetic in grades four, five and six can be introduced by studying a phase of this chapter. One need not relate it to the work of the grade level but introuduced as a technique for getting children involved in arithmetic and the workshop technique.

Study Questions

1. What characteristics of the Hindu–Arabic system of numbers caused it to be accepted universally?
2. What is the difference between number and numeral?
3. Illustrate the concept of regrouping using examples in base 5. Are the "crutches" used similar to those used in base 10?
4. What is the function of place value in our decimal system?
5. Construct an abacus for a base other than 10. Use it to illustrate regrouping.
6. Check several series of textbooks used by children for their presentation of number systems and bases. How is this unit presented?

Selected Text References

1. Grossnickle, Foster E., and Leo J. Brueckner, *Discovering Meanings in Elementary School Mathematics,* New York: Holt, Rinehart and Winston, Inc., 1963. Chapter 4.
2. Kramer, Klaas, *The Teaching of Elementary School Mathematics,* Boston: Allyn and Bacon, Inc., 1966. Chapter 4.
3. Meserve, Bruce E., and Max A. Sobel, *Introduction to Mathematics*, Englewood Cliffs, N.M.: Prentice–Hall, Inc., 1964. Chapter 2.
4. Mueller, Francis J., *Arithmetic, Its Structure and Concepts*, Englewood Cliffs, N.J.: Prentice–Hall, Inc., 1964. Chapters 1 through 5 and 10.
5. Peterson, John A., and Joseph Hashisaki, *Theory of Arithmetic,* New York: John Wiley and Sons, Inc., 1963. Chapters 1 and 4.
6. Swain, Robert L., and Eugene D. Nichols, *Understanding Arithmetic*, New York: Holt, Rinehart and Winston, Inc., 1965. Chapters 1 and 2.

Selected Readings from the Arithmetic Teacher

1. Claspill, Eileen K., "A Better Understanding of Our Number System," *9:* 71–73, February, 1962.
2. Hilaire, Paul, and Walter Westphal, "New Numerals for Basic–Five Arithmetic," *11:* 331–333, May, 1964.
3. Johnson, Paul B., "Modern Mathematics in a Toga," *12:* 343–347, May, 1965.
4. Peterson, Wayne, "Numeration—A Fresh Look," *12:* 335–338, May, 1965.
5. Rahlow, Harold F., "Understanding Different Number Bases," *12:* 339–340, May, 1965.
6. Stern, Catherine, and Margaret B. Stern, "Comments on Ancient Egyptian Multiplication," *11:* 254–257, April, 1964.
7. Willerding, Margaret F., "Other Number Systems—Aids to Understanding Mathematics," *8:* 350–356, November, 1961.

Chapter VIII

Fractions

Fractions have been in use for many centuries. The ancient Babylonians used a denominator of 60 and its multiples, while the Egyptians developed a fraction with a numerator of one and an unlimited denominator. Compared with the whole numbers (0, 1, 2, 3, etc.), the development of fractions was slow because they were motivated by need, and that need did not develop rapidly. As it became necessary for man to divide whole numbers to obtain more accurate measures, the pressure to extend the system of numbers to include a new notation became evident. This extension of whole numbers is called rational numbers, and they are governed by precisely the same laws and principles as operate for whole numbers.

The original meaning of the fraction was in terms of the unit, that is, one or more equal parts of a whole. With the passage of time, the "fraction" has come to mean any one of four things:
1. One or more parts of a unit. Example: 1/2 of a candy bar, 2/3 of a pie, 3/4 of 1.
2. One or more parts of a group. Example: 2/3 of a dozen, 3/5 of 15 feet, 1/2 of 6 apples.
3. The quotient of two numbers. Example: 5 feet of rope to be divided into 6 pieces. The quotient is 5/6 foot.
4. A comparison or a ratio. Jack has 3 apples and Jim has 5 apples. The number of apples which Jack has compared with the number of apples which Jim has is 3/5. (Also stated as 3 to 5 or 3:5).

The digits in a fraction have been given special names. The top numeral of the fraction is called the numerator and it points out the number of parts being considered. The bottom numeral of the fraction is called the denominator and it points out the number of parts into which a thing is divided. The symbol ($-$), called the fraction bar, separating the two digits, indicates division: 3/5 means 3 divided by 5.

$$\frac{3}{5} \quad \xleftarrow{\hspace{1cm}} \text{Numerator}$$
$$\xleftarrow{\hspace{1cm}} \text{Denominator}$$

Fractions may be classified into five groups according to form:
1. Simple fractions:
   a. Proper fractions: numerator is less than the denominator: 3/5, 5/6.
   b. Improper fractions: numerator is the same or greater than the denominator: 4/4, 7/5.
2. Mixed number: a whole number and a simple fraction: 2 2/3 → 2 + 2/3, 4 5/6 → 4 + 5/6.
3. Decimal fractions: the denominator is a power of ten: 3/10, 25/100.
4. Complex fractions: one or both terms of the fraction contain a fraction: $\frac{3/4}{6}$, $\frac{5/6}{1/2}$, $\frac{2}{4/5}$

5. Compound fractions: the numerator or the denominator or both involve an operation: $\dfrac{1/2 + 1/3}{1/6}$, $\dfrac{6 - 2}{4 + 2}$, $\dfrac{2}{2 \times 1/6}$.

The set of whole numbers is a subset of the set of fractional numbers and all the properties for the set of whole numbers hold for the set of fractional numbers.

Commutative property of addition and multiplication.

Examples: $1/2 + 1/3 \;=\; 1/3 + 1/2$

$a/b + c/d \;=\; c/d + a/b$

$2/3 \times 3/4 \;=\; 3/4 \times 2/3$

$a/b \times c/d \;=\; c/d \times a/b$

Associative property of addition and multiplication.

Examples: $2/3 + 1/2 + 3/4 \;=\; (2/3 + 1/2) + 3/4 = 2/3 + (1/2 + 3/4)$

$a/b + c/d + e/f \;=\; (a/b + c/d) + e/f \;=\; a/b + (c/d + e/f)$

$1/3 \times 3/4 \times 1/2 = (1/3 \times 3/4) \times 1/2 = 1/3 \times (3/4 \times 1/2)$

$a/b \times c/d \times e/f \;=\; (a/b \times c/d) \times e/f \;=\; a/b \times (c/d \times e/f)$

Distributive property of multiplication and division with respect to addition.

Examples: $3 \times 4\ 1/2 = 3 \times (4 + 1/2) = (3 \times 4) + (3 \times 1/2)$

$a \times (b + c) = (a \times b) + (a \times c)$

$4\ 1/2 \div 2 = (4 + 1/2) \div 2 = (4 \div 2) + (1/2 \div 2)$

$(a + b) \div c = (a \div c) + (b \div c)$

Identity element for addition.

Examples: $2/3 + 0 = 2/3$

$X + 0 = 0 + X$

Identity element for multiplication.

Examples: $3/5 \times 1 = 3/5$

$1 \times 4/5 = 4/5$

$a \times 1 = a$

Closure property for addition, multiplication and division.

Examples: $1/4 + 2/4 = 3/4$

$2/3 \times 4/5 = 8/15$

$2/3 \div 3/4 = 8/9$

Definitions

Addition: If a/b and c/d are fractions, $a/b + c/d \sim \dfrac{ad + bc}{bd}$ ($\sim$ is equivalent to)

Subtraction: If a/b and c/d are fractions and $a/b \geq c/d$, then $a/b - c/d = \dfrac{ad - bc}{bd}$

Multiplication: If a/b and c/d are fractions, $a/b \times c/d = \dfrac{ac}{bd}$

Division: If a/b and c/d are fractions, $c/d \neq 0/1$, $a/b \div c/d = a/b \times d/c$

Presentation of Fractions

The teacher who guides children into discovery must be well prepared in the art of asking questions. He must continually be answering the question, "What am I trying to teach?" By his questions, the teacher is challenging the students to serious thinking. He may also reveal, step by step, alternate possibilities as approaches to the problem. In a laboratory situation, the teacher moves about the room to observe what each student is doing. Later the class discusses the several approaches which individuals have discovered independently.

The properties and principles of the fractional numbers will not be discussed here in the detail it was done with whole numbers. Students are asked to call upon their knowledge of these properties to interpret fractional numbers. Methods and techniques acquired during the study of whole numbers will be adapted to each particular situation. Discovering relationships will be an important technique in teaching.

Children begin to use fractions before they enter school. Their experiences in sharing have helped them to develop ideas about one–half, one–third and one–fourth. The pupils speak of 1/2 hour, 1/2 day, half a cookie and half an apple with confidence, and they relate the fractions to the materials with which they work such as dividing a piece of paper into halves, thirds or fourths.

In kindergarten and grades one and two, the study of fractions is generally verbal. Children begin their work by identifying the elements of a fraction.

1. Into how many pieces is this pie divided?

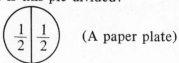   (A paper plate)

2. What are these parts called?
3. How many halves are there in one pie?
4. How many halves make 1 whole?
5. What is each part called?
6. What gives the fraction its name?

This early work with fractions should deal with concrete objects such as wooden discs, paper plates and real objects. This is followed by the use of the flannel board and finally by studying pictures and drawings. Units of measure such as the cup, the pint and the quart give children experience in identifying the elements of a fraction by using a liquid. In a similar manner, the fractions 1/3 and 1/4 are introduced.

As children are able to identify the number of parts and the size of the parts into which an object has been divided, they are ready to proceed to the next step, reproducing a fraction. The children are asked:

1. To divide a bar of candy into four equar parts:

$\frac{1}{4}$	$\frac{1}{4}$	$\frac{1}{4}$	$\frac{1}{4}$

2. What is each part called?
3. How many fourths are there in 1 bar of candy?
4. How many fourths are there in any whole?
5. What is one part called?
6. How many fourths are there in one–half of the bar? In three–fourths? (Children can color the parts called for.)

Ask the children to cut pieces of paper which show that a pie has been divided into thirds, fifths, etc. These can be placed on the flannel board and discussed with individuals or the total class. The problems which children structure are solved through the use of their manipulative materials (pie cutouts in this case).

Problem: We are having pie for supper. Mother said that she would cut the pie into 6 pieces. If 5 pieces of the pie are eaten, what part of the pie did we eat? How much pie is left?

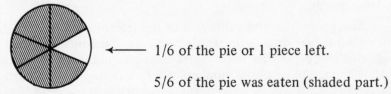

1/6 of the pie or 1 piece left.

5/6 of the pie was eaten (shaded part.)

Along with identifying the parts into which a whole has been divided and dividing a whole into some specified parts, a comparison of the size of the parts is made.

1. A pie has been divided into fourths. Are all the pieces in the pie the same size? Let the children prove that the pieces are the same size by matching the cutouts. Is this true if an object is divided into thirds? Sixths? Help the children to structure a generalization: whenever an object is divided into a specific number of equal parts, all the pieces of each object are of the same size.

2. Consider two pies. One pie is divided into halves and the other into thirds.

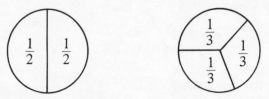

a. Are the pieces in each pie the same size? Ask the children to compare the pieces from each pie by using the cutouts.
b. Which is larger, 1/2 or 1/3?
c. How many pieces in each pie?
d. What is each piece called?
e. Help the children to generalize about the size of each part: the more equal parts into which a pie is equally divided, the smaller each part becomes.
f. Is 1/3 smaller than 1/2?

When children begin to write fractions, discuss the meaning of the terms numerator and denominator. Point out what happens to the denominator as an object is divided into more and more pieces, that is, that the denominator tells the number of parts (pieces) into which an object is divided, that the number becomes larger with each additional division and that the pieces become smaller. The denominator names the fraction.

A.   B.   C.

What is the denominator in A?

What is one of the parts in B called?

How many parts are there in all of C? (There are 6 sixths or 6/6 in C.)

The part of the fraction which tells the number of parts being taken away, eaten, considered, etc., is the numerator. It is the *numberer* of the part or parts being discussed. The fraction 1/4 should be read in several ways in the early stages in order to clarify its meaning.

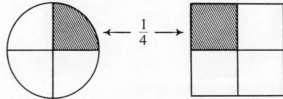

a. Something has been divided into 4 equal parts and 1 part is being considered.
b. We are considering 1 of the 4 equal parts into which something has been divided.
c. We are interested in 1 of the 4 equal parts.
d. One of four equal parts.
e. Eventually it is read one–fourth. Fractions with numerators of 1 are called *unit fractions.*

The fraction 5/6 is read:
a. Something has been divided into 6 equal parts and 5 of these parts are being considered.
b. We are considering 5 of the 6 equal parts into which something has been divided.
c. We are interested in 5 of the 6 equal parts.
d. 5 of 6 equal parts.
e. Eventually it is read five–sixths. Fractions with numerators of more than one are called *multiple fractions.*

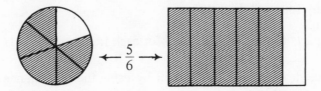

Shaded parts indicate the numerator. The total number of divisions indicates the denominator.

A fraction can also represent a part of a group. (For further detail, see Multiplication of Fractions.) Problem: Jack gave 1/2 of his 8 marbles to Jim. How many marbles did Jim receive?

Interpretation:
a. Jack gave 1 of 2 equal parts of 8 marbles to Jim.
b. 8 is to be divided into 2 equal groups (partition idea). One of these groups is given to Jim.

$$|\circ\circ\circ\circ|\circ\circ\circ\circ|$$
$$\quad 1/2 \qquad\quad 1/2$$

Jim receives 4 marbles

Problem: I have 3/4 of a dozen apples. How many apples do I have?

Interpretation:

a. I have 3 of 4 equal groups of 12 apples.

b. 12 is divided into 4 equal parts; I have 3 of the groups.

$$|\text{O O O}|\text{O O O}|\text{O O O}|\text{O O O}|$$

I have 9 apples

c. 3/4 of 12 is the same as dividing by 4 and multiplying the quotient by 3.

$$|\text{O O O}|\text{O O O}|\text{O O O}|\text{O O O}|$$
$$\quad 1/4 \qquad 1/4 \qquad 1/4 \qquad 1/4$$

4 equal groups
3 apples in each group
3/4 = 3 of the 4 groups = 9 apples
12 ÷ 4 = 3. Then 3 × 3 = 9 apples

The following chart is important in establishing the concept of equivalent fractions:

1 Whole															
$\frac{1}{2}$								$\frac{1}{2}$							
$\frac{1}{4}$				$\frac{1}{4}$				$\frac{1}{4}$				$\frac{1}{4}$			
$\frac{1}{8}$		$\frac{1}{8}$		$\frac{1}{8}$		$\frac{1}{8}$		$\frac{1}{8}$		$\frac{1}{8}$		$\frac{1}{8}$		$\frac{1}{8}$	
$\frac{1}{16}$	$\frac{1}{16}$	$\frac{1}{16}$	$\frac{1}{16}$	$\frac{1}{16}$	$\frac{1}{16}$	$\frac{1}{16}$	$\frac{1}{16}$	$\frac{1}{16}$	$\frac{1}{16}$	$\frac{1}{16}$	$\frac{1}{16}$	$\frac{1}{16}$	$\frac{1}{16}$	$\frac{1}{16}$	$\frac{1}{16}$

a. 1/2 is equal to how many fourths? Eighths?

b. How many 1/4's in 4/16?

c. Into how many equal parts is the whole divided for each fraction? (For 1/2, two equal parts.)

Two generalizations can be developed with children by using the equivalence chart. Guide them to discover these statements.

1. Multiplying the numerator and the denominator by the same nonzero number changes the fraction to higher equivalent terms. As the denominator increases, the size of each part decreases.

$$\frac{2 \times 1}{2 \times 4} = \frac{2}{8}$$

4ths →   8ths →

2. Dividing the numerator and the denominator by the same nonzero number changes the fraction to lower equivalent terms. As the fraction is divided, the size of each part increases.

$$\frac{2 \div 2}{4 \div 2} = \frac{1}{2}$$

Renaming fractions is first introduced when children are comparing fractions. Later, when addition and subtraction are developed, they will have had experience in expressing fractions with the same denominator. It is important that children understand the concept of "common denominators" as changing, expressing or renaming fractions so that each will have the same name. The following examples illustrate how children can develop facility comparing fractions.

Example: Change 1/2 and 1/3 to like fractions:

Multiply by 3:

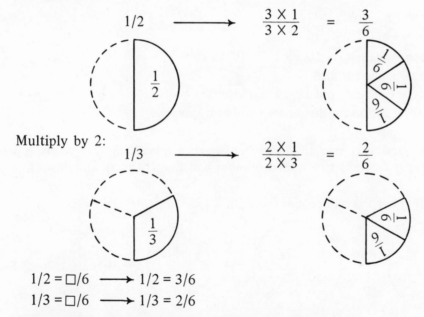

Multiply by 2:

$$1/2 = \square/6 \longrightarrow 1/2 = 3/6$$
$$1/3 = \square/6 \longrightarrow 1/3 = 2/6$$

Which fraction is the larger? 1/2 or 1/3? 3/6 or 2/6? One can compare when the denominators are the same. Why was 6 chosen as a common denominator? (2 × 3 = 6.) Can other common denominators be chosen? What is another name for 2/2? Has one multiplied by 1 when multiplying by 2/2? Yes, 1/2 is equivalent to 2/6 because 1 is the identity element for multiplication.

Example: Change 2/3 and 3/5 to like fractions:

Multiply by 5:

$$2/3 \longrightarrow \frac{5 \times 2}{5 \times 3} = \frac{10}{15}$$

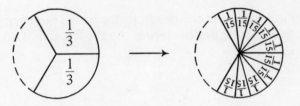

Multiply by 3:

$$3/5 \longrightarrow \frac{3 \times 3}{3 \times 5} = \frac{9}{15}$$

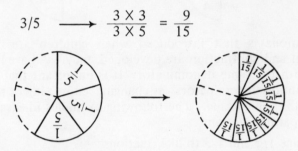

Concept of ratio (comparison):

2/3 = □/15 ⟶ 2/3 = 10/15

3/5 = □/15 ⟶ 3/5 = 9/15

Which fraction is the larger, 2/3 or 3/5? 10/15 or 9/15?

What is another name for 5/5?

Why are the fractions 2/3 and 10/15 equivalent?

State the generalization for dividing a number by itself.

Renaming a fraction is also applied to changing a mixed number to an improper fraction, an improper fraction to a mixed number and the writing of an integer as a fraction.

1. A mixed number to an improper fraction, 2 1/2:

1 whole	+	1 whole	+	1/2	⟶	2 + 1/2 = 2 1/2

How many fourths in any whole? In two wholes?

4/4 + 4/4 + 2/4 = 10/4

2 2/4 = 4/4 + 4/4 + 2/4 = 10/4

If numbers are used instead of drawings, how can the improper fraction be found? Example: 2 2/4.

a. What denominator is indicated in the example? (Fourths.)

b. How many fourths in any whole? How can one find the number of fourths in more than 1 whole? Multiply the number of wholes (4 × 2 = 8 fourths). Add to the fourths contained in the whole or wholes the numerator of the fraction (which states the number of original fourths).

8 fourths + 2 fourths = 10 fourths

8/4 + 2/4 = 10/4

2 2/4 → (4 × 2) + 2 = 10/4

2. Improper fraction to a mixed number, 8/3:

How many thirds in any whole?
How many wholes will 8/3 make?
How many thirds are left over? (2/3)

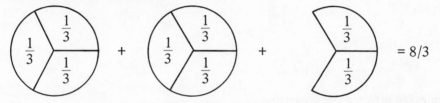

How many wholes can be made from 8/3?

3/3 + 3/3 + 2/3 = 1 + 1 + 2/3 = 2 2/3.

If numbers are used instead of drawings, how can the mixed number be found?

a. What is the denominator in the original fraction? (Thirds.) The denominator states the number of parts into which the wholes are divided. The number of thirds being considered is 8. The fraction $8/3 = 3\overline{)8} = 2\ 2/3$. Therefore, 8/3 = 2 2/3. The mixed number is 2 2/3.

3. Writing an integer as a fraction (other names for numbers): Any integer can be written as a fraction by writing it over a denominator of 1. This is true because any number divided by 1 is the number.

$$1/1 \rightarrow 1\overline{)1} 4/1 \rightarrow 1\overline{)4}$$

Sometimes it is necessary to write a whole number over denominators other than 1. This is true when the common denominator approach is used in solving problems such as 6 ÷ 2/3. In writing 6 as a fraction, there is no point in selecting a denominator other than 3. Let the 3 be the common denominator.

a. What is another name for 6 that has a denominator of 3? Apply Principle 1. Multiply the numerator and the denominator by the same nonzero number. (Multiply by 3 since it is given.)

Think: $6/1 \rightarrow \dfrac{3 \times 6}{3 \times 1} = \dfrac{18}{3}$ (6/1 and 18/3 are different names for 6)

The example now stated is $18/3 \div 2/3$.

b. Write 4 with a denominator of 8. ($4 \div 3/8$)

Think: $4/1 \rightarrow \dfrac{8 \times 4}{8 \times 1} = \dfrac{32}{8}$ (4/1 and 32/8 are different names for 4)

The example now stated is $32/8 \div 3/8$.

As children develop clearer concepts of fractions and can apply the principles and generalizations stated, they can begin to identify procedures for changing complex and compound fractions to proper and improper fractions. Although these fractions are not common to the elementary grades, there are pupils in grades 6, 7 and 8 who will profit from their introduction.

1. Complex fractions

Examples:

$$\dfrac{3/4}{6} \qquad\qquad \dfrac{5/6}{1/2} \qquad\qquad \dfrac{2}{4/5}$$

Interpretation:

$$\dfrac{3/4}{6} \qquad\qquad 3/4 \div 6 =$$

Divide 3/4 into 6 parts (partition).

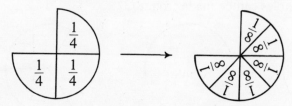

Each fourth is divided into 2 parts. Since the whole unit must be considered, the circle is divided into eighths. When the example is solved by inversion, the answer is 3/24; when renamed, each part is 1/8. Note that the renaming of these fractions requires knowledge of division of fractions. Is there a fraction in the numerator? Denominator? Can you state the generalization?

2. Compound fractions

Example:

$$\dfrac{1/2 + 1/3}{1/6} \qquad\qquad \dfrac{6 - 2}{2/3} \qquad\qquad \dfrac{1/2}{7 + 3}$$

Interpretation: Find the sum of $1/2 + 1/3$. (5/6.) The sum 5/6 is to be divided by 1/6.

$5/6 \div 1/6 = \square$ How many 1/6's in 5/6?

```
0                                                              1 unit
 | 1/6 | 1/6 | 1/6 | 1/6 | 1/6 | 1/6 |
    1     2     3     4     5
```

(There are 5 one-sixths in 5/6.)

Is there an operation in the numerator? Denominator? Can you state the generalization?

As children indicate their knowledge of the number of unit fractions in a whole (how many 1/4's in a whole), they should be challenged through discovery to find how many units of a multiple fraction are contained in a whole. This concept is used later to explain why the divisor is inverted when dividing by a fraction.

Examples:

1. How many 3/4's are there in one unit?

   a. Using the number line:

      Draw a line which is one unit long. Divide it into four equal parts.

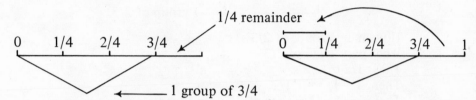

What part of 3/4's is the remainder 1/4?
Place 1/4 over the divisor 3/4.
1/4 is one of the 3 equal parts of 3/4's.
1/4 is 1/3 of 3/4's. Then, 1 + 1/3 = 1 1/3.
There are 1 1/3 groups of 3/4's in 1 whole.

   b. Using the circle:

      Divide a circle into 4 equal parts.

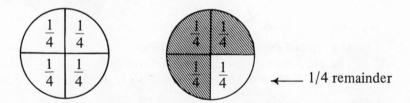

What part of 3/4's is the remainder 1/4?
The shaded area is 1 group of 3/4's.
Place the remainder 1/4 over the divisor 3/4's.
The 1/4 is one of the 3 equal parts of 3/4's.
Then 1 + 1/3 = 1 1/3.
There are 1 1/3 groups of 3/4's in 1 whole.

   c. Using arithmetic:

$$\begin{array}{r} 1 \\ 3/4 \overline{)\,1} \\ \underline{3/4} \\ \end{array} \quad \longleftarrow \quad \text{1 group of 3/4's}$$

$$\frac{1/4}{3/4} = \frac{1/4 \div 1/4}{3/4 \div 1/4} = \frac{1}{3}$$

There are 1 1/3 groups of 3/4's in 1 whole.

2. How many groups of 2/3's in 1 whole?

   a. Using the number line:

   Draw a line which is 1 unit long. Divide the line into 3 equal parts.

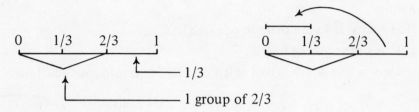

How many groups of 2/3's?
What part is 1/3 of 2/3's?
1/3 is 1/2 of 2/3's.
Then, 1 + 1/2 = 1 1/2.
There are 1 1/2 groups of 2/3's in 1 whole.

   b. Using the circle:

   Divide a circle into 3 equal parts. How many groups of 2/3's in 1 whole?

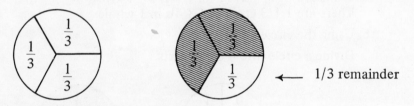

The shaded area is 1 group of 2/3's.
The 1/3 is one of the 2 equal parts of 2/3's.
Then, 1 + 1/2 = 1 1/2 groups of 2/3's in 1 whole.

3. How many groups of 2/5's in 1 whole?

   a. Using the number line:

   Draw a line 1 unit long and divide it into 5 equal parts.

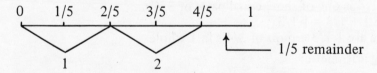

How many groups of 2/5's in 1 whole?
What part of 2/5's is the remainder 1/5?
The 1/5 is 1/2 of 2/5's.
Then, 1 + 1 + 1/2 = 2 1/2
There are 2 1/2 groups of 2/5's in 1 whole.

The development of insight into fractions is more involved as one begins work with the four operations. Children have worked with many different aids to interpret and discover the various concepts of fractions. Each part has been developed separately and in relationship to known ideas.

In presenting addition and subtraction, children are directed to use the insights developed when comparing fractions. The teacher's guidance becomes more effective now through the use of questions. The children are asked to think through these questions and to illustrate their understanding in different ways such as drawings, the number line and the equivalence charts. This interpretation is then put into writing. It is the purpose of the teacher to involve and encourage each child to observe, manipulate aids, and to write his understanding of the process. Techniques used previously are recalled and used.

Addition of Fractions

Addition of fractions is usually thought of as content in the fourth grade. Children, however, do add fractions as early as the first grade by manipulating objects and discussing the results. It is quite possible that many children are able to transfer the visual and oral approach to the writing of fractions before the fourth grade.

Ask children to solve several examples by using a drawing, cutouts or a method of their own choice.

Example: 1/4 and 2/4 (use the fractions in a story problem)

Possible solutions:

1. Drawing

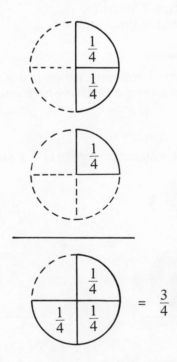

2. Cutouts

3. Words and symbols

```
  1 fourth           1/4
+ 2 fourths  ⟶    + 2/4
  3 fourths           3/4
```

Have the pupils discuss their solutions using questions similar to the following:

1. What does the denominator tell us?
2. Are the fractions alike? Do they have the same denominator?
3. Why are the numerators added?
4. Do the fractions agree in size of the parts?
5. Why can 1/4 be written 1 fourth?
6. Is the sum changed to the lowest terms?

Finding Common Denominators

Before attempting to find common denominators, review with children the techniques and generalizations discovered in changing fractions to higher terms.

Example:

1. $1/4 + 1/2 = \square$

Is the common denominator present? Is 2 a factor of 4?

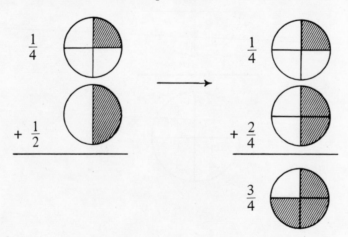

Finding equivalence

$$1/2 = ?/4 \rightarrow \frac{2 \times 1 = 2}{2 \times 2 = 4}$$

Multiply the numerator and the denominator by the same number.

$$
\begin{aligned}
1/4 &= 1/4 \\
\underline{1/2} &= \underline{2/4} \\
& 3/4
\end{aligned}
$$

What is the relationship of the factors to the product in any multiplication equation? The children have discovered that the product is always divisible by each of the factors.

Can we use this idea in finding the common denominator?

Will the common denominator always be the lowest common denominator?

Example:

1/2 + 1/3

2 × 3 = 6 the common denominator

$$
\begin{aligned}
1/2 &= 3/6 \\
\underline{1/3} &= \underline{2/6} \\
& 5/6
\end{aligned}
$$

Example:

2/6 + 3/4 =

6 × 4 = 24 the common denominator

$$
\begin{aligned}
2/6 &= 8/24 \\
\underline{3/4} &= \underline{18/24} \\
& 26/24 = 1\ 1/12
\end{aligned}
$$

How can one find the lowest common denominator?

Before finding equivalences, would it be good practice to divide by 2, 3 or 4 to check the denominator?

There is no one correct way to record the mechanics of solving an example in addition. However, there may be one way which is more acceptable because it is a common algorism to most people. Ask the children to solve the following examples in as many ways as possible. The following solutions are most common.

1. $12\ 3/4 = 12\ \ 9/12$
   $+\ \ \ 9\ 5/6 = \ \ 9\ 10/12$
                $21\ 19/12\ =\ 22\ 7/12$

2. $7\ 3/8\ -\ 3/8$
   $+\ \ \ 6\ 3/4\ -\ 6/8$
        $13\ \ \ \ \ \ \ \ 9/8\ =\ 1\ 1/8$
           $1\ 1/8$
        $14\ 1/8$

3. $3\ 4/6$ $\rightarrow$ $3\ +\ 4/6$
   $+\ \ \ 2\ 2/3$ $+\ 2\ +\ 4/6$
                  $5\ +\ 8/6\ =\ 6\ 1/3$

4. $1/6$
       $2/6$
   $+\ \ 1/6$
       $4/6$

5. $1/6\ =\ 2/12$
       $1/4\ =\ 3/12$
   $+\ \ 1/3\ =\ 4/12$
          $9/12\ =\ 3/4$

6. $2\ 1/2\ =\ 2\ \ 6/12$
       $3\ 4/6\ =\ 3\ \ 8/12$
   $+\ 1\ 2/4\ =\ 1\ \ 6/12$
         $6\ 20/12\ =\ 7\ 8/12\ =\ 7\ 3/4$

7. $3\ 1/3$ $3\ +\ 1/3$ $3\ +\ \ 4/12$
       $2\ 3/4$ $\rightarrow$ $2\ +\ 3/4$ $\rightarrow$ $2\ +\ \ 9/12$
   $+\ 4\ 2/6$ $4\ +\ 2/6$ $4\ +\ \ 4/12$
                              $9\ +\ 17/12$
                          $10\ +\ \ 5/12\ =\ 10\ 5/12$

Subtraction of Fractions

Subtraction of whole numbers is usually introduced when children are familiar with several addition facts. When children can add like fractions, they are ready to subtract like fractions.

By observation and manipulation, children discover that numerators are subtracted and the difference is written over the common denominator. The techniques discovered in addition of fractions can be transferred to developing meaning to subtraction. The following examples illustrate the common elements between addition and subtraction.

Addition

1.   1/4 Addend   3/4 Minuend (sum)   3/4 Minuend (sum)
   $+\ $ 2/4 Addend   1/4 Subtrahend (addend) $-\ $ 2/4 Subtrahend (addend)
       3/4 Sum   2/4 Difference (addend)   1/4 Difference (addend)

2.   3 2/5 (Addend)   4 3/5 (Minuend (sum)   4 3/5 (Minuend (sum)
   + 1 1/5 (Addend)   - 3 2/5 Subtrahend (addend) →   - 1 1/5 Subtrahend (addend)
     4 3/5 (Sum)   1 1/5 Difference (addend)   3 2/5 Difference (addend)

3.   5 5/6 = 5 5/6
   + 2 2/3 = 2 4/6
             7 9/6 = 8 1/2

   8 1/2 = 8 3/6 = 7 9/6   8 1/2 = 8 3/6 = 7 9/6
 - 2 2/3 = 2 4/6 = 2 4/6   - 5 5/6 = 5 5/6 = 5 5/6
                   5 5/6   2 4/6 = 2 2/3

Regrouping

Regrouping is necessary when the fraction in the minuend is less than the fraction in the subtrahend. Prepare for regrouping in fractions by reviewing with the children the thought process in regrouping of whole numbers. The base used in regrouping in whole numbers is always 10 or a power of 10. In fractions, the unit borrowed is expressed in terms of the common denominator established for each example.

Example:

   4 1/4 = 4 3/12   3 15/12   →   (12/12 + 3/12)
 - 1 2/3 = 1 8/12   →   - 1 8/12
                            2 7/12

What is the common denominator?
What is the total fraction in the minuend before subtraction?
What is the total fraction in the minuend after regrouping?
How is the one unit written after it is regrouped?

Examples:

1.   6 2/3 = 6 8/12 = 5 20/12
   - 2 3/4 = 2 9/12 = 2 9/12   12/12 + 8/12 = 20/12
                      3 11/12

     6 2/3 = 5 20/12
   - 2 3/4 = 2 9/12
             3 11/12

     5
   6 2/3 — 20/12
 - 2 3/4 —   9/12   Not an equals sign
   3   11/12 → 3 11/12

   6 2/3 → 6 + 2/3   →   5 + 12/12 + 8/12   →   5 + 20/12
 - 2 3/4   2 + 3/4   -(2 +   9/12)   -(2 + 9/12)
                                                   3 + 11/12 = 3 11/12

Broadening Experiences in Addition and Subtraction of Fractions

Challenge the children with new and exciting approaches to solving problems. Several of the activities in addition and subtraction of whole numbers can be applied to the operations in fractions. Provide opportunities for children to discover algorisms other than those presented here.

1. The additive method of subtraction

   Why is the approach used in the addition of whole numbers?

   Is it simple to perform with fractions?

   What is the first step before using the additive approach? (Change to common denominators.)

   Example:

   $$\begin{array}{r} 3\ 4/5 \\ -\ 1\ 2/5 \\ \hline \end{array}$$

   Language: 2/5 plus what number is 4/5?

   1 plus what number is 3?

   2 + 2/5 = 2 2/5

2. Compensation

   What is the generalization for compensation in addition of whole numbers?

   What is the generalization for compensation in subtraction of whole numbers?

   Can the generalization be applied to fractions?

   What is the first step before applying the principle of compensation?

   Example:

   $$\begin{array}{r} 8\ 3/6 = 8\ 6/12 \\ -\ 2\ 3/4 = 2\ 9/12 \\ \hline \end{array}$$

   What fraction added to 9/12 equals 12/12?

   9/12 + 3/12 = 12/12   Why was this done?

   12/12 = 1   1 + 2 = 3

   What happens to the fraction in the subtrahend? In the minuend?

   $$\begin{array}{r} 8\ 9/12 \quad \rightarrow \quad (6/12 + 3/12 = 9/12) \\ -\ 3 \qquad\qquad\qquad\qquad\qquad \\ \hline 5\ 9/12 \qquad\qquad\qquad\qquad\qquad \end{array}$$

   Check your work by using the common algorism.

3. Multiple Counting (addition)

   Count by 1/2 starting with 2.

   Count by 1/4 starting with 1/2.

   Count by 2/3 starting with 1.

4. Multiple Counting (subtraction)

   Count backwards by 1/2 starting with 6.

   Count backwards by 1/4 starting with 3.

   Count backwards by 3/4 starting with 5.

5. Ask the children to structure tables similar to the following:

+	1/2	1/3	1/4	1/5
1/2	1	5/6	3/4	7/10
1/3	5/6	2/3	7/12	8/15
1/4	3/4	7/12	1/2	9/20
1/5	7/10	8/15	9/20	2/5

Important Ideas Begun

1. Identify the elements of a fraction.
2. A fraction as one or more parts of a unit.
3. A fraction as one or more parts of a group.
4. A comparison of the size of fractions.
5. The concept of equivalence.
6. Changing fractions: multiplying the numerator and the denominator by the same number, zero omitted, does not change the value of the fraction.
7. Changing fractions: dividing the numerator and the denominator by the same number, zero omitted, does not change the value of the fraction.
8. Changing mixed fractions and improper fractions.
9. The relationship of the principle of compensation as used in whole numbers and fractions.
10. Writing a whole number as a fraction.
11. Interpreting complex and compound fractions.
12. The language used to interpret the fraction.

Multiplication of Fractions

Multiplication of whole numbers was introduced as a process for finding the sums when all the addends are equal. Review the relationships of addition and multiplication and other approaches used to interpret the operation such as the number line, drawings and arrays.

The mechanical operations involved with the multiplication of fractions are simple and easy to learn. We are concerned however, with the meaning for each thing that is done. With the development of understanding, generalizations are easily provided by the children.

To make the teaching of multiplication of fractions more meaningful, four types of examples are presented. Relationships are easily discernible as each type is developed. Mixed numbers are presented in order to show more clearly how these types are interrelated. A problem relevant to each type introduces the work. Ask the children to solve each problem in as many ways as they can. Build the class discussion about the solutions given.

1. A whole number times a fraction

   Problem: Fred lives 1/2 mile from school. He rides this distance on his bicycle 4 times a day. How far does Fred ride his bicycle each day?

   Read: 4 groups of 1/2
   4 1/2's (four halves)
   4 of the 1/2 values
   1/2 to be added 4 times

   Drawings

   2 halves = 1 whole   2 halves = 1 whole

Addition

```
  1/2
  1/2
  1/2          Adding 4 groups of 1/2
+ 1/2
  4/2 = 2
```

Using the ruler

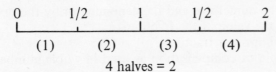

4 halves = 2

Use the following questions as a guide in discussing the various solutions:

What are the facts of the problem?
Do the illustrations show the facts of the problem?
Do the solutions show how the answer is established?
Which solutions seem to be the best? Why?
What known ideas were used to solve the problem?

Can you state a generalization for multiplying fractions? Children will express the rule in several ways, generally they say: the product of the numerators over the product of the denominators is the answer. 4 × 1/2 = 4/2 = 2. Fred rides 2 miles each day.

Example: 4 × 3/4 = □

Read: 4 groups of 3/4
              4 of the 3/4 values
              3/4 to be added 4 times

Drawings

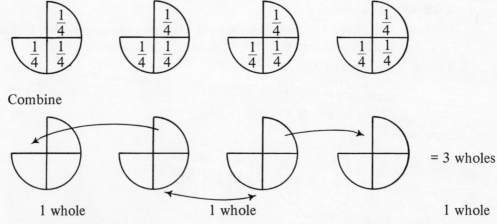

Combine

= 3 wholes

1 whole   1 whole   1 whole

a. 1/4 + 3/4 = 1 whole
b. 1/2 + 1/2 = 1 whole
c. 1/4 + 3/4 = 1 whole

Addition

$$\begin{array}{r} 3/4 \\ 3/4 \\ 3/4 \\ +\ 3/4 \\ \hline 12/4\ =\ 3 \end{array}$$

Adding 4 groups of 3/4

Using ruler (dividing into fourths)

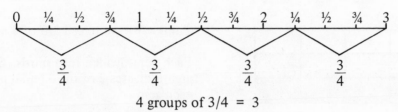

4 groups of 3/4 = 3

State the generalization.

4 × 3/4 = 12/4 = 3

2. A fraction times a whole number

Problem: A man has 4 acres of land. He wants to sell 1/2 of his land. How much land does he sell?

Read: 1 of 2 equal parts of 4

1/2 of 4

4 to be divided into 2 equal parts and one of the parts considered

Drawing:

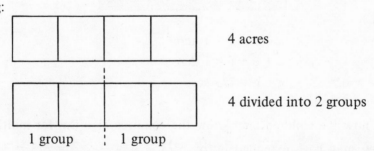

4 acres

4 divided into 2 groups

1 group   1 group

The numerator 1 (of 1/2) states that 1 of the two groups is taken. How many acres in each group? 2 acres. Then, 1 of 2 equal parts of 4 is 2.

State the generalization. Is there a change from the first type of fraction?

1/2 × 4 = 4/2 = 2. He sells 2 acres.

Can you identify the commutative property?

4 × 1/2 = 1/2 × 4

Example: 2/3 × 4

Read: 2 of 3 equal parts of 4

Divide 4 into 3 equal parts, consider 2 of the parts.

Drawing:

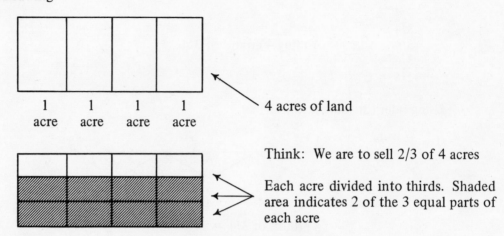

1 acre · 1 acre · 1 acre · 1 acre ← 4 acres of land

Think: We are to sell 2/3 of 4 acres

Each acre divided into thirds. Shaded area indicates 2 of the 3 equal parts of each acre

Into how many parts is each acre divided? (3 thirds.)
How many parts are considered in each acre? (2/3 shaded.)
Then, how many thirds are considered in the 4 acres? (8/3 shaded.)

a + b + c = 1 acre
d + e + f = 1 acre
g + h = 2/3 acre

By now the children may know the common algorism for multiplying fractions. They may have extended it to: $2/3 \times 4 = \dfrac{2 \times 4}{3} = 8/3 = 3/3 + 3/3 + 2/3 =$ 1 + 1 + 2/3 = 2 2/3

3. A fraction times a fraction

Example: 2/3 × 3/5

Problem: Jack has 3/5 of an acre of land. He wishes to sell 2/3 of it. How much land will he sell?

Read: 2 of 3 equal parts of 3/5.

3/5 is to be divided into 3 equal parts (groups) and 2 of the parts sold.

2/3 of 3/5.

Drawing:

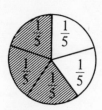

3/5 of a pie or circle. There are 3 equal parts the size of a fifth.

The multiplier states: 2 of 3 equal parts.

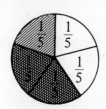

Since the part to be considered is already divided into 3 equal parts, shade 2 of the 3 equal parts.

2/3 X 3/5 then is 2 (shaded) of the 3 equal parts or 2/5 of the whole.

Drawing (rectangle)

a.

1/5
1/5
1/5
1/5
1/5

Divide into fifths.

Shaded portion not to be considered.

← 3/5 of an acre

b.

Divide the rectangle vertically into 3 equal parts.

c.

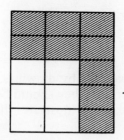

How many of the 3 parts are to be considered? (2 of the 3 parts.)

← Shade 1 part not to be considered.

How many divisions in the total rectangle? (15.)
How many of the 15 divisions are not shaded? (6.)
Therefore, 6/15 or 2/5 of the total rectangle (field) is not shaded. He sold 2/5 of an acre.

Multiplication:

$$2/3 \times 3/5 = \frac{2 \times 3}{3 \times 5} = 6/15 = 2/5$$

The shortened form is:

$$2/3 \times 3/5 = 6/15 = 2/5$$

Example: 1/2 × 1/2

Read: 1 of 2 equal parts of 1/2 (the multiplicand)

1/2 is to be divided into 2 equal parts and 1 of the parts taken.

1/2 of 1/2.

A pie has been cut into halves and only 1/2 remains. How much is 1/2 of the piece remaining?

Ruler

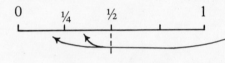

Divide 1/2 into 2 equal parts.

Each part is 1/4. The fraction calls for 1 of the parts. (1/4.)

Drawing

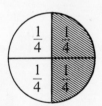

1/2 of a pie

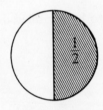

The half has been divided into 2 equal parts. What part of the total pie is one of the pieces? The piece is 1/4 in size.

1/2 of 1/2 is 1/4

Multiplication

1/2 × 1/2 = 1/4 the size of the piece remaining

4. Mixed Numbers

At this point there is little need to present fractions by drawings, the use of rulers or other aids. When pupils can interpret fractions, they should be permitted to solve the problems using multiplication. One example illustrates that drawings can be used to find the solution.

a. A whole number times a mixed number

Children discover in the use of the distributive property that this example is made up of two parts: a whole number times a whole number and a whole number times a fraction.

$$4 \times 2\ 3/4 = 4 \times (2 + 3/4) = (4 \times 2) + (4 \times 3/4)$$
$$= 8 + 3 = 11$$

If 2 3/4 is changed to an improper fraction, one has merely changed names.

$$4 \times 2\ 3/4 = 4 \times 11/4 = 44/4 = 11$$

Lay out 4 groups 2 3/4 inches long on a ruler.

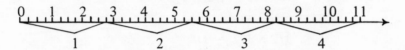

Drawings at this point tend to become cumbersome.

4 groups of 2 3/4

Can one add to find the answer to this example?

b. A mixed number times a whole number

What two parts should children discover present in this example? The distributive property helps us to identify a whole number times a whole number and a fraction times a whole number.

$$2\ 3/4 \times 4 = (2 + 3/4) \times 4 = (2 \times 4) + (3/4 \times 4)$$
$$= 8 + 3 = 11$$

Then, 2 3/4 × 4 = 11/4 × 4 = 44/4 = 11

c. A mixed number times a mixed number

What patterns can you identify?

$$3\ 2/3 \times 2\ 3/5\ =\ 11/13 \times 13/5 = 143/15 = 9\ 8/15$$
$$3\ 2/3 \times 2\ 3/5\ =\ (3 + 2/3) \times (2 + 3/5)$$
$$=\ (3 \times 2) + (3 \times 3/5) + (2/3 \times 2) + (2/3 \times 3/5)$$
$$=\quad 6\quad +\ 9/5\quad +\ 4/3\quad +\quad 6/15$$
$$=\ 9\ 8/15$$

Patterns to observe:

    A whole number times a whole number

    A whole number times a fraction

    A fraction times a whole number

    A fraction times a fraction

What is the meaning of $a/b \times c/d = \dfrac{ac}{bd}$?

Broadening Experiences for Multiplication of Fractions

Review with children various activities learned in multiplication of whole numbers. As home assignments, ask them to relate these algorisms to the solution of fractions. Several possibilities are presented here.

1. Squaring any fraction ending in 1/2. (Recall squaring any two–digit number ending in 5.)

$$6 \ 1/2 \times 6 \ 1/2 \ = \ (6 \times 7) + (1/2 \times 1/2)$$
$$= \ 6 \times 7 \ = \ 42$$
$$1/2 \times 1/2 \ = \ 1/4$$
$$\text{Then, } 42 + 1/4 \ = \ 42 \ 1/4$$

2. Compensation: In whole numbers it was learned that when one factor is multiplied by a number, the second factor must be divided by that number to produce the correct product. Apply this principle to fractions. Examples:

a. $64 \times 2 \ 1/2 =$

Multiply by 2 to get a whole number

Divide by 2 to maintain balance

$64 \times 2 \ 1/2 \ =$ What number times 2 1/2 equals a whole number?

$$\begin{array}{r} 2 \ 1/2 \\ \times \ 64 \\ \hline 8 \\ 120 \\ 32 \\ \hline 160 \end{array}$$

2 1/2 × 2 = 5 (A whole number)

64 ÷ 2 = 32

Then 32 × 5 = 160

b. $3 \ 1/3 \times 120$ What number times 3 1/3 equals a whole number?

$$\begin{array}{r} 120 \\ \times \ \ \ 3 \ 1/3 \\ \hline 360 \\ 40 \\ \hline 400 \end{array}$$

3 × 3 1/3 = 10

120 ÷ 3 = 40

Then, 10 × 40 = 400

c. $96 \times 1 \ 1/4$ What number times 1/4 equals a whole number?

$$4 \times 1/4 = 4/4 = 1$$
$$1 + (4 \times 1) = 5$$
$$(4 \times 1) + (4 \times 1/4) = 5$$

$$\begin{array}{r} 1 \ 1/4 \\ \times \ 96 \\ \hline 6 \\ 90 \\ 24 \\ \hline 120 \end{array}$$

4 × 1 1/4 = 5

96 ÷ 4 = 24

Then, 5 × 24 = 120

3. Structure tables similar to the following:

$\overset{\times}{\div}$	1/2	1/3	1/4	1/5
1/2	1/4	1/6	1/8	1/10
1/3	1/6	1/9	1/12	1/15
1/4	1/8	1/12	1/16	1/20
1/5	1/10	1/15	1/20	1/25

Division of Fractions

Children must be clear on the language and meanings of division of whole numbers before division using fractions can be understood. A good starting point can be a review of the division concepts by analyzing the example $12 \div 4$ through:

1. Language:

   How many fours in 12?
   What number times 4 equals 12?
   12 divided into 4 parts, how much in 1 part?
   How many groups of 4 in 12?

2. Using a ruler:

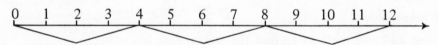

   How many groups of 4 in 12?

   3 groups of 4 in 12.

3. Addition and subtraction:

$$\begin{array}{r} 4 \\ +\ 4 \\ \hline 8 \\ +\ 4 \\ \hline 12 \end{array}$$

Three groups of 4 are added to reach the sum of 12

There are 3 groups of 4 in 12

$$\begin{array}{r} 12 \\ -\ 4 \\ \hline 8 \\ -\ 4 \\ \hline 4 \\ -\ 4 \end{array}$$

Three groups of 4 are subtracted from 12

The procedure to be used in presenting the division of fractions is similar to that used in presenting the multiplication of fractions. Children are asked to solve the problems using drawings, the ruler and then to derive number solutions from the drawings. Finally, they are asked to state the generalization.

The conventional method used in dividing fractions is to invert the divisor and multiply. To give the children an opportunity to understand division of fractions, four types are presented. Mixed numbers are included as a type so that students can observe patterns within mixed numbers as being the three types discussed first.

1. A whole number divided by a fraction:

Problem: John has a board 4 feet long. He intends to divide the board into pieces 1/2 foot long. How many pieces can he get?

Solve the problem in as many ways as you can.

Ruler:

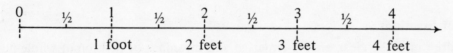

Each piece is one–half foot. Count the 1/2's. There are 8 halves in 4.

Drawing:

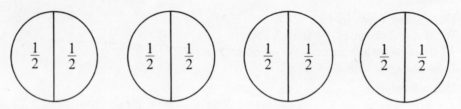

How many halves in 4 circles?

Can one add and subtract to find the answer?

Common denominator: The common denominator involves the concept of dividing like units. In the example 4 ÷ 1/2, the 4 is changed to have a denominator of 2. Since 2 is the denominator in the divisor, there is no point in selecting another denominator.

How does one find an equivalent fraction for 4? 4 ÷ 1/2 is now written 8/2 ÷ 1/2. To give more meaning to the example, write it as $\frac{8 \div 1}{2 \div 2}$.

Then $\frac{8 \div 1}{2 \div 2} = \frac{8}{1} = 8$

What happens to the denominator when division is performed?

What generalization describes division by 1?

Inverting the divisor: The rule points out that to divide fractions, invert the divisor and multiply.

What does this mean? Why does it work?

$4 \div 1/2 = 4 \times 2/1 = 8/1 = 8$

Compare the divisor 1/2 to any unit of length. We have learned that there are 2/2, 3/3, 4/4 and so on in every whole.

How many halves are there in 1 unit? If 1 unit has 2 halves, how many halves are there in 4 units? $4 \times 2 = 8$.

Reciprocal Method: The principle in arithmetic which permits us to multiply the divisor and the dividend by the same nonzero number explains the use of the reciprocal idea in division.   This implies that by changing the divisor to 1, one has only to multiply the dividend by the reciprocal to arrive at the quotient.

Rewrite 4 ÷ 1/2 to:

$$\frac{4}{1/2} = \frac{4 \times 2/1}{1/2 \times 2/1} = \frac{8}{1} = 8$$

What is the reciprocal of 1/2?
What is the reciprocal of any number?
What happens to the denominator when the reciprocal is used?

Problem: Mary has a piece of lace 6 feet long. How many pieces can she get if she divides the lace into pieces 2/3 foot long?

Solve the problem in as many ways as you can.

Ruler:

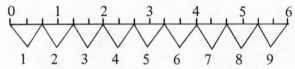

Divide each unit into thirds

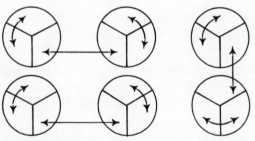

How many groups of 2/3 are there in 6?

Drawings:

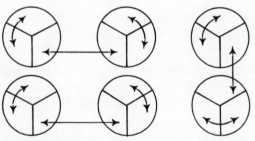

How many groups of 2/3's in 6? (9.)

Ask the children to add and subtract as solutions to this problem.

Common denominator: What denominator can be chosen for this example? Would it make a difference if some other denominator were selected?

    6 ÷ 2/3 → 18/3 ÷ 2/3

Rewrite for clairty

$$\frac{18 \div 2}{3 \div 3} = \frac{9}{1} = 9$$

What pattern is repeating in the denominator?
Would it be possible to solve an example using only the numerators?

If the children have not observed a pattern, challenge them to structure examples to solve until they do see a pattern.

Generalization: Whenever the common denominator method is used, the denominator is reduced to 1 and the quotient is found by dividing the numerators.

Inverting the divisor

$$6 \div 2/3 = 6 \times 3/2$$

Why is the divisor inverted?

Compare the divisor 2/3 to any unit of length.

How many 2/3 in one unit?

What part of 2/3 is the remainder 1/3?

Think 1/3 over 2/3

Reduce the fraction dividing by 1/3

$$\frac{\frac{1}{3}}{\frac{2}{3}} = \frac{\frac{1}{3} \div \frac{1}{3}}{\frac{2}{3} \div \frac{1}{3}} = \frac{1}{2}$$

How many 1/3 in 1/3? How many 1/3 in 2/3?

There are 1 and 1/2 groups of 2/3 in 1 unit. What is the improper fraction for 1 1/2?

Then $6 \times 1\ 1/2$ or $6 \times 3/2 = 18/2 = 9$.

What does the inverted number tell us? Can you generalize? The inverted number always states how many groups the size of the divisor there are in one unit. To find how many in all, multiply by the dividend.

Reciprocal method: The children soon discover that fractions have an important property which the set of whole numbers does not have. This is the reciprocal property. It states that for every fraction number a there is another fraction number b such that $a \times b = 1$.

$$6 \div 2/3$$

$$\frac{6 \times 3/2}{2/3 \times 3/2} = \frac{18/2}{1} = 9$$

What do we do with the divisor to get a product of 1? For pupils to understand division of fractions, they must understand division of whole numbers. Is the principle of multiplying the dividend and the divisor in the set of whole numbers similar to what is done using the reciprocal? In the use of the reciprocal, is the solution reduced to multiplying the numerator? (Yes.)

2. A fraction divided by a whole number:

Problem: One half of a watermelon is to be divided among 4 boys. What part of the watermelon will each boy receive?

Before attempting to solve this problem, review with the children partition division of whole numbers. Then direct them to solve the problem using a ruler and by drawing pictures before solving the problem using the common denominator approach, inverting the divisor and the reciprocal method.

Ruler

Divide 1/2 into 4 equal parts. What is one of the 4 parts called. Why must the total unit be considered in naming the 1 part? What part of the watermelon does each boy get?

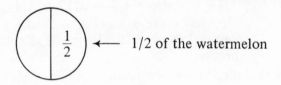

Drawing:

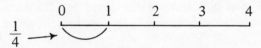

$\longleftarrow$ 1/2 of the watermelon

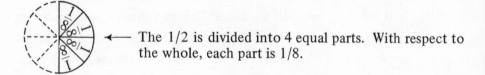

$\longleftarrow$ The 1/2 is divided into 4 equal parts. With respect to the whole, each part is 1/8.

Can addition be a solution to this example? Subtraction? What is the language of partition division?

Inverting the divisor

$1/2 \div 4 = 1/2 \times 1/4$

Why is the divisor inverted? Compare the divisor 4 to a unit of length.

The space between 0 and 1 is what part of the 4 parts? It is 1 of the 4 parts of the divisor or 1/4. What does the inverted number mean? The inverted number always tells how many groups the size of the divisor there are in 1 unit. To find what 1 part is called, we multiply by the dividend. $1/2 \div 4 = 1/2 \times 1/4 = 1/8$. The one part is 1/8. Because we operate on numbers and not on labels, we can repeat the first generalization here: the inverted number always states how many groups the size of the divisor there are in one unit. To find how many in all, multiply by the dividend.

Example:

3/4 ÷ 3 = ☐

What does the example state? In 3/4 ÷ 3, the 3/4 is to be divided into 3 equal parts. To determine what 1 part is called, the total unit is considered.

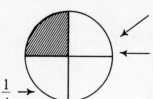

3/4 the dividend

By observation the dividend is already divided into 3 equal parts. What is 1 part called when the whole is considered?

$\frac{1}{4}$ →

Can each part be divided into 3 equal parts? Into how many parts is the total divided?

each part is 1/12

3/12 = 1/4

3/4 ÷ 3 = 3/4 × 1/3 = 3/12 = 1/4

Can you make a drawing to illustrate why the 3 becomes 1/3 when it is inverted? Explain the thought process.

When we divide, we find the answer to a question. In fractions we ask the same questions we asked in division of whole numbers.

18 ÷ 2 =   asks, "How many 2's are in 18? What number times 2 is 18?"

20 ÷ 5 =   asks, "If we divide 20 into 5 groups, how many are in each group?"

6 ÷ 2/3 =   asks, "How many 2/3's are in 6? What number times 2/3 is 6?"

3/4 ÷ 3 =   asks, "If we divide 3/4 into 3 parts, what is one part called?"

Division by the common denominator method becomes a division of whole numbers in the numerator since the denominator becomes 1. Changing to a common denominator should be well known to children because of their experience with addition and subtraction of fractions. Therefore, children seem to accept it as a reasonable method. In fact, when pictures are drawn as a solution, the dividend and the divisor are changed to fractions with common denominators. Continue to solve each type of fraction using the common denominator approach.

Compensation in division of whole numbers is a prerequisite to understanding the use of the reciprocal. A review of the principles of multiplication and division of whole numbers will give direction to the steps for thinking through the sequence. To children who can move ahead, the approach can be looked upon as enrichment.

3. A fraction divided by a fraction:

Example:

1/2 ÷ 1/4 = ☐

What does the example state? How many 1/4's in 1/2?

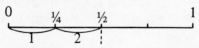

How many 1/4's in 1 whole?

Then 1/2 ÷ 1/4 = 1/2 × 4/1 = 4/2 = 2

Example:

$3/4 \div 1/2 = \square$

What does the problem state? How many 1/2's in 3/4?

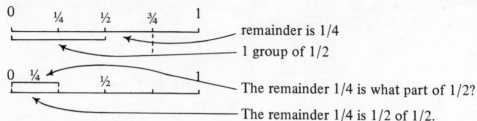

remainder is 1/4

1 group of 1/2

The remainder 1/4 is what part of 1/2?

The remainder 1/4 is 1/2 of 1/2.

There are 1 1/2 groups of 1/2 in 3/4.

$3/4 \div 1/2 = 3/4 \times 2/1 = 6/4 = 1\ 2/4 = 1\ 1/2$

How many 1/2's in 3/4?

1 group of 1/2

remainder is 1/4

The remainder 1/4 is what part of 1/2?

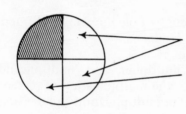
$$\frac{\frac{1}{4}}{\frac{1}{2}} = \frac{1}{2}$$
The remainder 1/4 is 1/2 of 1/2.

Then $3/4 \div 1/2 = 3/4 \times 2/1 = 6/4 = 1\ 1/2$

4. Mixed numbers:

Example:

$4 \div 1\ 1/2 = \square$

How many 1 1/2's in 4?

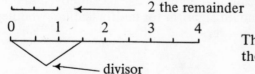

2 parts the remainder

What is the ratio of the remainder to the divisor?

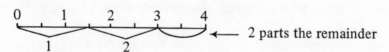

2 the remainder

The reaminder is 2 of the 3 equal parts of the divisor.

divisor

The remainder is 2/3 of the divisor.

There are 2 2/3 groups of 1 1/2 in 4.

Example:

1 1/2 ÷ 4 = □

1 1/2 is to be divided into 4 equal parts.

When 1 1/2 is changed to 3/2 we have a fraction divided by a whole number, type 2. 3/2 ÷ 4 = 3/2 × 1/4 = 3/8

Example:

3 1/3 ÷ 1 3/4 = □

Change the mixed numbers to improper fractions. Type 3.

10/3 ÷ 7/4 = 10/3 × 4/7 = 40/21 = 1 19/21

What does the equation mean? If a/b and c/d are fractions (c/d ≠ 0/1) then a/b ÷ c/d = a/b × d/c.

Important Ideas Begun

1. Relationship of multiplication and division of whole numbers and fractions.
2. The multiplicand indicates the size of the group.
3. The multiplier indicates the number of groups.
4. The term "factor" can replace the terms "multiplier" and "multiplicand."
5. The distributive principle can be applied to the multiplication of mixed numbers.
6. Interpreting the four major fraction forms in multiplication and division of fractions.
7. Division is the process of finding the number in each group or the number of groups.
8. Examples in division may be computed by using the common denominator method, the reciprocal method or the inversion method.
9. The "principle of multiplication and division" as applied to whole numbers is applicable to multiplication and division of fractions.
10. Any number multiplied by its reciprocal is 1.
11. When the dividend is less than the divisor, the quotient is less than one.
12. The importance of drawings to the explanation of the processes.

Summary of Fractions

Children use fractions before they come to school. Throughout the grades, visual materials should be available so that fractions can be represented to them in a meaningful way. Emphasis upon the terms which describe fractions must be a part of their daily lessons in fractions.

The four fundamental operations of fractions are best taught when they are related to the operations of whole numbers. Language will establish the similarities in each process and is the "carry–over" element from operation to operation. Three groups of four and three groups of one–half clearly indicate that addition can be employed in each situation. The child who cannot use the standard algorism for multiplication, whether whole numbers or fractions, can add to find the answer.

Study Questions

1. Use the distributive property in multiplying (4 × 6 2/3.)
2. What understandings are required to change an improper fraction to a mixed number?
3. Illustrate in three different ways how a child might indicate to you the meaning of (2/3 × 3/4).

4. Illustrate and explain the mathematical reason for inverting the divisor when dividing by a fraction.

5. What are the related subtraction examples for the following addition examples?

	a.	3/4		b.	2 3/5
		+ 2/4			+ 1 3/5

6. Construct a problem in division of fractions which uses the measurement concept. Solve the problem in at least three different ways.

7. Check several series of textbooks used by children for their presentation of fractions. What is their approach?

Selected Text References

1. Dwight, Leslie A., *Modern Mathematics for the Elementary Teacher*, New York: Holt, Rinehart and Winston, Inc., 1966. Chapter 12.

2. Grossnickle, Foster E., and Leo J. Brueckner, *Discovering Meanings in Elementary School Mathematics*, New York: Holt, Rinehart and Winston, Inc., 1963. Chapters 10 and 11.

3. Howard, Charles F., and Enoch Dumas, *Basic Procedures in Teaching Arithmetic*, Boston: D. C. Heath and Company, 1963. Chapters 9 and 14.

4. Kramer, Klaas, *The Teaching of Elementary School Mathematics*, Boston: Allyn and Bacon, Inc., 1966. Chapter 14.

5. Marks, John L., C. Richard Purdy, and Lucien R. Kinney, *Teaching Elementary School Mathematics for Understanding*, New York: McGraw-Hill Book Company, 1966. Chapter 9.

6. Mueller, Francis J., *Arithmetic, Its Structure and Concepts*, Englewood Cliffs, N. J.: Prentice-Hall, Inc., 1964. Chapters 17-20 and 23.

7. Spencer, Peter Lincoln and Marguerite Brydegaard, *Building Mathematical Competence in the Elementary School*, New York: Holt, Rinehart and Winston, Inc., 1966. Chapter 9.

Selected Readings from the Arithmetic Teacher

1. Aranti, Frank C., "The Use of '1' in Building Concepts," *8:* 299-300, October, 1961.

2. Gunderson, Ethel, "Fractions—Seven-Year Olds Use Them," *5:* 233-238, November, 1958.

3. Johnson, Harry C., "Division With Fractions—Levels of Meanings," *12:* 362-368, May, 1965.

4. Lutz, Marie, "Multiplication Memos for Dr. Mower," *9:* 317-320, October, 1962.

5. McMeen, George N., "Division by a Fraction—A New Method," *9:* 122-126, March, 1962.

6. O'Brien, Thomas C., "Two Approaches to the Algorism for Multiplication of Fractional Numbers," *12:* 552-555, November, 1965.

7. Sanders, Walter, J., "The Use of Models in Mathematics Instruction," *11:* 157-165, March, 1964.

Chapter IX

Decimal Fractions and Percent

Fractions were man's attempt to extend the number system to meet the needs of an expanding society. When compared with the set of whole numbers, these numbers involved a new set of rules to carry on the four fundamental operations. It was this "new set of rules" which probably, through the centuries, challenged man to explore the set of whole numbers for another technique in dealing with "broken" numbers.

The set of whole numbers has two characteristics which makes it unique, place value and the base of 10. In the number 666, each 6 from right to left is 10 times greater than the preceding 6. It was these concepts that early mathematicians explored and developed, and eventually provided us with the set of numbers called decimal fractions.

Decimal fractions permit us to operate on "broken" numbers using the same rules and algorisms as used in the set of whole numbers. One addition was necessary to indicate to the user that the number was extended. This was the decimal point.

The units place is the center of our decimal system. To the left of the units is the tens place, to the right of the units place is the tenths place, etc. Each place to the left is a power of ten: tens, hundreds, etc., to the right one-tenth, one–hundredth, etc. In writing three hundred twenty–one and twenty–three hundredths, (321.23), the decimal point indicates the extension of the number to the right. In writing a number, the decimal point is thought of as occupying the units place.

PLACE VALUE CHART

Hundreds	Tens	Units	Tenths	Hundredths
3	2	1	2	3
		Symmetry		

$$321.23 = (3 \times 10 \times 10) + (2 \times 10) + (3 \times 1/100)$$

Many variations in form have been used to indicate extension of our number system. Some of the earlier notations were quite awkward to record. Several of the forms are:

23.67 as:

$$23\overline{)67}$$

23'6"7"

$23_16_27_3$

23_{67}

23 67   (used in England)

23,67   (used in Europe)

Kinds of Decimal Fractions

Decimal fraction: The value is less than 1: 0.10, 0.25 and 0.75

Mixed decimal fraction: A combination of a whole number and a decimal fraction: 1.2, 4.75.

Generalizations and Properties

1. The number to the right of the decimal point is the numerator.

$$0.27 = \frac{27}{100}$$

2. The number of places to the right of the decimal point indicates the denominator. The last place position names the fraction.

$$0.27 = \frac{27}{100} \qquad \text{(7 is in the hundredths place)}$$

3. To change a common fraction to a decimal fraction, multiply both the numerator and the denominator by a number to produce 10 or a power of 10.

$$2/5 = \frac{2 \times 2}{2 \times 5} = \frac{4}{10} = 0.4$$

$$3/4 = \frac{3 \times 25}{4 \times 25} = \frac{75}{100} = 0.75$$

4. To change a decimal fraction to a common fraction, divide both the numerator and the denominator of the fraction by the same nonzero number.

$$0.4 = \frac{4}{10}, \ \frac{4 \div 2}{10 \div 2} = \frac{2}{5}$$

$$0.60 = \frac{60}{100}, \ \frac{60 \div 10}{100 \div 10} = \frac{6}{10}, \ \frac{6 \div 2}{10 \div 2} = \frac{3}{5}$$

5. Commutative law:

$$0.3 + 0.8 = 0.8 + 0.3$$
$$2.65 + 3.23 = 3.23 + 2.65$$
$$3.4 \times 5.3 = 5.3 \times 3.4$$

6. Associative law:

$$(0.7 + 0.6) + 0.8 = 0.7 + (0.6 + 0.8)$$
$$(2.34 + 1.75) + 1.52 = 2.34 + (1.75 + 1.52)$$
$$2.3 \times (3.9 \times 5.6) = (2.3 \times 3.9) \times 5.6$$

7. Distributive law:

$$0.4 \times 2.4 = 0.4 \times (2 + 0.4) = (0.4 \times 2) + (0.4 \times 0.4)$$
$$= \quad 0.8 \quad + \quad 0.16 \quad = 0.96$$
$$38 \times 3.6 = (30 \times 3.6) + (8 \times 3.6) = 108 + 28.8 = 136.8$$
$$6.8 \div 2 = (6 + 0.8) \div 2 = (6 \div 2) + (0.8 \div 2)$$
$$= \quad 3 \quad + \quad 0.4 \quad = 3.4$$

8. Algorisms:

$$\begin{array}{r} 5.4 \\ \times\ 3.7 \\ \hline .28 \\ 3.50 \\ 1.20 \\ 15.00 \\ \hline 19.98 \end{array}$$

Decimal point may be placed in the partial product by thinking place value as you multiply.

9. Inequalities:

a. $0.5 > 0.3,$ $1.57 > 0.376$

b. $1.7 < 2.4,$ $3.09 < 3.21$

c. $0.3 + 0.4 \neq 0.5 + 0.3,$ $2.5 - 0.6 \neq 3.15 - 1.12$

$>$ is greater than
$<$ is less than
$\neq$ is not equal to

Presentation of Decimal Fractions

One cannot assume that children have a basic background in decimal fractions because they have handled money or added and subtracted numbers involving money. In most situations, the concept of place value has not been involved.

Decimal fractions are usually introduced through the children's knowledge of fractions and their use of money.

One unit has been divided into 100 equal parts:

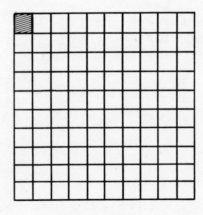

What is 1 small square of the total? As a fraction, 1/100. It is read as 1 over 100 or as one one–hundredth. Which place to the right of units is called "hundredths?" Write the fraction 1/100 as a decimal fraction. (0.01, read as one-hundredth.)

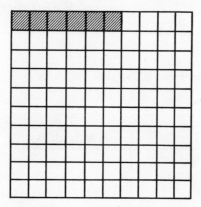

What part of 100 is shaded? As a fraction, 6/100. As a decimal fraction, 0.06.

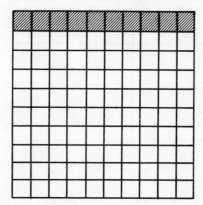

How many of the squares are shaded? What part of the 100 squares is shaded? As a fraction, 10/100. As a decimal fraction 0.10 (ten hundredths).

Review with children place value and how regrouping in the set of whole numbers is accomplished before using a decimal place value chart. The purpose of this exercise is to guide children to discover that regrouping in decimal fractions is the same as in whole numbers and that decimal fractions may have several names. For example, .14 may be read .1 + .04.

Whole numbers

Tens	Units	
	/ / / / / /	
	/ / / /	One can think 10 units
	10	

Tens	Units
1	0

To write the number, a collection is made of the 10 sticks into 1 group of ten and no ones (10).

Decimal fractions

Units	Tenths	Hundredths
		/ / / / /
		/ / / /
		10

One can think 10 hun-hundredths

Units	Tenths	Hundredths
	1	0

Can 10 hundredths be re-grouped to 1 tenth?

10 hundredths = one tenth and no hundredths

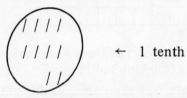

← 1 tenth

Units	Tenths	Hundredths
		/ / / / /
		/ / / /
		/ / / /
		/ / / /
		18

0.18 hundredths

Units	Tenths	Hundredths
	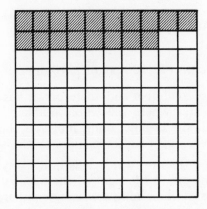	/ / / / / / / /
	1	8

Regroup:

18 hundredths regrouped to 1 tenth and 8 hundredths. (0.1 + 0.08 = 0.18)

Read as 1 tenth and 8 hundredths or as 18 hundredths

(Recall that in whole numbers, 18 may be read as 18 ones or as 1 ten and 8 ones)

Give the children an opportunity to discuss this material. Help them to see that regrouping and renaming in decimal fractions is not different from regrouping and renaming in whole numbers. Have the children recognized a change in the spelling of each place value? What is the change?

How many parts are shaded? As a fraction, 18/100. As a decimal fraction, 0.08. How many tenths and hundredths in 18 hundredths? 0.18 = 0.1 + 0.08. (Add 0.01 10 times.)

Ask the children to complete exercises similar to this. Help them to observe how decimal fractions are read. How does one identify the total number of parts in the group and the number of parts being considered?

0.1		0.10
0.1		0.10
0.1		0.10
0.1		0.10
0.1		0.10
0.1		0.10
0.04		0.04
0.64		0.64

How many parts are shaded? (0.64.) How many tenths? (0.6.) How many hundredths? (0.04.) Each row is 10 hundredths or 1 tenth.

0.1		0.10
0.1		0.10
0.1		0.10
0.1		0.10
0.1		0.10
0.1		0.10
0.1		0.10
0.1		0.10
0.1		0.10
0.1		0.10
1.00		1.00

How many hundredths? (100.) 100/100 = 1.00. (1 whole.) How many tenths? (10.) 10/10 = 1.0. (1 whole.)

Explore the dollar in terms of: 100 pennies, 10 dimes.

The decimal point is not a number and, therefore, it has no number value. It is, however, a symbol which indicates where the whole number ends and where the decimal fraction begins. In 3.6 feet, the decimal point indicates the whole number to be 3 and the decimal fraction to be 0.6. It is read three and 6 tenths. Expanded, it is 3 + 0.6.

The part of the decimal fraction which tells how many parts of the whole are being considered is the set of numbers to the right of the decimal point. In 0.25, the 25 specifically states that 25 parts of something are being compared in some way. In common fractions, the numerator expressed this idea. To complete the comparison, the number of places to the right of the decimal point provides us with the total number of parts in the group and corresponds to the denominator in common fractions. The first digit indicates that the object has been divided into tenths; the second digit indicates that the object has been divided into hundredths. In the example 0.25, the decimal fraction is read as 25 hundredths, or 25 of 100 parts are being considered. The denominator in a decimal fraction is always 10 or a power of 10.

Example: 0.6   = 6 of 10 parts. As a fraction, 6/10.

0.32 = 32 of 100 parts. As a fraction, 32/100.

0.257 = 257 of 1000 parts. As a fraction, 257/1000.

FRACTION–DECIMAL FRACTION EQUIVALENCE CHART

1				(whole)			
0.5 (1/2)				0.5 (1/2)			
0.25 (1/4)		0.25		0.25		0.25	
0.125(1/8)	0.125	0.125	0.125	0.125	0.125	0.125	0.125

NUMBER LINE FRACTION–DECIMAL FRACTION EQUIVALENCE

					1/2					4/4
	1/5				2/4	3/5		4/5		5/5
0	1/10	2/10	3/10	4/10	5/10	6/10	7/10	8/10	9/10	10/10
	0.1	0.2	0.3	0.4	0.5	0.6	0.7	0.8	0.9	1.0

How many 0.5 in 1 whole? 0.5 + 0.5 = 1.0. Use the place value charts to establish these facts.

Units	Tenths	
	/ / / / /	0.5
	/ / / / /	0.5

Units	Tenths	
(circle)		Tenths are regrouped to 1. Ten tenths = 1
1	0	

How many 0.25 in 0.5? How many 0.125 in 0.25? In 0.5? In 1?

In the study of common fractions, it was necessary to change fractions to higher terms or to lower terms in order to perform addition and subtraction as operations. While this is not necessary in decimal fractions, there is a need to change common fractions to decimal fractions and decimal fractions to common fractions in transition from one number form to another.

Two principles discussed in Chapter VIII "Fractions," are applicable here. They are:

1. Changing a common fraction to a decimal fraction: Multiply the numerator and the denominator by the same nonzero number.

a. 1/2 = how many tenths?

$$1/2 = \frac{n}{10} \qquad \frac{5 \times 1}{5 \times 2} = \frac{5}{10} = 0.5$$

1/2 is equivalent to 0.5.

1/2 = how many hundredths?

$$1/2 = \frac{n}{100} \qquad \frac{50 \times 1}{50 \times 2} = \frac{50}{100} = 0.50$$

1/2 is equivalent to 0.5 or 0.50.

b. 1/4 = how many hundredths?

$$1/4 = \frac{n}{100} \qquad \frac{25 \times 1}{25 \times 4} = \frac{25}{100} = 0.25$$

c. 3/4 = how many hundredths?

$$3/4 = \frac{n}{100} \qquad \frac{25 \times 3}{25 \times 4} = \frac{75}{100} = 0.75$$

d. 2/5 = how many tenths?

$$2/5 = \frac{n}{10} \qquad \frac{2 \times 2}{2 \times 5} = \frac{4}{10} = 0.4$$

2/5 = how many hundredths?

$$2/5 = \frac{n}{100} \qquad \frac{20 \times 2}{20 \times 5} = \frac{40}{100} = 0.40$$

e. 3/8 = how many thousandths?

$$\frac{n}{1000} \qquad \frac{125 \times 3}{125 \times 8} = \frac{375}{1000} = 0.375$$

f. Using prime factors to find the ratio of demonimators:

$$1/4 = \frac{n}{100} \rightarrow \frac{1}{2 \times 2} = \frac{n}{2 \times 2 \times 5 \times 5} \rightarrow \frac{25}{100} = 0.25$$

Cancel primes common to each denominator to establish the ratio.

The ratio of 4 to 100 is 1 to 25. The numerator must maintain the same ratio, therefore, 1 × 25. The equation is 1/4 = 25/100 = 0.25.

$$3/5 = \frac{n}{100}$$

$$3/5 = \frac{n}{10 \times 10}$$

$$3/5 = \frac{n}{2 \times 2 \times 5 \times 5} \qquad \text{The ratio of 5 to 100 = 1 to 20}$$

$$3/5 = \frac{3 \times 20}{100} = \frac{60}{100} = 0.60$$

2. Changing a decimal fraction to a common fraction: Divide the numerator and the denominator by the same nonzero number.

a. Change 0.5 to a common fraction:

$$0.5 = 5/10 \qquad \frac{5 \div 5}{10 \div 5} = 1/2. \text{ Then } 0.5 = 1/2$$

$$0.50 = 50/100 \qquad \frac{50 \div 10}{100 \div 10} = 5/10, \frac{5 \div 5}{10 \div 5} = 1/2 . \text{ Then } 0.50 = 1/2$$

b. 0.75 to a common fraction:

$$0.75 = 75/100 \qquad \frac{75 \div 5}{100 \div 5} = \frac{15}{20}, \frac{15 \div 5}{20 \div 5} = \frac{3}{4} . \text{ Then } 0.75 = 3/4$$

c. 0.80 to a common fraction:

$$0.80 = 80/100 \qquad \frac{80 \div 5}{100 \div 5} = \frac{16}{20}, \qquad \frac{16 \div 4}{20 \div 4} = \frac{4}{5} \qquad \text{Then } 0.80 = 4/5$$

Practice Activities

Ask the children to find the equivalents for the following using the above approach;

Fraction	Decimal Fraction
1/4	?
?	0.40
5/8	?
1/3	?
?	0.875

Interpret the following graphs: Is the fraction easier to interpret than the decimal? If so, what explanation can you give for your choice?

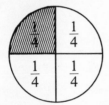
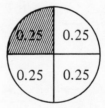

Identify with the children that the principles used here were first identified in division of whole numbers, later in fractions and now in decimal fractions. This will develop stronger relationships and give strength to the concept that each set of numbers studied conform to a set of principles.

Addition and Subtraction of Decimal Fractions

The meanings and thought processes related to adding and subtracting whole numbers and fractions apply to these operations for decimal fractions.

Addition of decimal fractions:

Ask the children to solve several problems, similar to the types below in any way they can or in as many ways as they can recalling previous experiences.

Problem: John walked 0.2 of a mile to his friend's home. Later he walked 0.3 of a mile to his father's place of business. How far did John walk?

1.

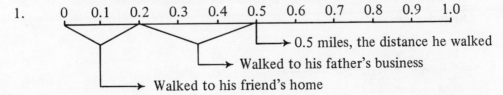

2. The circle is divided into tenths:

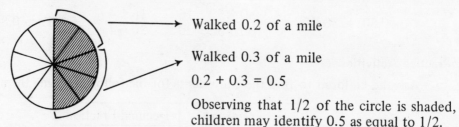

Walked 0.2 of a mile

Walked 0.3 of a mile

0.2 + 0.3 = 0.5

Observing that 1/2 of the circle is shaded, children may identify 0.5 as equal to 1/2.

3. Place value chart:

Ones	Tenths
	/ /
	/ / /
	5 → 0.5

4.   2 tenths   0.2
   + 3 tenths ⟶   + 0.3
     5 tenths   0.5

5.   2/10   0.2
   + 3/10   ⟶   + 0.3
     5/10 = 0.5   0.5

6.   0.2 miles
   + 0.3 miles
     0.5 miles   Total distance John walked

Discuss the solutions using the following questions as guides:

1. What are the facts of the problem?
2. Do the illustrations show the facts of the problem?
3. Do the solutions show how one arrived at the answer?
4. Which solution seems best? Why?
5. What concepts did you discover? Were they new?

Problem: The weather bureau listed the following amounts of rain for a 2-day period: 1.54 inches on Tuesday, and 1.67 inches of rain on Wednesday. What was the total amount of rain during the 2 days?

1. The use of a number line having divisions of one-hundredths.

2. Expanded notation:

   1 + 0.5 + 0.04   2.00
 + 1 + 0.6 + 0.07   ⟶   1.10   Partial sums
   2 + 1.1 + 0.11   0.11
                                     3.21   Inches of rain

3. Partial sums:

$$
\begin{array}{ll}
1.54 & \text{Inches of rain} \\
+\ 1.67 & \text{Inches of rain} \\
\hline
0.11 & \\
1.10 & \\
2.00 & \\
\hline
3.21 & \text{Total inches of rain}
\end{array}
$$

4. Fractions:

$$
\begin{array}{l}
1\ \ 54/100 \\
+\ 1\ \ 67/100 \\
\hline
2\ 121/100\ =\ 3\ 21/100\ =\ 3.21
\end{array}
$$

5. Regrouping

$$
\begin{array}{l}
\overset{1}{}\overset{1}{}1.54 \\
+\ 1.67 \\
\hline
3.21
\end{array}
$$

4 hundredths + 7 hundredths = 11 hundredths. 11 hundredths = 1 tenth and 7 hundredths. Carry the one tenth to the tenths column. 12 tenths = 1 and 2 tenths (1.2). 2 + 1 = 3.

Examples for study:

1.
$$
\begin{array}{l}
0.68 \\
+\ 0.57 \\
\hline
\end{array}
\qquad
\begin{array}{l}
6/10\ +\ 8/100 \\
5/10\ +\ 7/100 \\
\hline
11/10\ +\ 15/100\ =\ 1\ 2/10\ +\ 5/100\ =\ 1.25
\end{array}
$$

2.
$$
\begin{array}{l}
2.74 \\
+\ 1.49 \\
\hline
4.23
\end{array}
\longrightarrow
\begin{array}{l}
2\ +\ 0.7\ +\ 0.4 \\
+\ 1\ +\ 0.4\ +\ 0.9 \\
\hline
3\ +\ 1.1\ +\ 0.13\ =\ 4.23
\end{array}
\longrightarrow
\begin{array}{l}
0.13 \\
1.1 \\
3.0 \\
\hline
4.23
\end{array}
$$

3.
$$
\begin{array}{l}
3.24\ +\ 2.38\ = \\
(3\ +\ 0.24)\ +\ (2\ +\ 0.38)\ = \\
(3\ +\ 2)\ +\ (0.24\ +\ 0.38)\ = \\
5\ \ +\ \ \ \ \ \ \ 0.62\ \ =\ 5.62
\end{array}
\longrightarrow
\begin{array}{l}
3.24 \\
+\ 2.38 \\
\hline
5.62
\end{array}
$$

4.
$$
\begin{array}{l}
12.35 \\
+\ \ 8.21 \\
\hline
\end{array}
$$

$$
\begin{array}{l}
(12\ +\ 3/10\ +\ 5/100)\ +\ (8\ +\ 2/10\ +\ 1/100)\ = \\
(12\ +\ 8)\ +\ (3/10\ +\ 2/10)\ +\ (5/100\ +\ 1/100)\ = \\
20\ \ +\ \ \ \ \ 5/10\ \ +\ \ \ \ \ \ 6/100\ \ \ \ \ \ \ \ = \\
20\ \ +\ \ \ \ \ 0.5\ \ \ \ +\ \ \ \ \ \ \ 0.06\ \ \ \ \ \ \ =\ 20.56
\end{array}
$$

Column addition: Similar patterns and thought processes as used for whole numbers are applicable to column addition.

Ones	Tenths	
	3	0.3
	1	0.1
	5	→ + 0.5
	9	0.9

Review with children:
Hidden numbers
Addition by endings
Various crutches

Ones	Tenths
^{1}1	6
4	7
3	5
9	8

$$\longrightarrow \quad \begin{array}{r} 1.6 \\ 4.7 \\ + 3.5 \\ \hline 1.8 \\ 8.0 \\ \hline 9.8 \end{array} \quad \longrightarrow \quad \begin{array}{r} 1.6 \\ 4.7 \\ + 3.5 \\ \hline 9.8 \end{array}$$

Tens	Ones	Tenths	Hundredths
^{1}2	^{1}3	^{2}3	7
4	6	0	9
1	2	7	4
8	2	2	0

$$\longrightarrow \quad \begin{array}{r} ^{1\ 1\ 2} \\ 23.37 \\ 46.09 \\ + 12.74 \\ \hline 82.20 \end{array}$$

$$\begin{array}{r} 3.4 \\ 5.1 \\ + 2.2 \\ \hline 10.7 \end{array}$$

$$3.4 + 5.1 + 2.2 =$$
$$(3 + 0.4) + (5 + 0.1) + (2 + 0.2) =$$
$$(3 + 5 + 2) + (0.4 + 0.1 + 0.2) =$$
$$10 \quad + \quad 0.7 \quad = 10.7$$

Generalizations for addition:

1. Only units of like value can be added.
2. When a place value has 10 or more units, regroup as in whole numbers.
3. The decimal points are placed in a straight line.
4. When adding digits in the hundredths place or any place, we are adding numerators with a common denominator.

Subtraction of decimal fractions

Without regrouping:

$$\begin{array}{r} 0.9 \\ - 0.6 \\ \hline 0.3 \end{array} \quad \rightarrow \quad \begin{array}{r} 9/10 \\ - 6/10 \\ \hline 3/10 \end{array} = 0.3$$

Using fractions to establish placement of the decimal point

$$\begin{array}{r} 0.48 \\ - 0.13 \\ \hline 0.35 \end{array} \quad \rightarrow \quad \begin{array}{r} 48/100 \\ - 13/100 \\ \hline 35/100 \end{array} = 0.35$$

$$\begin{array}{r} 3.59 \\ - 1.27 \\ \hline 2.32 \end{array}$$

Can subtract from the left or from the right

Regrouping:

$$\begin{array}{r} 0.70 \\ - 0.38 \\ \hline \end{array} \quad \rightarrow \quad \begin{array}{r} ^{6\ 1} \\ 0.\cancel{7}0 \\ 0.38 \\ \hline 0.32 \end{array}$$

1 tenth regrouped to 10 hundredths

$$\begin{array}{r} 81.53 \\ -\ 27.86 \end{array} \quad \rightarrow \quad \begin{array}{r} 80 + 1 + 0.5 + 0.03 \\ \underline{20 + 7 + 0.8 + 0.06} \end{array}$$

Regrouping:

Tens	Ones	Tenths	Hundredths
7	10	14	13
– 2	– 7	– 8	– 6
5	3	6	7

56.3 – 23.8 =
(56 + 0.3) – (23 + 0.8) =
(55 + 1.3) – (23 + 0.8) =
(55 – 23) + (1.3 – 0.8) =
32   +   0.5   = 32.5

$$\text{Regrouping} \rightarrow \quad \begin{array}{r} 5\ 13 \\ 56.3 \\ -\ 23.8 \\ \hline 32.5 \end{array}$$

In subtracting a decimal fraction from a whole number, children must be helped to discover that adding zeros to the whole number makes it easier to subtract. As abstract numbers, 6, 6.0 and 6.00 have equivalent values. In money values, $6 is written $6.00.

$$\begin{array}{r} \$6 \\ -\ \ 0.24 \end{array} \quad \rightarrow \quad \begin{array}{r} {}^{5\ 9\ 1} \\ \$6.00 \\ \underline{0.24} \\ \$5.76 \end{array}$$

We may utilize the writing of 10 as 10.0 in solving another type of problem such as: Jim runs the 100 yard dash in 10 seconds. However, to win in a race, he must reduce his time by 0.3 of a second. In what time is he expected to run the race?

$$\begin{array}{l} {}^{9} \\ 10.0 \\ \underline{0.3} \end{array} \quad \begin{array}{l} \text{Jim's time now in seconds} \\ \text{Reduction in time} \end{array}$$
9.7 seconds, Jim's new time in order to win

Generalizations for subtraction:
1. Only units of like value can be subtracted.
2. When a place value in the minuend is less than the place value in the subtrahend, regrouping is necessary.
3. The decimal points are placed in a straight line.
4. When one is subtracting digits in the hundredths place, or any place, one is subtracting numerators.

Multiplication of Decimal Fractions:

The only new generalization to be established with children in multiplying decimal fractions is that regarding the placement of the decimal point. Before instruction in multiplication of decimal fractions is begun, a careful review of multiplication by powers of 10 should be provided in order to re-establish rules discovered earlier. Examples:

$$\begin{array}{cccccccc} 10 & \quad 12 & \quad 100 & \quad 234 & \quad 1000 & \quad 100 & \quad 1000 \\ \times\ 10 & \quad \times\ 10 & \quad \times\ \ 10 & \quad \times\ \ \ 10 & \quad \times\ \ \ \ 10 & \quad \times\ 100 & \quad \times\ \ 100 \end{array}$$

Re–introduction of the language of multiplication is also important at this time in order to guide the children in their discovery of the rule for the placement of the decimal point.

```
    12              12
  X  3              12           3 groups of 12
    36            + 12           12 is added 3 times
                    36
```

```
   10 + 2          3 X 12 = n
  X      3         3 X (10 + 2) =          Renaming 12
                   (3 X 10) + (3 X 2) =    Distributive property
   30 + 6 = 36     30   +   6   = 36
```

To make the teaching of multiplication of decimal fractions more meaningful, four types are presented. Mixed decimal fractions are presented as a type to emphasize their structure and to show their relationship to the first 3 types.

Procedures in teaching developed earlier are continued. It is most important that children continue to be directed to observe what is happening, to think about what they see, to try out their findings and to state what was discovered as a generalization.

1. A whole number times a decimal fraction.

   Problem: Mary lives 0.3 mile from school. She walks this distance 4 times each day. How far does she walk each day?

   Solutions:

   (1) $4 \times 0.3 =$ $4 \times 3/10 =$
        0.3   3/10
        0.3   3/10
        0.3   3/10
        0.3   3/10
        1.2 $12/10 = 1\ 2/10$

      a. How is the sum of the fraction read?
      b. How is the decimal fraction read?
      c. How many places are there to the right of the decimal point in the original example? Does the pattern of the decimal place hold for the product in this example?

   (2) Prove your answer using the decimal fraction number line.

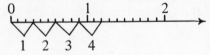

   4 groups of 0.3 is 1.2

   Examples:

      $3 \times 0.23 = 3 \times (0.2 + 0.03) =$ Renaming 0.23
      $(3 \times 0.2) + (3 \times 0.03) =$ Distributive property
      0.6   +   0.09   =   0.69

$$\begin{array}{r} 0.526 \\ \times \quad 4 \\ \hline 2.104 \end{array} \qquad \begin{array}{r} 0.526 \\ 0.526 \\ 0.526 \\ \underline{0.526} \\ 2.104 \end{array}$$

$$4 \times 0.526 = 4 \times (0.5 + 0.02 + 0.006) \quad =$$
$$(4 \times 0.5) + (4 \times 0.02) + (4 \times 0.006) \quad =$$
$$2.0 \quad + \quad 0.08 \quad + \quad 0.024 \quad = 2.104$$

$$\begin{array}{r} 0.26 \\ \times \quad 24 \\ \hline 0.24 \\ 0.8 \\ 1.2 \\ \underline{4.0} \\ 6.24 \end{array}$$
Units × hundredths = hundredths
Units × tenths = tenths
Tens × hundredths = tenths (12 tenths = 1.2)
Tens × tenths = units

2. A decimal fraction times a whole number.

Problem: A man has 4 acres of land. He can sell 0.3 of his land. How many acres does he sell?

Solutions:

(1) Decimal fraction number line

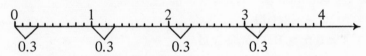

He sells 0.3 acre from each acre.
0.3 × 4 = 1.2 acres

(2) Use of a rectangle

Divide each acre into 10 equal parts. Three of 10 equal parts in each acre is to be sold. The shaded area indicates the land to be sold.

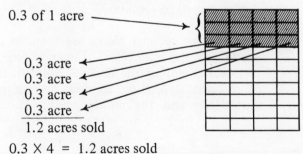

0.3 of 1 acre

0.3 acre
0.3 acre
0.3 acre
0.3 acre
1.2 acres sold

0.3 × 4 = 1.2 acres sold

Examples:

$$\begin{array}{r} 46 \\ \times \, 0.37 \\ \hline 322 \\ \underline{138} \\ 17.02 \end{array}$$

In each of the activities, encourage the children to look for patterns concerning the placement of the decimal point. By observation, there are two decimal places in the multiplier. Therefore, there must be two places in the product.

$$(40 + 6)$$
$$\underline{\times\ (0.3 + 0.07)}$$
$$2.80 + 0.42$$
$$\underline{12.0 + 1.8}$$
$$12.0 + 4.60 + 0.42\ =\ 17.03$$

$0.43 \times 56 = (0.4 + 0.03) \times 56 =$ Renaming 0.43

$= (0.4 \times 56) + (0.03 \times 56) =$ Distributive property

$=\quad 22.4 \quad + \quad 1.68 \quad = 24.08$

76	
$\times\ 0.34$	
0.24	Hundredths $\times$ units = hundredths
2.8	Hundredths $\times$ tens = tenths (28 tenths = 2.8)
1.2	Tenths $\times$ units = tenths (12 tenths = 1.2)
21.0	Tenths $\times$ tens = units
25.24	

3. A decimal fraction times a decimal fraction.

Problem: Mr. Brown owns 0.6 acre of land. He sells 0.4 of it. What part of his land does he sell?

Solutions:

(1)   Use of the common fraction:

$4/10 \times 6/10\ =\ 24/100$

Then $0.4 \times 0.6\ =\ 0.24$ acre sold.

(2)   Explore the use of the rectangle in solving this problem.

(3)   Examples:

0.53	$(0.5 + 0.03)$
$\times\ 0.49$	$\underline{\times\ (0.4 + 0.09)}$
0.0027	$0.045 + 0.0027$
0.045	$\underline{0.20 + 0.012}$
0.012	$0.20 + 0.057 + 0.0027\ =\ 0.2597$
0.20	
0.2597	

How many decimal places are there in the multiplicand and the multiplier? Can you generalize about the placement of the decimal point in the product? By observation, there are four decimal places in the multiplier and the multiplicand. Therefore, there must be four places in the product.

$$0.67$$
$$\underline{\times\ 0.54}$$
$$268$$
$$\underline{335}$$
$$0.3618$$

4. Mixed decimal fractions.

Type 1. A whole number times a mixed decimal fraction.

Problem: A board is 3.4 feet long. If 2 boards this length are laid end to end, what is the total length?

Solutions:

(1)   3.4   3.4
    + 3.4   X   2
    6.8 feet   6.8 feet

(2) $2 \times 3.4 = 2 \times (3 + 0.4) =$ Renaming 3.4

        $(2 \times 3) + (2 \times 0.4) =$ Distributive property

          $6 \quad + \quad 0.8 \quad =$ 6.8 feet

Examples:

    2.75
 X   7
   0.35
   4.9   Partial products
  14.0
  19.25

    $7 \times 3.54 = 7 \times (3 + 0.5 + 0.04) =$

        $(7 \times 3) + (7 \times 0.5) + (7 \times 0.04) =$

          $21 \quad + \quad 3.5 \quad + \quad 0.28 \quad =$ 24.78

Patterns to observe in multiplying mixed decimal fractions:

(1) A whole number times a whole number.
(2) A whole number times a decimal fraction.

Type 2. A mixed decimal fraction times a whole number.

Problem: A recipe calls for 3 cups of flour. The portion is to be increased 2.5
        times. How much flour is needed?

Solutions:

(1)   3
   X 2.5
    1.5   ←   15 tenths = 1.5
     6
   7.5   cups of flour

(2) 2.5×3

   $(2 + 0.5) \times 3 =$ Renaming 2.5

   $(2 \times 3) + (0.5 \times 3) =$ Distributive property

      $6 \quad + \quad 1.5 \quad =$ 7.5 cups of flour

Examples:

    36
 X 2.3
  108
   72
  82.8   Why does one point off 1 place in the product?

$$2.3 \times 36 = (2 + 0.3) \times 36 =$$
$$(2 \times 36) + (0.3 \times 36) =$$
$$72 \quad + \quad 10.8 \quad = 82.8$$

Patterns to observe in the multiplication of a mixed decimal fraction times a whole number:

(1)   A whole number times a whole number.

(2)   A decimal fraction times a whole number.

Type 3. A mixed decimal fraction times a mixed decimal fraction.

Problem: A rectange is 4.6 feet long and 3.7 feet wide. How many square feet are there in the rectangle?

Solutions:

(1)   4.6
       $\times$ 3.7
       ———
        322
        138
       ———
       17.02 sq. ft.   Why does one point off 2 places in the product?

(2)   Use of the common fraction and the distributive property

$$3\ 7/10 \times 4\ 6/10 =$$
$$37/10 \times 46/10 = 1702/100 = 17\ 2/100$$
$$3.7 \times 4.6 =$$
$$(3 + 0.7) \times (4 + 0.6) = \text{ Renaming 4.6 and 3.7}$$
$$(3 \times 4) + (3 \times 0.6) + (0.7 \times 4) + (0.7 \times 0.6) =$$
$$12 \quad + \quad 1.8 \quad + \quad 2.8 \quad + \quad 0.42 \quad = 17.02$$

Examples:

         3.24
       $\times$ 27.6
       ———
        1944
        2268
         648
       ———
       89.424

$$42.6 \times 3.78 =$$
$$(42 + 0.6) \times (3 + 0.78) =$$
$$(42 \times 3) + (42 \times 0.78) + (0.6 \times 3) + (0.6 \times 0.78) =$$
$$126 \quad + \quad 32.76 \quad + \quad 1.8 \quad + \quad 0.468 \quad = 161.028$$

Patterns to observe in multiplying mixed decimal fractions times mixed decimal fractions:

(1)   A whole number times a whole number

(2)   A whole number times a decimal fraction.

(3)   A decimal fraction times a whole number

(4)   A decimal fraction times a decimal fraction.

The teacher must continually set the stage for thinking. In working with mixed decimal fractions, the pupils are guided through questions to identify patterns similar to those discovered in fractions.

Activities to Broaden the Scope in Multiplying Decimal Fractions

Review the activities presented in the multiplication of whole numbers before involving the children in these exercises. These problem situations will provide opportunities to relate past knowledge to new situations. Activities of this nature are excellent homework for individuals or for group study. Challenge them to generalize about their work when a pattern is developed.

Multiplication by elevens, twelves, etc.

```
    1.2          1.2          3.2
 X  11        X  11        X 1.3
    12          13.2          4.16
    12
   13.2
```

Teens times teens

```
    1.6            .18
 X 1.4          X 1.7
    2.24          .306
```

Multiplying numbers ending in 5

```
    3.5          8.5          .75
 X 3.5        X 6.5        X .45
  12.25        55.25        .3375
```

Complement approach

```
    .98      2
 X .87     13
   .8526
```

Division of Decimal Fractions

There is a simple, easily explained method for placing the decimal point in the quotient. The principle of multiplying the dividend and the divisor by the same nonzero number does not change the quotient.

Ask the children to review this principle. When they indicate a working knowledge of this rule, have them reason what could happen if this concept were applied to division of decimals. What numbers can be used as multipliers? What is the purpose of multiplying the dividend and the multiplier?

Multiplying by 10's, 100's and so on, is not new to the students. They will very rapidly recognize the value of the principle in changing the divisor to a whole number.

To expedite the teaching of division of decimal fractions, four types are presented. Because of earlier experiences with fractions, children will find many relationships to help them gain a quick recognition and understanding of the process.

Recall with children the history in the development of decimal fractions. Why did the people of the past who were interested in mathematics look for another way to extend the number system when fractions were available? What do the decimals permit us to do that fractions did not do?

1. A whole number divided by a decimal fraction.

   Problem: A rope is 4 yards long. How many lengths 0.5 yards long can be cut?

   Solutions. Measurement division:

   (1) Decimal fraction number line

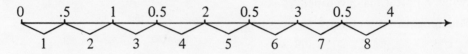

   (2) Addition

0.5	1.0	1.5	2.0	2.5	3.0	3.5
+ 0.5	+ 0.5	+ 0.5	+ 0.5	+ 0.5	+ 0.5	+ 0.5
1.0	1.5	2.0	2.5	3.0	3.5	4.0

   There are 8 groups of 0.5 in 4.

   (3) Subtract to find the number of 0.5 in 4.

   (4) Common fraction

   $4 \div 5/10 =$

   $4 \times 10/5 = 40/5 = 8$

   (5) Division by a decimal fraction.

   $$0.5)\overline{\,4\,} \quad \to \quad 10 \times 0.5)\overline{10 \times 4} \quad \to \quad 5)\overline{40} \;^8$$

   Example: Multiplying the divisor and the dividend by 100.

   $$0.46)\overline{\,12.68\,} \quad \to \quad 46)\overline{1268.} \;^{28.}$$
   $$\underline{92}$$
   $$328$$
   $$\underline{328}$$

2. A decimal fraction divided by a whole number.

   Problem: Nine–tenths pound of candy is divided into 3 equal parts. How much candy is in each part?

   Solutions. Partition division:

   (1) Decimal fraction number line

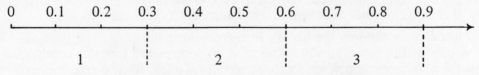

   There is 0.3 pound of candy in each part.

(2) Division by a whole number.

$3\overline{)0.9}$
0.3	0.1	Units × tenths = tenths
0.6		
0.3	0.1	Units × tenths = tenths
0.3		
0.3	0.1	Units × tenths = tenths
	0.3	0.3 pound in each part.

Examples:

$2\overline{)0.24}$
0.2	0.1	Units × tenths = tenths
0.04		
0.04	0.02	Units × hundredths = hundredths
	0.12	

$$\begin{array}{r} 0.36 \\ 24\overline{)8.64} \\ 7\,2 \\ \hline 1\,44 \\ 1\,44 \end{array}$$

Think 24 as units. Then, units × tenths = tenths. 8.6 is also thought of as tenths. Units × hundredths = hundredths

3. A decimal fraction divided by a decimal fraction.

Problem: Jan has a ribbon 0.8 yard long. She is to cut strips 0.2 yard long as markers for books. How many markers can she cut?

Solutions:

(1) Decimal fraction number line

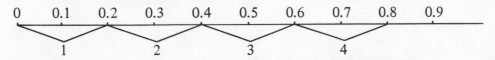

There are 4 groups of 0.2 in 0.8. She can cut 4 markers.

(2) Solve by addition.

(3) Solve by subtraction.

(4) Common fraction.

8/10 ÷ 2/10 =

8/10 × 10/2 = 80/20 = 4

(5) Division: Multiply by 10.

$$0.2\overline{)0.8} \qquad \begin{array}{r} 4 \\ 2\overline{)8} \end{array}$$

4 groups of 0.2 in 0.8.

Example: Multiply by 100.

$$0.23\overline{)\,0.276} \qquad \rightarrow \qquad 23\overline{)27.6}$$

$$\begin{array}{rr} \underline{23} & 1.0 \\ 4.6 & \\ \underline{4.6} & \underline{0.2} \\ & 1.2 \end{array}$$

Think 4.6 as tenths. Then tenths $\times$ units = tenths.

4. Mixed decimal fractions.

Problem: Jack saved $16.20. He told his friend, Tom, that he had saved $1.35 each month. How many months had it taken him to save his money?

Solutions:

(1) Multiplying by 100.

$$1.35\overline{)\,16.20} \qquad \rightarrow \qquad 135\overline{)1620}$$

$$\begin{array}{rr} \underline{1350} & 10 \\ 270 & \\ \underline{270} & \underline{2} \\ & 13 \text{ months} \end{array}$$

(2) Solve by addition and subtraction.

Examples: Annexing zeros.

$$1.76\overline{)\,651.4} \qquad \rightarrow \qquad \begin{array}{r} 370.1 \\ 176\overline{)65140.0} \\ \underline{528} \\ 1234 \\ \underline{1232} \\ 200 \\ \underline{176} \\ 24 \quad \text{Remainder} \end{array}$$

$$21.4\overline{)\,47.789}$$

$$\begin{array}{r} 2.233 \\ 214\overline{)\,477.890} \\ \underline{428} \\ 48\;8 \\ \underline{42\;8} \\ 7\;09 \\ \underline{6\;42} \\ 670 \\ \underline{642} \\ 28 \quad \text{Remainder} \end{array}$$

Summary for Decimal Fractions

1. A common fraction and a decimal fraction are different names for a given number.
2. The decimal point indicates an extension of a number.
3. One adds tenths and tenths, hundredths and hundredths, etc.

4. The commutative and associative properties apply to addition and multiplication of decimal fractions.
5. The distributive property applies to the multiplication and division of decimal fractions.
6. The principle of multiplication changes a decimal in the divisor to a whole number. This implies multiplying the dividend by the same power of 10.
7. A decimal fraction can be changed to a common fraction by first writing the decimal fraction as a common fraction and then changing the common fraction to its lowest term.

Teaching the Meaning of Percent

There is no new arithmetic in percent. The idea that "percent" means "hundredths" should make it easy to learn. We have seen how reducing a quantity by multiplying leads to a fraction which is either a common fraction or a decimal fraction. If the choice is to express these fractions with denominators of 100, then we have a form which is called percent.

$$3/4 = \frac{3 \times 25}{4 \times 25} = \frac{25}{100} = 0.25 = 25\%$$

Common fractions, decimal fractions and percent are fractions. In a common fraction, the denominators are unlimited; in a decimal fraction, the denominator is 10 or a power of 10; in percent the denominator is 100.

ALTERNATE FORMS

Fractions	Decimal Fractions	Percent
3/4	0.75	75%
2/5	0.4	40%
1/8	0.125	12.5% or 12½%
2 3/4	2.75	275%

Percent is always used to express a relationship. When one quantity is divided by another, the result may be written as a fraction, a decimal or a percent.

Because percent means hundredths, it is easily illustrated using drawings similar to those introducing decimals. The symbol, %, is a way to indicate percent.

A SQUARE DIVIDED INTO 100 PARTS

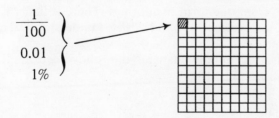

1. What part of the large square is shaded;
2. What is the relationship between percent, decimal fraction and fractions?
3. What happens to the decimal point in changing from a decimal fraction to a percent?

10/100 = 0.10

Also, 10%

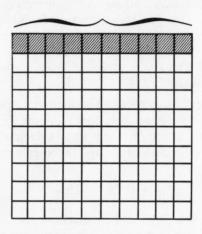

1. How many hundredths are shaded? (10/100 = 0.10.)
2. What percent is shaded? (10%.)
3. What happens to the decimal point in changing from a decimal to a percent? (Multiply 0.10 by 100.)

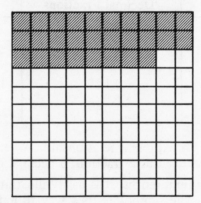

1. How many hundredths are shaded? Write this as a fraction and as a decimal fraction.
2. What percent of the square is shaded?
3. Generalize about the change from one form to another. There actually is no need to think in terms of a rule if the concept of hundredths is understood. Thirty–five hundredths is 35%.
4. Ask children to analyze their procedure in changing the following examples.

$$1/100 = 0.01 = 1\%$$
$$7/100 = 0.07 = 7\%$$
$$25/100 = 0.25 = 25\%$$
$$85/100 = 0.85 = 85\%$$
$$124/100 = 1.24 = 124\%$$

Changing Percent to Fractions and Decimal Fractions

It should not be difficult for children to change percent to other forms because of their knowledge of changing decimal fractions to fractions. Guide the children to identify the pattern in the change from percent as merely dropping the symbol %, and dividing by 100. After developing some skill with this approach, students may complete the change by moving the decimal point.

Examples:

25% = 25/100 = .25
65% = 65/100 = .65
81 1/3% = 81 1/3 ÷ 100 = .81 1/3
1% = 1/100 = .01
½% = ½/100 = 0.005
½% = 0.5% = .005

An activity similar to the one above helps students to discover that fractions, decimal fractions and percents are different ways representing the same number.

Changing a Decimal Fraction to a Percent

In changing a decimal fraction to a percent one should adopt a procedure which will put a common fraction into a decimal fraction before writing a percent to strengthen the concept of hundredths.

Examples:

2/5 = 40/100 = 0.40
Then, 100 × 0.40 = 40%

3/8 = 375/1000 = 0.375
Then, 100 × 0.375 = 37.5% or 37½%

1/100 = 0.01
Then, 100 × 0.01 = 1%

1¼ = 5/4 = 125/100 = 1.25
Then, 100 × 1.25 = 125%

2/1 = 200/100 = 2.00
Then, 100 × 2.00 = 200%

Applications:

In any problem situation involving percent, there are three basic numbers. They are the base, the rate (percent) and the percentage. Each problem to be solved will state two of these conditions and requires that the third be found.

Examples:
a. percent (rate) × base = percentage
   base equals the total of something
   percentage is a part of something

b. □ × base = percentage
   Then, percentage ÷ base = percent
   some percent times the base equals percentage

c. percent $\times$ □ = percentage

Then, percentage $\div$ percent = base

percent times some base equals percentage

Finding the percentage of a number:

Problem: Jack earned $20 mowing lawns one week. He spent 25% of his earnings for repairs and gasoline. How much money did he spend?

Solutions:

1. Change the percent to a decimal and multiply.

$$\begin{array}{r} \$20 \\ \times\ .25 \\ \hline 100 \\ 40 \\ \hline \$5.00 \end{array}$$

$\$20 \quad \leftarrow$ Base: the total or 100% which he has.

$\times\ .25 \quad \leftarrow$ Rate: the ratio of the percentage to the base. The rate is always a percent.

$\$5.00 \quad \leftarrow$ Percentage: the quantity obtained when multiplying rate times base. A percentage is never indicated by a percent symbol.

2. The Proportion Approach

A common approach to the solution of problems with percent is by using proportion. A ratio is a comparison of two or more numbers; two ratios that represent an equality is called a proportion.

Terms of the equation:

N = Percentage, the money he spent

$\$20$ = Base, the total amount of money earned

25% = Rate, the number of parts to be considered

100 = The total number of parts

Equation:

$\dfrac{N}{20} = \dfrac{25}{100}$ The ratio in the denominator is 1 : 5. This ratio must be maintained in the numerators.

$\dfrac{5}{20} = \dfrac{25}{100}$ Cross multiply to check your ratios:

$5 \times 100 = 20 \times 25$

Key ideas:

The denominator tells how many in all, how much in all and the total or the 100% of a quantity.

The numerator tells the quantity of the part to be considered.

How much did Jack earn; How much did Jack spend?

Problem: Jack earned $20 mowing the lawn one week. He spent $5 for repairs and gasoline. What percent of his money did he spend?

Solutions:

1. Base and the percentage are given: the rate is to be found. The question asked is, "What part of $20 is $5?"

percent (rate) $\times$ base = percentage

□ $\times$ $20 = $5

Then $5 $\div$ $20 = □

$$\begin{array}{r} 0.25 \\ 20\overline{)5.00} \\ 4\ 0 \\ \hline 1\ 00 \\ 1\ 00 \\ \hline \end{array}$$

Jack spent 25% of his money.

2. The Proportion Approach

Terms of the equation:

$5 = Percentage, the money he spent
$20 = Base, the total amount of money earned
N = The number of parts to be considered (rate)
100 = The total number of parts

Equation:

$\dfrac{5}{20} = \dfrac{N}{100}$ The ratio in the denominators is 1 : 5. This ratio must be maintained in the numerators

$\dfrac{5}{20} = \dfrac{25}{100}$ Cross multiply to prove your answer: (5 × 100) = (20 × 25)

Problem: Jack earned some money mowing the lawn one week. He spent $5 for repairs and gasoline. This was 25% of the total money earned. How much money did he earn mowing the lawn?

Solutions:

1. rate × N = percentage
   25% × N = $5. Then, $5 ÷ .25 = N

$$0.25\overline{)5} \qquad\qquad \begin{array}{r} 20. \\ 25\overline{)500.} \\ 50 \\ \hline 0 \\ 0 \\ \hline \end{array}$$

0.25 × 20 = 5. Jack earned $20 mowing the lawn.

2. The Proportion Approach

Terms of the equation:

$5 = Percentage, the money he spent
N = Base, the total amount of money earned
25% = Rate, the number of parts to be considered
100 = The total number of parts

$\dfrac{5}{N} = \dfrac{25}{100}$ The ratio in the numerators is 1 : 5. This ratio must be maintained in the denominators

$\dfrac{5}{20} = \dfrac{25}{100}$ Cross–multiply to prove your answer: (5 × 100) = (20 × 25)

When students can interpret a problem in percent as a problem in hundredths, and recognize what is given, they can write the equation for its solution regardless of what type it may be. The understanding of how to set up the solution equation is of greater importance than recognizing a percent problem as a particular type. Practice in looking for and recognizing relationships between numbers in a problem are vital to successful problem solving.

There are many situations in which percentage applies, but there are only three applications which have been called the three types of problems. To know that they can have only three major types of problems that involve percent gives the pupils a security and insight that they might not have otherwise. The following outline groups the several applications into the three types of problems.

1. Given: Percent and the base
          Interest on a loan
          Discount
          Commission
          Profit or loss

2. Given: Percentage and base
          Rate of interest
          Rate of commission

3. Given: Percent and percentage
          Amount of a loan
          Value of an investment
          Assessment of property

Summary

1. Fractions, decimals and percent are different names for the same numeral. 3/4   0.75   75%.
2. Percent means hundredths.
3. Percents are useful in making comparisons because they all have the same denominator.
4. Problems in percent may be solved using the proportion approach.

Study Questions

1. What principle defines the changing of a decimal fraction to a common fraction? Illustrate.
2. Give two explanations for the placement of the decimal point in the following examples: 3×2.4, 1.2×0.34.
3. State the principle which defines the method used in making the divisor a whole number. Illustrate.
4. What language related to whole numbers and common fractions may be applied to the multiplication and division of decimal fractions?
5. What is the meaning of "percent"? What is the relationship between fractions, decimal fractions and percent?
6. What is the question asked in each of the three types of percent problems? Construct a problem for each type and set up the necessary equation for each one.

Selected Text References

1. Dwight, Leslie A., *Modern Mathematics for the Elementary Teacher*, New York: Holt, Rinehart and Winston, Inc., 1966. Chapters 13 and 14.
2. Grossnickle, Foster E., and Leo J. Brueckner, *Discovering Meanings in Elementary School Mathematics*, New York: Holt, Rinehart and Winston, Inc., 1963. Chapters 12 and 13.
3. Howard, Charles, F., and Enoch Dumas, *Basic Procedures in Teaching Arithmetic,* Boston: D. C. Heath and Company, 1963. Chapters 10 and 11.
4. Kramer, Klaas, *The Teaching of Elementary Mathematics*, Boston: Allyn and Bacon, Inc., 1966. Chapters 15 and 16.
5. Marks, John L., C. Richard Purdy and Lucien B. Kinney, *Teaching Elementary School Mathematics for Understanding*, New York: McGraw-Hill Book Company, 1966. Chapters 10 and 11.
6. Mueller, Francis J., *Arithmetic, Its Structure and Concepts*, Englewood Cliffs, N. J.: Prentice-Hall, Inc., 1964. Chapters 21-24.
7. Spencer, Peter Lincoln, and Marguerite Brydegaard, *Building Mathematical Competence in the Elementary School*, New York: Holt, Rinehart and Winston, Inc., 1966. Chapter 8.

Selected Readings from the Arithmetic Teacher

1. Hauck, E., "Concrete Materials for Teaching Percentage," *1:* 9-12, December, 1954.
2. Jones, Emily, "Historical Conflict-Decimal Versus Vulgar Fractions," *7:* 184-188, April, 1960.
3. Kessler, Rolla, "The Equation Method of Teaching Percentage," *7:* 90-92, February, 1960.
4. Rappaport, David, "Percentage-Noun or Adjective," *8:* 25-26, January, 1961.
5. Spencer, Peter L., "Do They See the Point," *5:* 271-272, January, 1958.
6. Swart, William L., "Don't Move the Point, Move the Number," *7:* 204-205, April, 1960.

Chapter X

Measurement

Man has always had a need for measurement. The world of the caveman necessitated judgments of distances, the size of objects and some method for comparison. His world of measurement did not demand accuracy and precision, but was one which satisfied the individual or several members of a group. As his needs grew for greater accuracy in measurement, primitive man chose to use those units of measurement which were most readily available to him, namely, the members of his body. If he wished to measure distance, he used his foot or the length of his step, the pace. To measure small objects, he used some part of a finger, the hand or the length of his arm.

In traveling about the world today, it is not unusual to see a woman measuring cloth by placing her elbow on one end of the material and marking the cloth at the end of her middle finger and, from this point, placing the width of two or three fingers to arrive at an approximate 18 inches, one–half yard.

1. Ask the children to find the approximate length of their arms from the elbow to the end of the middle finger.
2. What added measurement must they make to arrive at 18 inches?
3. If the distance from the elbow to the tip of the middle finger on any child is accepted as a standard unit of measure by the children, what reactions are forthcoming as they begin to measure various objects in the room?
4. Do they agree on the measurement of each object?

Some Early Units Used in Measurement

1. Cubit: The distance from the elbow to the tip of the middle finger. Approximately 18 inches.
2. Span: The distance between the tip of the thumb and the tip of the little finger when the hand is spread. Approximately 9 inches or ½ cubit.
3. Palm: The distance across four fingers. Approximately 3 inches or 1/6 of a cubit.
4. Digit: The width of the middle finger. Approximately ¾ inch or 1/24 cubit.
5. Inch: The breadth of the thumb.
6. Foot: Approximately 12 inches. Equivalent to 2/3 cubit, 4 palms or 16 digits.
7. Rod: Eight cubits or approximately 12 feet.

Ask the children to use the above units in measuring objects in the classroom and outside the classroom. What discrepancies do they find?

As each community grew in social structure and as commerce increased between communities, the controversies over the units of measure increased. The units based upon the body were inconsistent because people differed in size. From this confusion man developed the concept of measure which eventually led to a standard unit.

Measurement requires that a unit which tells something about the quantity to be measured be selected. Measurement is finding how many times a given unit is contained in a given quantity. What units might be appropriate for measuring the following quantities? Why? What arguments are advanced by the students?

1. A line segment:

A _____ B

   a. A mile
   b. A yard
   c. An inch
   d. A foot

   Our system of units of length is based upon the inch as the smallest unit. If units smaller than the inch are needed, fractional parts of the inch may be used.

   For larger units of measurement, multiples of the inch are used. As the unit increases, the less likely we are to think about the number of inches the unit in question contains. We can easily understand this because we would not be likely to think about the number of inches there are in a mile.

2. An enclosed figure:

   a. Circles
   b. Rectangles
   c. Triangles
   d. Trapezoids
   e. Squares

   The choice of a unit to be used is always a part of measurement. Any of the units listed may be used. However, one unit is more adaptable to the measurement of area, and this unit is easily recognized when the measurement is attempted. Ask the children to cut out different shaped units using tagboard or cardboard. Measure the object using these units.

   In the sense of applied measurement, an object can never be measured exactly. The children will discover this quickly when several are permitted to measure a length of rope or the sides of a table. It is most likely that each measurement will be different. Have the children use different units of measure, for example, the foot, the inch, 1/2 inch, 1/4 inch, etc. What do they discover about their measurement now? It is generally stated that the error can be as much as 1/2 of the unit being used. Explore this statement by using the units of measure presented below in finding the length of the segment AB. Do not estimate the smaller portion left over for each unit by using the smaller units on the ruler. Estimate only in terms of the unit used. Construct a ruler which has only one unit represented. For example, 1/8, 1/4 or 1 inch.

A _____ B

Generalization: If the quantity to be measured contains 19 units, the measurement is somewhere between 18½ and 19½ units. The smaller the unit for a given quantity, the more accurate the measurement.

To have zero error, the unit must be zero. Since a unit of zero length cannot be produced, an exact measure can never be produced when using some physical scale. On the other hand, one can divide exactly if it is merely a manipulation of numbers.

Problem: Jack has a rope 13 feet long. He wishes to divide the rope into three pieces. How long will each section of rope be?

$$
\begin{array}{r}
4 \\
3)\overline{13} \\
12 \\
\hline
1 \\
\hline
3
\end{array}
$$
          Each piece will be 4 1/3 feet long

The Old English system of measures attempted to standardize measurement throughout the world. For many centuries, it had little competition as a system but, as time passed and its structure was scrutinized, men began to see internal inadequacies. This system does not group to higher terms in a logical pattern and the units are ill defined and unrelated. What relationships exist between 1 inch and 1 gallon? Are they related in a well defined number? Some common units of measure from the Old English system are listed in the tables below.

OLD ENGLISH SYSTEM OF MEASURES

Measures of Length:

12 inches	= 1 foot
3 feet	= 1 yard
16½ feet	= 1 rod
5½ yards	= 1 rod
40 rods	= 1 furlong
8 furlongs	= 1 statute mile
5280 feet	= 1 mile
1760 yards	= 1 mile
320 rods	= 1 mile
3 miles	= 1 league

Square Measure:

144 square inches	= 1 square foot
9 square feet	= 1 square yard
272¼ square feet	= 1 square rod (16½ × 16½)
30¼ square yards	= 1 square rod (5½ × 5½)
43,560 square feet	= 1 acre
160 square rods	= 1 acre
640 acres	= 1 square mile

Cubic Measures:

1728 cubic inches	= 1 cubic foot
27 cubic feet	= 1 cubic yard
231 cubic inches	= 1 standard gallon
1 cubic foot	= approximately 4/5 bushel
40 cubic feet	= 1 ton
128 cubic feet	= 1 cord (wood)

Measures of Time:

60 seconds	= 1 minutes
60 minutes	= 1 hour
24 hours	= 1 day
7 days	= 1 week
365 days	= 1 common year
366 days	= 1 leap year

Liquid Measures:

4 gills	= 1 pint
2 pints	= 1 quart
4 quarts	= 1 gallon
31½ gallons	= 1 barrel
2 barrels	= 1 hogshead

Surveyor's Measures:

7.92 inches	= 1 link
25 links	= 1 rod
4 rods	= 1 chain
10 square chains	= 1 acre
160 square rods	= 1 acre
640 square acres	= 1 square mile

Dry Measures:

2 pints	= 1 quart
8 quarts	= 1 peck
4 pecks	= 1 bushel

Avoirdupois Measures (Weight):

27 11/32 grains	= 1 dram
16 drams	= 1 ounce
16 ounces	= 1 pound
2000 pounds	= 1 short ton
2240 pounds	= 1 long ton

Apotheciaries' Measures (Weight):

20 grains	= 1 scruple
3 scruples	= 1 dram
8 drams	= 1 ounce
12 ounces	= 1 pound

Troy Measure (Weight):

20 grains	= 1 pennyweight
20 pennyweights	= 1 ounce
12 ounces	= 1 pound

Most of the uses of arithmetic in problems relating to length involve three units; the inch, the foot and the yard. Tables similar to the following may be used to show relationships between the units.

	Inch (A)	Foot (B)	Yard (C)
Inch	1	12	36
Foot	1/12	1	3
Yard	1/36	1/3	1

Begin with Column A and work down putting in each number which shows the relationship of the inch to each unit on the left. What part of a foot is 1 inch? What part of a yard is 1 inch? In Column B, work out the relationship of 1 foot to each of the units on the left. If 3 feet equal 1 yard, we know that 1 foot must be 1/3 of a yard.

Reduction is perhaps the most common exercise with lengths. This means simply that a unit is changed to another unit within a system. When we write 3 feet equals 1 yard, we are reducing feet to yards. Examples:

1. 2 feet 3 inches = 2¼ feet
2. 2 feet 3 inches = 27 inches

   2 feet 3 inches = (2 X 12 inches) + 3 inches = 27 inches

Express the following measurements in terms of inches, feet, yards, fractions of units and miles:

1. 9 yards
2. 2 feet, 4 inches
3. 100 feet

4. 1158 yards
5. 2640 feet
6. 9 inches

Dissatisfaction with the Old English system of measures was the incentive for man to look for a related and a well defined system. Just as man had looked for help in the structure of our number system for a way to extend the number system as in the case of decimals, man again looked to the number system for clues which might lead to the establishing of a new system of measurement. The French discovered a grouping scheme for measurement which was similar to place value in the Hindu–Arabic number system. The relationship between units in the metric system is in the powers of 10. Reduction from one unit to another is indicated by the use of prefixes and is accomplished through multiplication or division by 10 or a power of 10. To express a given unit in a smaller unit, multiply; to express a given unit in a larger unit, divide.

PREFIXES FOR THE METRIC SYSTEM

micro – one millionth
milli – one thousandth
centi – one hundredth
deci – one tenth

deca – ten
hecto – one hundred
kilo – one thousand
mega – one million

METRIC LINEAR MEASURE

10 millimeters(mm.)	= 1 centimeter (cm.)
10 centimeters	= 1 decimeter (dm.)
10 decimeters	= 1 meter (m.)
10 meters	= 1 dekameter (dkm.)
10 dekameters	= 1 hectometer (hm.)
10 hectometers	= 1 kilometer (km.)
10 kilometers	= 1 myriameter (M.)

The basic units are meter, gram and liter. The tables for weight and capacity are constructed in the same manner as the linear table, but use the gram as the basic unit for weight and the liter for capacity.

UNIT: GRAM

10 milligrams	=	1 centigram
10 centigrams	=	1 decigram
10 decigrams	=	1 gram
10 grams	=	1 dekagram
10 dekagrams	=	1 hectogram
10 hectograms	=	1 kilogram
10 kilograms	=	1 myriagram

UNIT: LITER

10 milliliters	=	1 centiliter
10 centiliters	=	1 deciliter
10 deciliters	=	1 liter
10 liters	=	1 dekaliter
10 kekaliters	=	1 hectoliter
10 hectoliters	=	1 kiloliters
10 kiloliters	=	1 myrialiter

The metric system is a tremendous improvement over the Old English system because it relates length, weight and volume. For example, 1 cubic centimeter of water which weighs 1 gram under certain standard conditions is translated to be one–thousandth of a liter. Thus 1 liter of water (1000 cubic centimeters) has a weight of 1000 grams or 1 kilogram.

$$1000 \text{ cubic centimeters} = 1000 \text{ grams}$$
$$1000 \text{ grams} = 1 \text{ kilogram}$$

Because England has now adopted the metric system, it becomes apparent that we, too, must put greater emphasis on the metric system. Conversion tables will help children to make comparisons between the two systems. Some of the most frequently used conversion constants are the following:

1 inch	= 2.54 centimeters	1 centimeter	= 0.3997 inch, 2/5 inch
1 foot	= 0.3048 meter	1 meter	= 39.37 inches
1 yard	= 0.9144 meter	1 meter	= 3 ft. 3 3/8 inches
1 mile	= 1.609 kilometers	1 kilometer	= 0.62 mile, 5/8 mile
1 ounce	= 28.35 grams		
1 pound	= 0.4536 kilogram	1 kilogram	= 2.20 pounds
1 quart	= 0.9464 liter	1 liter	= 1.06 quarts
1 gallon	= 3.785 liters		

Presentation of the Metric Scale

1. Have the pupils identify the millimeter, centimeter and the meter. Measure objects in the room and draw line segments of specific lengths.
2. Cut out units of measure such as a millimeter, a centimeter and a decimeter. Compare each unit to the meter. How many millimeters in a centimeter? A decimeter? A meter? How many centimeters in a meter?
3. Help the child to generalize as he changes from one unit to another. What operation is involved when converting smaller units to larger units?
4. Compare the centimeter to the inch. How many centimeters in an inch? In a foot? Continue to measure objects in the room.
5. Compare the yard and the meter. What fractional part of the meter is the yard? It takes about 11 yards to equal 10 meters; therefore, a yard is 10/11 of a meter.
6. Measure objects using the metric scale; then express the measures in inches, feet or yards.
7. Develop the measures of weight and volume in a similar manner to length.

The meter is the primary unit upon which the metric system is based, and is also the unit of length. It is 39.37 inches long, which is very nearly 1 ten-millionth part of the distance on the earth's surface from the equator to the pole, as measured on the meridian through Paris.

The names of the lower denominations in each measure of the metric system are formed by prefixing the Latin numerals—deci (0.1), centi (.01), and milli (0.001)—to the unit of measure; those of the higher denominations, by prefixing Greek numerals—deka (10), hekto (100), kilo (1000)—to the unit used. The name of each denomination immediately shows its relationship to the unit of measure. Thus, a centimeter is 1 one-hundredth of a meter and a hektoliter is 100 liters.

Denominate Numbers

A number which is labeled such as 36 inches or 3 feet or 4 hours is a denominate number. It consists of two parts, the number and the name. The introduction of denominate numbers is not an extension of the set of rational numbers and does not require a new set of operations before they can be used. In decimals, the operations previously learned for whole numbers were applicable with some adaptation. So it is with denominate numbers.

The process of changing measures from one unit to another within a given system, as in the Old English or metric system, is called reduction. In the study of place value in whole numbers, one is continually changing units to tens, tens to hundreds, etc., with the grouping always in terms of 10. In the study of other bases than 10, the grouping was in terms of the base given. Now with denominate numbers, the grouping is in terms of the units being used. To change from a larger unit (the yard) to a smaller unit (the foot), multiplication is employed; to change from smaller units to larger units, division is used. Exercises such as the following help children to see relations between the various units of measure:

1. To change inches to feet, we ___divide___ by _12_.

2. To change bushels to quarts, we _____ by _____.

3. To change yards to feet, we _____ by _____.

4. To change minutes to hours, we _____ by _____.

When children perform the operations, they must deal with various units and sometimes change from one unit to another to acquire like units. Since most measures are stated in simple units, for example, in yards, feet, inches or fractional parts of a unit; the processes of combining are generally similar to the following examples:

1.   3 1/2 yds.
    × 4
    ‾‾‾‾‾‾‾
    12   (4 × 3)
     2   (4 × ½)
    ‾‾‾‾‾‾‾
    14 yds.

2.   3 5/6 feet − 3 10/12
    1 3/4 feet − 1 9/12
    2 2/3 feet − 2 8/12
                8 3/12 = 8 1/4 ft.

3.   4 hr. 25 min.
    × 3
    ‾‾‾‾‾‾‾‾‾‾‾
    12 hr. 75 min.   Regroup by: 60 (60 min. = 1 hr.)
    13 hr. 15 min.

4.   2 gal. 3 qt. 3 pt.
    3 gal.   2 pt.
 +   4 qt. 2 pt.
    ‾‾‾‾‾‾‾‾‾‾‾‾‾‾‾‾‾
    7 gal. 2 qt. 1 pt.

5.

$$\begin{array}{r} \\ 2\text{ ft.})\overline{15\text{ ft. }30\text{ in.}} \end{array} \longrightarrow \begin{array}{r} 8\ 3/4\text{ pieces} \\ 24\text{ in.})\overline{210\text{ in.}} \\ \underline{192} \\ \frac{18}{24} = \frac{3}{4} \end{array}$$

Measurement division

Addition and Subtraction of Denominate Numbers

In presenting denominate numbers to children, it is good to emphasize the similarities of action in the procedures to place value. Notice that the groupings in Example 1 are based on 10. However, in Example 2, the grouping is based on inches to feet. Similar units are added or subtracted.

	Tens	Ones	
1. 3 tens + 9 ones Adding like units	3	9	
+ 2 tens + 6 ones	+ 2	6	
5 tens + 15 ones Regrouping by tens	5	15	
6 tens + 5 ones	6	5	65

	ft.	in.
2. 3 ft. + 8 in. Adding like units	3	8
+ 1 ft. + 6 in.	1	6
4 ft. + 14 in. Regrouping by 12	4	14
5 ft. + 2 in. (12 in. = 1 ft.)	5 ft.	2 in.

3.   1 yd. + 1 ft.

        2 yds. + 2 ft. + 7 in.   Regrouping by: 12 (12 in. = 1 ft.); 3 (3 ft. = 1 yd.)

        3 yds. + 2 ft. + 9 in.

        8 yds. + 0 ft. + 4 in.

4.   6 tens + 5 ones → 5 tens + 15 ones

    − 3 tens + 9 ones   − 3 tens + 9 ones   Regrouping based on changing

      2 tens + 6 ones   2 tens + 6 ones   1 ten to 10 ones

5.   5 ft. 2 in. → 4 ft. 14 in.

    − 3 ft. 8 in.   − 3 ft. 8 in.   Regrouping based on changing

      1 ft. 6 in.   1 ft. 6 in.   1 ft. to 12 in.

6.   4 ft.

     5   1 ft.   16

     6 yds. + 2 ft. + 4 in.   Regrouping by: 12 (1 ft. = 12 in.)

  − 3 yds. + 2 ft. + 9 in.   3 (1 yd. = 3 ft.)

     2 yds. + 2 ft. + 7 in.

Exercise:

1. Apply the commutative and associative laws to addition of denominate numbers.
2. Use the principle of compensation in subtraction.

Multiplication of Denominate Numbers

The product will have the same name as the multiplicand since the multiplicand continues to state the size of each group. The multiplier cannot be a denominate number; it continues to state the number of groups the size of the multiplicand.

1.   2 tens + 3 ones   Multiplicand

          × 4   Multiplier

    8 tens + 12 ones   Regrouping by: 10 (10 ones = 1 ten)

    9 tens + 2 ones

2.   4 hr. + 16 min.
         X 4
    ─────────────────
     16 hr. + 64 min.   Regrouping by: 60 (60 min. = 1 hr.)
     17 hr. + 4 min.

3.   2 gal. + 3 qt. + 1 pt.
                X 3
    ──────────────────────────
     6 gal. + 9 qt. + 3 pt.   Regrouping by: 2 (2 pt. = 1 qt.) 4 (4 qt. = 1 gal.)
     6 gal. + 10 qt. + 1 pt.
     8 gal. + 2 qt. + 1 pt.

4. Exercise: Apply the commutative and distributive laws to multiplication of denominate numbers. Examples:

$$4 \times (4 \text{ hr.} + 16 \text{ min.}) =$$
$$(4 \times 4 \text{ hr.}) + (4 \times 16 \text{ min.}) =$$
$$16 \text{ hr.} + 64 \text{ min.} =$$
$$17 \text{ hr.} + 4 \text{ min.}$$

$$3 \times (2 \text{ gal.} + 3 \text{ qt.} + 1 \text{ pt.}) =$$
$$(3 \times 2 \text{ gal.}) + (3 \times 3 \text{ qt.}) + (3 \times 1 \text{ pt.}) =$$
$$6 \text{ gal.} + 9 \text{ qt.} + 3 \text{ pt.} =$$
$$8 \text{ gal.} + 2 \text{ qt.} + 1 \text{ pt.}$$

Division of Denominate Numbers

Denominate numbers are expressed in both measurement and partition situations. Ask the children to solve the following problems in as many ways as they can.

1. Measurement: How many pieces of rope 18 inches long can be cut from a rope 24 feet long?
    a. The dividend and the divisors are regrouped to like units. 24 feet = 288 inches.)

```
                16 pieces
    18 inches) 288 inches
                18
               ───
               108
               108
               ───
```

    b. The divisor is regrouped to feet.
        (18 inches = 1 1/2 feet.)
        24 ft. ÷ 1 1/2 ft. =
        24 ft. ÷ 3/2 ft. =
        24 ft. X 2/3 ft. = 16 pieces

Can one add or subtract to find the answer?

2. Partition: Find the length of each piece when a rope 8 ft. 6 in. is divided into 3 sections.

```
    a.      2 ft. 10 in.
         3) 8 ft.  6 in.
            6 ft.
            ──────────
            2 ft.  6 in.  = (Regroup 2 feet to inches, 24 in.)
               30 in.       Then, 24 in. + 6 in. = 30 in.
               30 in.       30 in. ÷ 3 = 10 in.
               ──────
```

b. In this type of example, it may be simpler to regroup the dividend to one unit or to a mixed number.

(1) Change 8 ft. 6 in. to inches = 102 in.

$$
\begin{array}{r}
34 \text{ in.} \\
3)\overline{102 \text{ in.}} \\
\underline{9} \\
12 \\
\underline{12}
\end{array}
$$

34 in. can be reduced to (changed to) 2 ft. 10 in.

(2) Regrouped to a mixed number

8 ft. 6 in. = 8 1/2 ft.

The 8 1/2 ÷ 3 =
17/2 ÷ 3 =
17/2 × 1/3 = 17/6 = 1 5/6 ft.
2 5/6 ft. = 2 ft. 10 in.
5/6 ft. = 5 of 6 equal groups of 12 in.

c. A fundamental principle of division is that the dividend may be expanded. In giving the number another name, the process of division is simplified.

$$
3)\overline{8 \text{ ft. } 6 \text{ in.}} \qquad \rightarrow \qquad
\begin{array}{r}
2 \text{ ft. } 10 \text{ in.} \\
3)\overline{6 \text{ ft. } 30 \text{ in.}}
\end{array}
$$

Compare this transformation with the expansion of the dividends in a whole number.

$$
4)\overline{144} \qquad \rightarrow \qquad
\begin{array}{r}
30 + 6 \\
4)\overline{120 + 24}
\end{array}
$$

Are there similarities?

We find occasion to perform the fundamental operation with denominate numbers. This leads to a regrouping within a particular system of measures comparable to the work with place values in our decimal system.

It is unfortunate that children are faced with the learning of so many units in measuring activities. The concept of place value prevails in the number system when the children deal with whole numbers. The same relations should be maintained in the scale from one unit to another. This, then, is a plea for more emphasis on the use of metric measurement. Give the children an opportunity to make and compare metric units.

Learning to use denominate numbers does not present anything new in each process. Grouping depends upon the unit to be regrouped and the operation is essentially the same as with other numbers. Activities such as the following will help children to develop greater insights into denominate numbers and their use.

1. What relationships are present in the following examples:

$$
\begin{array}{r}
2.37 \\
+ 1.94 \\
\hline
4.31
\end{array}
\qquad
\begin{array}{r}
3\ 3/4 \\
+ 2\ 2/4 \\
\hline
6\ 1/4
\end{array}
\qquad
\begin{array}{r}
2 \text{ yds. } 3 \text{ ft. } 7 \text{ in.} \\
+ 1 \text{ yd. } 1 \text{ ft. } 9 \text{ in.} \\
\hline
1 \qquad 4 \\
1 \\
\underline{3 } \\
4 \text{ yds. } 2 \text{ ft. } 4 \text{ in.}
\end{array}
$$

Check units, regrouping and partial sums.

2. What relationships exist in subtraction, multiplication and division of denominate numbers and the same operations with decimals and fractions?

3. Measure the length and width of your room. Is your measurement in even number of feet? Yards? What is the measurement?

4. Find the perimeter of the room? What units of measure were necessary?

Geometry

Geometry is taught in the elementary school on an informal basis. Informal geometry works with length, area, volume and shape of various kinds of figures. Measurement and construction of figures are used to verify questions about these figures. In contrast, formal geometry uses logical arguments to prove questions or statements (theorems) about various figures. Children enjoy the tangible experiences which geometry provides. In the early grades, children manipulate blocks of different shapes and sizes and learn the names of the various shapes. They reproduce the geometric figures in their drawings, be they lines, squares or circles. Some can begin early in the use of the ruler, the compass and other instruments in reproducing models. The concept of a point, a line, a line segment and a ray must be developed slowly through the uses of many aids. Children should be given the opportunity to touch and to see familiar objects which will demonstrate these concepts. They can be helped to observe many geometric designs in their classrooms, designs such as the surface of the walls, corners where the floor and the walls come together and the straight lines. There are many geometric patterns in every room that can be observed.

The basic elements of geometry are points, lines, surfaces and solids. Measurement which involves length, area and volume are metric relationships. The relationships which exist among them other than measurement are known as nonmetric concepts.

Nonmetric Concepts

1. **Point**: A point is a mathematical idea. If we wish to record the number of rooms in a house, we do so with a symbol. This symbol, for example 7, is not the number. When we wish to identify the point where two lines meet, the dot is a convenient symbol to represent this point. Students in discussing points should become aware of the following concepts:

   a. A point has no size, it cannot be seen. Make points of different sizes and ask the children why a fine, sharp point such as (·) is better than this large (●). The dot represents the point for us. It has no length or width.

   b. A point has position. The dot places the point.

   c. A point is an idea, just as "number" is an idea.

2. **Lines**: A line may be considered as a set of infinite points. The symbol for a line is $\xleftarrow{\underset{X \quad Y}{\bullet \quad \bullet}}\rightarrow$. The arrowheads indicate that the line XY extends indefinitely in either direction. The names for any two points on a line with the symbol $\longleftrightarrow$ written above them may be used to name the line. Thus the line $\xleftarrow{\underset{X \quad Y}{\bullet \quad \bullet}}\rightarrow$ may be represented as $\overleftrightarrow{XY}$. (Read "Line XY"). Guide the children to discover properties of lines through many activities.

   a. A line does not have width, only length.

   b. A line is infinite in length, it has no end.

c. Two points on a line can be used to name the line. The symbol  is read "Line AB". We can also write $\overleftrightarrow{AB}$ for "line AB".

d. A line is an infinite set of points. We cannot see a point, and since a line is made up of points we cannot see a line. A line is an idea.

3. **Line segments**: A line segment is a part of a line. It consists of two points and all the points between them.

In the line segment L ▬ M, the points L and M are called the end points of the segment. Another way to write "line segment LM" is LM. The word "segment" means "a part," thus, a part of a line.

The sides of such figures as triangles and squares are line segments. Draw line segments between the labeled points:

Properties of a line segment:
a. The line segment, AB, consists of two endpoints, A and B.
b. A line is an extension of a line segment in both directions shown by using arrowheads.
c. A line segment is a portion of a line. Line segment AB ($\overline{AB}$) begins at A and ends at B.

Activities:
a. Draw a line segment from point A to B.
b. Can one point determine a line segment? Ask the children to illustrate why the answer is no.
c. Given points A, B, C and D. Connect the points with line segments.

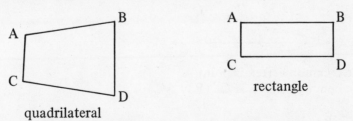

square

A polygon with four sides is called a quadrilateral. (See figure below.) If the four sides of the quadrilateral are all right angles, the quadrilateral is called a rectangle. When the sides of the rectangle have the same measure, that is, the sides are congruent, we have a square.

quadrilateral

rectangle

Encourage the children to construct different figures. What characteristics are present which will help them in naming the figures?

4. **Rays**: A part of a line consisting of one endpoint and all the points in one direction from the endpoint is a ray. In the figure $\xrightarrow{A \quad B}$, A is the endpoint of the ray. All the points to the right of A belong to the ray. The endpoint and another point on the ray are used in naming a ray. The symbol is read, the "Ray AB." The ray is also identified by the symbol $\overrightarrow{AB}$.

Activities: From any endpoint, an infinite number of rays exist, but only one ray can be drawn from the endpoint through any one point on the line.

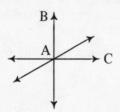

a. Identify the endpoints. (A.)
b. An infinite number of rays can be drawn from the endpoint. Add several rays to the figure.
c. How many rays can there be between A B and A C?

5. **Angles**: Angles are constructed by using rays having a common endpoint. The length of the ray does not determine the size of the angle.

Activities:
1. Draw an angle using two rays having a common endpoint.

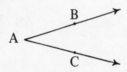

a. Point A is the common endpoint.
b. Point A names the angle. The name for this angle is "Angle BAC."
c. The angle can be named using the symbol ∠ BAC. (Read "Angle BAC".)
d. The endpoint common to both rays is the vertex and the rays are called sides.
e. The letter at the vertex may be used to name the angle.

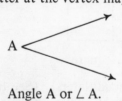

Angle A or ∠ A.

2. Ask the children to draw pictures of angles. Label each angle. Examples:
   a. Draw two angles having the same vertex and a common side.

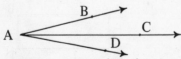

(1) The common vertex is point A.
(2) The common side is A C. (Ray AC.)

$\xrightarrow{A \qquad B}$ How many rays can be drawn through Points A and B?

b. Draw two angles with a common vertex but not a common side.

    (1) The common vertex is point P.

    (2) Angles APB and DPC do not have a common side.

    (3) How many angles are shown? (4.) Name the angles.

3. Angles are classified into three types:

    a. Angles "of 90°" are right angles. Draw a right angle using a protractor. Ask the children to identify right angles in the classroom.

    b. Angles less than 90° are acute angles. Draw acute angles using a protractor. Identify acute angles in the structure of the building, for example, the angle of the stairs.

    c. Angles more than 90° and less than 180° are obtuse angles. Identify obtuse angles in the local architecture.

6. **Planes**: Some flat surface, such as a tabletop, will help children form some concepts of a plane. Three points not in a line determine a plane. If these points are connected with line segments, they form the simple closed figure, a triangle. The figures below are flat surfaces and are called plane figures. The set of points which determine these figures all lie in one plane.

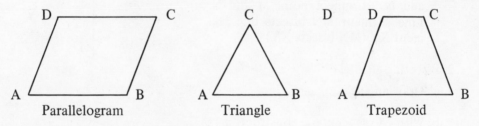

Parallelogram   Triangle   Trapezoid

How many sides has each figure?

What is the shape of the angle in each figure?

Are the lines parallel in each figure?

How long is segment A B in each figure? (Use a ruler and a compass.)

Is the distance around each figure the same? This is the perimeter. (Use a ruler and a compass.)

7. **Circles**: A circle is a simple closed figure. Each point in the circle is the same distance from a fixed point called the center of the circle. A line segment passing through the center with endpoints on the circle is the diameter. A line segment with one endpoint the center and the other endpoint on the circle is a radius of the circle. The length of the circle is the circumference and the surface enclosed by the circle is its area.

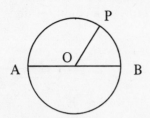

Line segment AB is a diameter

Line segment OP is a radius

Geometric Construction

Children find satisfaction in the preciseness of construction. They are challenged by the need for accuracy in reproducing models and in comparing figures (congruence). They discover that the tools such as the ruler, the compass and protractor must be precise or their work is in error.

1. Bisecting a line segment:

  a. Draw a line segment XY.

  X ———————— Y

  b. With X and Y as centers, draw arcs above and below the given segment.

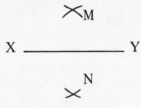

  c. Label the points of intersection M and N. Connect point M and N. Line segment MN bisects line segment XY (MN bisects XY).

2. Bisecting an angle:

  a. Draw an angle.

  b. With A as center, construct arcs intersecting the two rays. Name these points B and C.

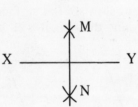

  c. With B as center, construct an arc between the two rays. With C as center, construct an arc between the two rays with the same radius, intersecting the first arc. Name this point of intersection D.

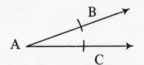

  d. Draw a ray from point A through point D. Angles BAD and CAD are the same size (congruent). $\overrightarrow{AD}$ bisects ∠BAC.

3. Drawing a perpendicular to a line from a point on the line:

  a. Construct a line and locate point M on the line.

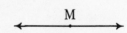

b. With point M as the center, construct two arcs intersecting the line at O and P.

c. With points O and P as centers, construct arcs above and below the line. Let X and Y be the points of intersection of the arcs.

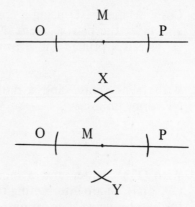

d. Draw a line through points X and Y. Line $\overleftrightarrow{XY}$ is perpendicular to line OP. ($\overleftrightarrow{XY}$ is perpendicular to $\overleftrightarrow{OP}$.)

4. Drawing a perpendicular to a line from a point not on the line:

a. Given a line and a point, E, not on the line.

b. With point E as center, construct an arc intersecting the line at C and D.

c. Using C and D as centers, construct two arcs below the line. Label their intersection G.

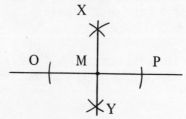

d. Draw a line through points E and G. Line $\overleftrightarrow{EG}$ is perpendicular to line CD. ($\overleftrightarrow{EG}$ is perpendicular to $\overleftrightarrow{CD}$.)

5. Drawing a triangle congruent to another triangle. A triangle is a closed figure formed by connecting three line segments.

a. Given a triangle, NOP.

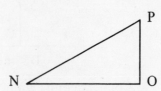

b. Copy segment NO using a compass and label the new segment N' and O'. (Read N' primed and O' primed.)

c. With N' as center and a radius of NP, draw an arc.

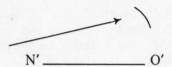

d. With O' as center and a radius of OP, draw an arc intersecting the arc formed by using N' as center. Label the point of intersection P'.

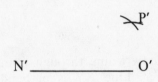

e. Draw the segments N'P' and O'P'. The △ N'O'P' is congruent to △ NOP.

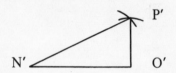

6. Constructing a rectangle with the sides equal in length to the given line segments, AB and CD. Given:

A ——————— B
C ——————————D

a. Draw line segment CD. (Use a compass or a ruler.)

b. Extend line segment CD and construct perpendiculars to C and D.
   (1) With C and D as centers, draw arcs R, S and T, U.
   (2) With R and S as centers, construct the arcs which locate point X. With T and U as centers, construct the arcs which locate point Y.
   (3) Construct the perpendiculars, XC and YD.

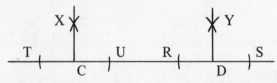

c. With C and D as centers, draw arcs with the radius of segment AB, intersecting the perpendiculars. Name these points E and F.

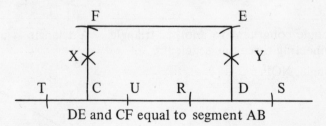

DE and CF equal to segment AB

Connect points E and F to complete the rectangle CDEF.

Activities

1. A triangle has how many points of intersection? A square?

2. The points of intersection are also called vertices. How many vertices are there in a triangle? A square?
3. A polygon is a geometric figure with several sides. A rectangle is a polygon with four sides. What polygon has three sides? Five sides?
4. Construct an equilateral triangle using a compass. Measure each angle using a protractor. Given, line segment AB.

A ———————— B

5. Construct a triangle. Bisect each line segment and then construct a perpendicular to each line segment.
6. Use the point of intersection of the perpendiculars in Example 5 as the center point and construct a circle within the triangle.

Metric Geometry

Metric concepts are concerned with the measurement of length, area and volume. In finding area of a rectangle, a square, etc., the area enclosed by the figure is in question.

Area:

1. **Squares and rectangles**: A square which measures 1 inch on each of its four sides has an area of 1 square inch.

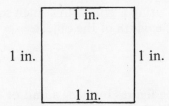

Construct a square having 6 inches on each side from a piece of tagboard. Using the square inch, find the area of the square. How many square inches were counted? Place a plastic grid having 1-inch squares over the square. How many square inches did you count?

Answer the following questions about the square.

a. What is the length of the square? (6 inches.)

b. What is its width? (6 inches.)

c. How many 1-inch squares in the length? (6.)

d. How many rows of 1-inch squares? (6.) (The number of rows is the width.)

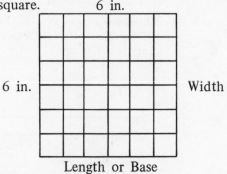

To find the number of square units in the area, multiply the number of rows times the number of square inches in each row. (6 rows × 6 square inches = 36 square inches.) In multiplication of whole numbers, children learned that the multiplier always tells how many groups and that the multiplicand states how many things are in each group. This concept is also applicable here.

6 apples	6 square inches
× 6 (groups)	× 6 (rows)
36 apples	36 square inches

As a final step, children can express and use the relation "area equals width times length," "side times side" or "the number of units in the width times the number of units in the length." This is represented by the formula: A = lw where A = area, l = length and w = width.

The area of a rectangle is represented in the same manner.

a. What is the length of the rectangle? How many 1–inch squares in the length? (4.)
b. What is the width of the rectangle? How many rows of 1–inch squares?
c. What is the area? 2 × 4 square inches = 8 square inches.

Area of a rectangle equals:

a. Side times side.   a × b = Area
b. Length times width. l × w = Area
c. Base times height.   b × h = Area

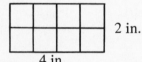

2 in.

4 in.

Activities:

a. Find the area of the following articles using a grid with 1–inch squares and by measuring with a ruler the length and the width of the object.
   (1) A sheet of paper.
   (2) A book cover.
   (3) Top of a child's desk.
b. Find the area of the following geometric figures by using a unit of 1 square foot and by measuring the length and the width of each plane using a ruler. Approximate the measurement to the nearest foot.
   (1) Top of the teacher's desk.
   (2) A table.
   (3) A large map.
   (4) The classroom floor.
c. Compare the area of the rectangles below. If these rectangles are the plans for a room, which one provides the greatest area? Note that the perimeter of each rectangle is the same.

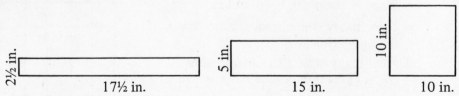

2½ in.   17½ in.   5 in.   15 in.   10 in.   10 in.

2. **Triangles**: The formula for finding the area of a triangle is derived from the formula for finding the area of a square or a rectangle (a parallelogram). A parallelogram is a quadrilateral (4 sides) whose opposite sides are parallel.

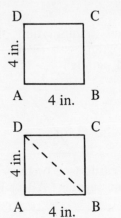

The area of square ABCD is 16 square inches. Base × height = area

Fold along diagonal DB so that point C falls on point A. Cut along the diagonal. Use a plastic grid to estimate the area

 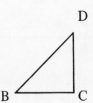

a. What is the area of triangle ABD with respect to rectangle ABCD? Triangle BCD with respect to rectangle ABCD?

b.

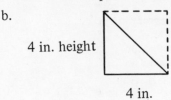

4 in. height

The area of a rectangle is 1 × w or b × h.

4 in.

c.

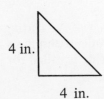

4 in.

The area of a triangle is one–half the area of a rectangle.

4 in.

(1) $\dfrac{1 \times w}{2} = \dfrac{4 \times 4}{2} = 8$ square inches, the area

(2) $\dfrac{\text{base} \times \text{height}}{2} = \dfrac{4 \times 4}{2} = \dfrac{16}{2} = 8$ square inches

(3) $A = \frac{1}{2} \times 1 \times w$ or $\frac{1}{2}(1 \times w)$
   $= \frac{1}{2} \times 4 \times 4$
   $= 2 \times 4$
   $= 8$ square inches

(4) A = ½ × b × h or ½ (b × h)
   = ½ × 4 × 4
   = 2 × 4
   = 8 square inches

3. **Parallelogram**:   Through observation and manipulation of cardboard cutouts, children come to recognize the parallelogram as a figure in which the opposite sides are equal in length (congruent) and parallel.

a. Place a plastic grid over a parallelogram made from a cardboard and count the squares. Is it easy to establish the number of squares by counting?

b. Make a parallelogram from a piece of cardboard or tagboard. Draw a line segment from Point D perpendicular to line segment AB at E.

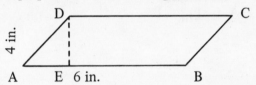

c. Cut along the dotted line, DE. Place triangle AED on the right side of the figure. What is the result? A rectangle is formed with the sides perpendicular to the base. The width of the rectangle is the same as the height of the parallelogram. The length, base, of the rectangle is the same as the length, base, of the parallelogram.

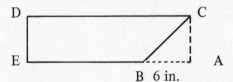

Then, b × h = Area

   6 × 4 = 24 square inches

The formula b × h = A is equivalent to l × w = A. During early presentation, "height" may be used instead of "width" to lend emphasis to the fact that the concept of height and not the length of the side is called for in the formula.

Activities:

(1) Make a parallelogram from a cardboard. Instead of cutting the triangle away, slit the top surface of the card and fold the triangle back under the cardboard. Make a triangle the same size as the triangle folded under and place this on the right side of the parallelogram. In this way, the parallelogram remains intact.

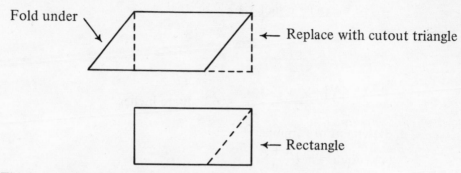

Fold under →

← Replace with cutout triangle

← Rectangle

(2) Think through the reasons which make the following statements true:
   (a) A square is a rectangle, a parallelogram and a quadrilateral.
   (b) A trapezoid is a quadrilateral.
   (c) A rectangle is a square, a quadrilateral.
   (d) All parallelograms are quadrilaterals.

4. **Trapezoid**: A trapezoid is a four–sided figure with one pair of parallel lines. The most common approach to discovering the formula for finding the area of a trapezoid is to show its relationship to a parallelogram.

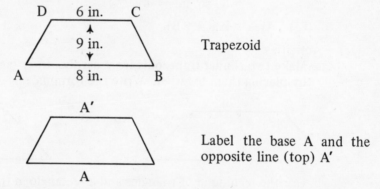

Trapezoid

Label the base A and the opposite line (top) A′

Extend Base A by the length of A′ and extend A′ by the length A. In doing this, a similar trapezoid has been added in an inverted position. The resulting figure is a parallelogram.

a. What has been added to the original trapezoid? (A trapezoid of the same size.)
b. How is the area of a parallelogram found? The formula is base × height (b × h = A).
c. Since the original trapezoid is one–half of the parallelogram, the formula must be the sum of A + A′ which is the base, times the height, divided by 2.

$$\frac{8 \text{ in. } (A) + 6 \text{ in. } (A') \times 9 \text{ in. } (h)}{2} =$$

$$\frac{(8 + 6) \times 9}{2} =$$

$$\frac{14 \times 9}{2} = \frac{126}{2} = 63 \text{ square inches}$$

d. Statement of formula:

(1) Area $= h \left(\dfrac{A + A'}{2}\right)$

$= 9 \left(\dfrac{8 + 6}{2}\right) = 9\left(\dfrac{14}{2}\right)$

$= 9 \times 7 = 63$ sq. in.

(2) Area $= \frac{1}{2}h(A + A')$

$= \frac{1}{2} \times 9(8 + 6)$

$= 4\frac{1}{2} \times 14$

$= 63$ sq. in.

(3) Area $= \frac{1}{2}h(A + B)$

Activities:

a. Make two similar trapezoids from cardboard or tagboard. Make a parallelogram by placing them together. Write the formula.

b. Use the technique of triangles and a rectangle in finding the area of a trapezoid. Use a cutout similar to the one shown. What is the area of each triangle? Of the rectangle? Make the measurements carefully. Is the answer the same as above?

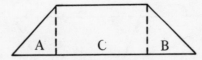

c. Check the answers with a grid. Are the partial unit squares difficult to estimate?

5. Circles: The rotation of a line segment about one of its endpoints describes a line equidistant from the endpoint. This line is the circumference of the circle.

Ask the children to use a tape and to measure circular objects in the room. Measure the diameter and the circumference of each object. Place the results in table form.

Object	Diameter	Circumference	Ratio
Plate	8 in.	25 in.	?
Bucket	1.5 ft.	4.8 ft.	?
Hoop	24 in.	72 in.	?

What ratio is expressed when the circumference is divided by the diameter for each object? Ratio of circumference to diameter:

25 in. ÷ 8 in. = 3.12

4.8 ft. ÷ 1.5 ft. = 3.20

72 in. ÷ 24 in. = 3.00

Find the average of 3.12, 3.20 and 3.00.

$$\begin{array}{r} 3.12 \\ 3.20 \\ +\ 3.00 \\ \hline 3\overline{)9.32} \\ \end{array}$$

3.10   Average c/d.   This average is a little less than pi (π), 3.14

As children continue to measure objects and to arrive at the ratio, the pupils will soon establish the concept of pi. This ratio (pi) is the same for all circles. There are approximately 3.14 diameters in every circle.

a. Finding the circumference when the diameter is given:

Problem: Mr. Jones' swimming pool has a diameter of 18 feet. What is the circumference? Equation:

Diameter times the ratio (pi) = circumference.

$D \times \pi = C$

18 ft. $\times$ 3.14 = 56.52 ft.

b. Finding the circumference when the radius is given: Since there are 2 radii in any diameter, the diameter may be written as 2r. Then the equation for the above problem becomes:

$2r \times \pi = C$

$(2 \times 9 \text{ ft.}) \times 3.14 = 56.52$ ft.

The commonly used formula is $2\pi r = C$. Because of the commutative law in multiplication, it does not matter whether we say $2r\pi$ or $2\pi r$.

$2\pi r = C$

c. Finding the diameter when the circumference is given: A circular tent has a circumference of 205 feet. What is its approximate diameter? Equation:

$D \times \pi = C$

$N \times 3.14 = 205$ ft.

Divide both sides by π:

$N \times \dfrac{3.14}{3.14} = \dfrac{205}{3.14}$

Then N = 205 ÷ 3.14.

N = 65 ft., approximate diameter.

6. **Area of circles**: The area of a figure is the number of square units in its surface. To develop this concept for circles, have pupils draw circles on graph paper and approximate the number of square units. They will encounter difficulty in estimating a square unit when only parts of the square unit appear because of the curved boundary.

Children, working individually or in groups, will work along with the teacher as she presents the following steps.

a. Draw a circle and divide it into eight equal parts. Cut out each part.

b. Fit the eights together to form the following figure:

A

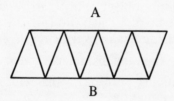

B

Note that the figure resembles a parallelogram. The top and the base of the figure are each one–half of the circumference. A + B equals the circumference of the circle.

c. The formula for finding the circumference is $2\pi r$. Since one–half of C is the base of the parallelogram, the base of the parallelogram is $2\pi r/2$ or πr. The height of the figure is the radius, r.

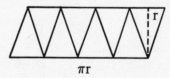

πr

Area of a parallelogram = b X h = πr X r.
Then, the area of a circle is πr X r = πr^2. Therefore, A = πr^2.

7. **Volume of a cube**: Measures of volume are commonly expressed in cubic inches, cubic feet and cubic yards. A cubic unit of measure has three dimensions: length, width and height. When each side of a cube is 1 inch long, it is called a cubic inch.

Ask the children to make a unit cube using tagboard. The pattern presented here may be used as a guide in making the cube. If 1–inch cubes of wood are not available, the paper cubes can be used to find the volume of a figure. For example, pupils will use 24 one-inch cubes to show that a cube 3 inches by 4 inches by 1 inch has a volume of 24 cubic inches.

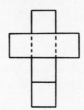

Pattern for making a cube

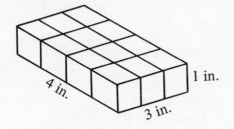

a. How many cubic inches are there in one row? How many rows with 4 cubic inches in each row? How many cubic inches in the first layer? 3 × 4 cubic inches = 12 cu. in.

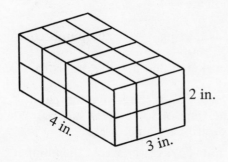

b. How many cubic inches in the second layer? How many cubic inches in this cube?

4 in. × 3 in. × 1 in. = 12 cubic in.
in one layer

4 in. × 3 in. × 2 in. = 24 cubic in.
in two layers

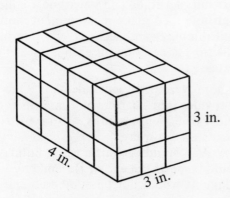

c. How many 1-inch cubes will make one layer? How many layers in the figure? What is the volume of this figure?

3 layers × 12 one-inch cubes =
36 cubic in.

The students discover that the volume of a rectangular cube is equal to the product of the area of the base and the height. In general, the volume of a rectangular cube is the product of three dimensions, the length, the width and the height. In other words, V = lwh. Calling the area of the base B, the volume may be represented by the formula V = Bh.

Time

Concepts of time are quite complex and must evolve at different levels of maturity. Time means little to the young child; his idea of time is very limited.

Children begin to tell time before coming to school. Their activities in the primary grades are centered about ways to tell time and the skill of telling time. The following outline enumerates some of the common activities in telling time.

1. The numerals on the clock.
2. The long hand tells the minutes and moves around the face of the clock once every hour.
3. The short hand tells the hour. It moves slowly from one numeral to the next.
4. The children first tell time by the hour. Then the half hour and then finer distinctions are made. The parts of the hour are taught with fractions.
5. Types and history of clocks.
6. Materials: old clocks, paper clocks, sundials.
7. Worksheets
   a. Show the dial with one or both hands missing. Have the pupils complete the dial to show a certain hour.
   b. Have numerals or hands missing on a sketch and ask the pupils to supply the missing information.
   c. Have clocks without hands, or movable hands, and have the pupils draw the hands or move the hands to show the time of some event such as: When does school start? When is recess? When do we have lunch? etc.

Time is comprehensive. The calendar with its days of the week, the number of days in a month, the number of weeks in a year is somewhat evasive because they are abstract. In science, the light year measures distance using time. Science speaks of the sidereal day and solar time as time marked by stars and our sun. Latitude and longitude are measures of time. One hour of latitude equals 1° of latitude. To make measurement more accurate, 1° of latitude and longitude is divided into minutes and seconds. By international agreement, the world has been divided into 24 time zones, one for each hour of the day. Of these 24 time zones, 4 are in the United States.

Constructive efforts are being made to improve our present calendar. One of the proposed calendars is the World Calendar. It provides four quarters of 3 months each.

1. Each quarter has a 31-day month and two 30-day months, a total of 91 days. Every quarter begins on Sunday and ends on Saturday.
2. The day which is left over in an ordinary year would become a world holiday. The day would not be numbered, but it would come at the end of December.
3. Leap Year Day is another world holiday. It would not be numbered and would come at the end of June.
4. January 1 is always on Sunday.
5. The second month of each quarter begins on Wednesday; the third month begins on Friday.

In our calendar, Easter can come as early as March 22 and as late as April 25. Easter is the first Sunday after the full moon that falls on or after the spring equinox, March 21. If the full moon falls on Sunday, Easter is observed 1 week later. On the World Calendar, Easter would be April 15 in each year.

Measures and the process of measurement have been important to man's progress through the centuries. Man has used geometry for developing his civilization; he has used the tools of measurement to answer his questions of "how many." Dissatisfaction with his knowledge of measurement forced him to invent new systems during his centuries of growth. The metric system, one of his inventions, has provided simplicity and relatedness to measurement. Man will continue to search for more accurate ways of answering the questions of measurement.

Questions

1. How early do children recognize geometric shapes such as the square, rectangle and the circle? Do they learn the terms for these shapes at the same time?
2. Note that we avoid such expressions as "3 inches × 4 inches equal 24 square inches." Why are such expressions objectionable in the early stages of teaching?
3. Illustrate how to develop the formula for finding the area of a circle.
4. Develop the concept of a unit for measuring area of a rectangle, for measuring volume of a cube.
5. Describe and illustrate how to proceed to teach children the nature of a unit.
6. Make a list of activities in measurement which you can use at your grade level.
7. Compare the merits of the Old English system and the metric system of measures.
8. Develop a lesson which demonstrates that all measurement is approximate.
9. Have the children estimate the length, height and width of your classroom. How great was their error?
10. What ratio is expressed by pi? Develop a lesson which will illustrate this concept to children.
11. Try a day in class when the use of numbers is not permitted. What ideas about numbers soon develop with the children?
12. What computational skills are used in solving problems of measurement?
13. Check several arithmetic series for their presentation of measurement.

Selected Text References

1. Dwight, Leslie A., *Modern Mathematics for the Elementary Teacher*, New York: Holt, Rinehart and Winston, Inc., 1966. Chapters 16 and 17.
2. Hollister, George E., and Agnes G. Gunderson, *Teaching Arithmetic in the Primary Grades*, Boston: D. C. Heath and Company, 1964. Chapters 9 and 10.
3. Howard, Charles F., and Enoch Dumas, *Basic Procedures in Teaching Arithmetic*, Boston: D. C. Heath and Company, 1963. Chapter 12.
4. Kramer, Klaas, *The Teaching of Elementary School Mathematics*, Boston: Allyn and Bacon, Inc., 1966. Chapter 17.
5. Marks, John L., C. Richard Purdy and Lucien B. Kinney, *Teaching Elementary School Mathematics for Understanding*, New York: McGraw–Hill Book Company, 1966. Chapters 8 and 12.

6. Mueller, Francis J., *Arithmetic, Its Structure and Concepts*, Englewood Cliffs, N.J.: Prentice–Hall, Inc., 1964. Chapters 24 and 25.
7. Spencer, Peter Lincoln, and Marguerite Brydegaard, *Building Mathematical Competence in the Elementary School*, New York: Holt, Rinehart and Winston, Inc., 1966. Chapters 10 and 12.

Selected Readings from the <u>Arithmetic Teacher</u>

1. Bowles, D. Richard, "The Metric System in Grade 6," *11:* 36–38, January, 1964.
2. DeGroff, Homer R., "Teaching Square Root Meaningfully in Grade 8," *7:* 100–102, February, 1960.
3. Hawley, N. S., "Geometry for the Primary Grades," *8:* 374–376, November, 1961.
4. Mascho, George, "Familiarity with Measurement," *8:* 164–167, April, 1961.
5. Miller, G. H., "Geometry in the Elementary Grades: A Comparative Study of Greek Mathematics Education," *11:* 85–88, February, 1964.
6. Pray, Richard H., "The Metric System is Easy," *8:* 179, April, 1961.
7. Smart, James R. and John L. Marks, "Mathematics Measurement," *13:* 283–287, April, 1966.

Bibliography

1. Banks, J. Houston, *Elementary School Mathematics,* Boston: Allyn and Bacon, Inc., 1966.
2. Corle, Clyde G., *Teaching Mathematics in the Elementary School,* New York: Ronald Press, 1964.
3. DeMay, Amy J., *Guiding Beginners in Arithmetic,* Evanston, Ill.: Row, Peterson and Company, 1957.
4. Dutton, W. H., and L. J. Adams, *Arithmetic For Teachers,* Englewood Cliffs, N.J.: Prentice-Hall, Inc., 1961.
5. Dwight, Leslie A., *Modern Mathematics for the Elementary Teacher,* New York: Holt, Rinehart and Winston, Inc., 1966.
6. Flournoy, Frances, *Elementary School Mathematics,* New York: The Center for Applied Research in Education, Inc., 1964.
7. Grossnickle, Foster E., and Leo J. Breuckner, *Discovering Meaning in Elementary School Mathematics,* New York: Holt, Rinehart and Winston, Inc., 1963.
8. Hollister, George E., and Agnes G. Gunderson, *Teaching Arithmetic in the Elementary Grades,* Boston: D. C. Heath and Company, 1964.
9. Howard, Charles F., and Enoch Dumas, *Basic Procedures in Teaching Arithmetic,* Boston: D. C. Heath and Company, 1963.
10. Kramer, Klaas, *The Teaching of Elementary School Mathematics,* Boston: Allyn and Bacon, Inc., 1966.
11. Marks, John L., C. Richard Purdy, and Lucien B. Kinney, *Teaching Elementary School Mathematics for Understanding,* New York: McGraw-Hill Book Company, 1966.
12. Meserve, Bruce E., and Max A. Sobel, *Introduction to Mathematics,* Englewood Cliffs, N.J.: Prentice-Hall, Inc., 1964.
13. Mueller, Francis, J., *Arithmetic, Its Structure and Concepts,* Englewood Cliffs, N.J.: Prentice-Hall, Inc., 1964.
14. Peterson, John and Joseph Hashisaki, *Theory of Arithmetic,* New York: John Wiley and Sons, Inc., 1963.
15. Shipp, Donald, and Sam Adams, *Developing Arithmetic Concepts and Skills,* Englewood Cliffs, N.J.: Prentice-Hall, Inc., 1964.
16. Spencer, Peter Lincoln, and Marguerite Brydegaard, *Building Mathematical Competence in the Elementary School,* New York: Holt, Rinehart and Winston, Inc., 1966.
17. Swain, Robert L., and Eugene D. Nichols, *Understanding Arithmetic,* New York: Holt, Rinehart and Winston, Inc., 1965.
18. Swenson, Esther, *Teaching Arithmetic to Children,* New York: The Macmillan Company, 1964.

Selected Readings from the Arithmetic Teacher, an Official Journal of the National Council of Teachers of Mathematics, 1201 Sixteenth Street, N.W., Washington, D.C. 20036.

1. Adkins, Bryce, E., "Adapting Magic Squares to Classroom Use," *10:* 525-532, November, 1965.
2. Adler, Irving, "The Cambridge Conference Report: Blueprint or Fantasy?" *13:* 179-186, March, 1966.
3. Aranti, Frank D., "The Use of '1' in Building Concepts," *8:* 299-300, October, 1961.
4. Beard, Virginia, "Mathematics in Kindergarten," *9:* 22-25, January, 1962.
5. Bender, Marvin L., "Dividing by Zero," *8:* 176-179, April, 1961.
6. Botts, Truman, "Numbers, Sets and Counting," *8:* 281-286, October, 1961.
7. Bowles, D. Richard, "The Metric System in Grade 6," *11:* 36-38, January, 1964.
8. Brace, Alec and L. Doyal Nelson, "The Preschool Child's Concept of Number," *12:* 126-133, February, 1965.
9. Capps, Lelon R., "Making Division Meaningful and Logical," *9:* 198-202, April, 1962.
10. Clark, John R., "Looking Ahead at Instruction in Arithmetic," *8:* 388-394, December, 1961.
11. Clary, Robert C., "Teaching Aids for Elementary School Arithmetic," *13:* 135-136, February, 1966.
12. Claspill, Eileen K., "A Better Understanding of Our Number System," *9:* 71-73, February, 1962.
13. Coon, Lewis H., "Number Line Multiplication for Negative Numbers," *13:* 213-217, March, 1966.
14. Corle, Clyde G., "The New Mathematics," *11:* 242-247, April, 1964.
15. Deans, Edwina, "Independent Work in Arithmetic," *8:* 77-80, February, 1961.
16. _____ , "Practice in Renaming Numbers—An Aid to Subtraction," *12:* 142, February, 1965.
17. DeGroff, Homer R., "Teaching Square Root Meaningfully in Grade 8," *7:* 100-102, February, 1960.
18. Easterday, Kenneth and Helen, "A Logical Method for Basic Subtraction," *13:* 404-406, May, 1966.
19. Fehr, Howard F., "Sense and Nonsense in a Mathematics Program," *13:* 83-91, February, 1966.
20. Fisher, Alan A., "The Peg Board—A Useful Aid in Teaching Arithmetic," *8:* 186-188, April, 1961.
21. Flournoy, Frances, "Applying Basic Mathematical Ideas in Arithmetic," *11:* 104-108, February, 1964.
22. Grossnickle, Foster E., "Verbal Problem Solving," *11:* 12-17, January, 1961.
23. Gunderson, Ethel, "Fractions—Seven-Year Olds Use Them," *5:* 233-238, November, 1958.
24. Hannon, Herbert, "A New Look At Basic Principles of Multiplication With Whole Numbers," *7:* 357-361, November, 1960.
25. Hauck, E., "Concrete Materials for Teaching Percentage," *1:* 9-12, December, 1954.
26. Hawley, N. S., "Geometry For The Primary Grades," *8:* 374-376, November, 1961.
27. Heard, Ida Mae, "Developing Concepts of Time and Temperature," *8:* 124-126, March, 1961.
28. Hess, Marvel, "Second-Grade Children Solve Problems," *13:* 317-318, April, 1966.

29. Hilaire, Paul A., "Let's Take a Look at Division," *8:* 220-225, May, 1961.
30. Hilaire, Paul, and Walter Westphal, "New Numerals for Basic-Five Arithmetic," *11:* 331-333, May, 1964.
31. Inbody, Donald, "Helping Parents Understand New Mathematics," *11:* 530-537, December, 1964.
32. Irwin, Evelyn S., "An Approach to Substraction Using Easy Facts," *11:* 260-261, April, 1964.
33. Jackson, Humphrey C., "Tables and Structures," *7:* 71-76, February, 1960.
34. Johnson, Harry C., "Division With Fractions—Levels of Meanings," *12:* 362-368, May, 1965.
35. Johnson, Paul B., "Modern Mathematics in a Toga," *12:* 343-347, May, 1965.
36. Jones, Emily, "Historical Conflict — Decimal Versus Vulgar Fractions," *7:* 184-188, April, 1960.
37. Kaliski, Lotte, "Arithmetic and the Brain-Injured Child," *9:* 245-251, May, 1962.
38. Kessler, Rolla, "The Equation Method of Teaching Percentage," *7:* 90-92, February, 1960.
39. Lutz, Marie, "Multiplication Memos for Dr. Mower," *9:* 317-320, October, 1962.
40. Machlin, Ruth, "The Use of Overlay Charts," *8:* 433-435, December, 1961.
41. Marks, John, "The Uneven Progress of the Revolution in Elementary School Mathematics," *10:* 474-478, December, 1963.
42. Mascho, George, "Familiarity with Measurement," *8:* 164-167, April, 1961.
43. McMeen, George N., "Division by a Fraction—A New Method," *9:* 122-126, March, 1962.
44. Michalov, Mary, "The Versatile Number Runner," *8:* 182-186, April, 1961.
45. Miller, G. H., "Geometry in the Elementary Grades, A Comparative Study of Greek Mathematics Education," *11:* 85-88, February, 1964.
46. O'Brien, Thomas C., "Two Approaches to the Algorism for Multiplication of Fractional Numbers," *12:* 552-555, November, 1965.
47. Oesterle, Robert A., "What About Those Zero Facts?" *6:* 109-111, March, 1959.
48. Paschal, Billy J., "Teaching the Critically Disadvantaged Child," *13:* 369-374, May, 1966.
49. Peterson, John A., and Joseph Hashisaki, "Patterns in Arithmetic," *13:* 209-212, March, 1966.
50. Peterson, Wayne, "Numeration—A Fresh Look," *12:* 335-338, May, 1965.
51. Philips, Jo, "Basic Laws for Young Children," *12:* 525-532, November, 1965.
52. Pray, Richard H., "The Metric System is Easy," *8:* 179, April, 1961.
53. Rahlow, Harold, F., "Understanding Different Number Bases," *12:* 339-340, May, 1965.
54. Rappaport, David, "Percentage — Noun or Adjective," *8:* 25-26, January, 1961.
55. Rasmussen, Don and Lore Rasmussen, "The Miquon Mathematics Program," *9:* 188-192, April, 1962.
56. Rivera, Emilio, "Adding by Endings, Some Important Considerations," *12:* 204-206, March, 1965.
57. Ruddell, Arden K., "Levels of Difficulty in Division," *6:* 97-99, March, 1959.
58. Sanders, Walter J., "The Use of Models in Mathematics Instruction," *11:* 157-165, March, 1964.
59. Smart, James R. and John L. Marks, "Mathematics Measurement," *13:* 283-287, April, 1966.
60. Spencer, Peter L., "Do They See the Point," *5:* 271-272, January, 1958.

61. Spooner, George, "Divisibility and the Base-Ten Numeration System," *11:* 563-568, December, 1964.
62. Spross, Patricia, "Considerations in the Selection of Learning Aids," *11:* 350-353, May, 1964.
63. Stern, Catherine and Margaret B. Stern, "Comments on Ancient Egyptian Multiplication," *11:* 254-257, April, 1964.
64. Stutler, Mary S., "Arithmetic Concepts in the First Grade," *9:* 81-85, February, 1962.
65. Sueltz, Ben A., "A Time for Decision," *8:* 274-280, October, 1961.
66. Swart, William L., "Don't Move the Point, Move the Number," *7:* 204-205, April, 1960.
67. Volpel, Marvin C., "The Hundred Board," *6:* 295-301, December, 1959.
68. Weaver, Fred J., "The School Mathematics Study Group Project in Elementary School Mathematics," *8:* 32-35, January, 1961.
69. Willerding, Margaret F., "Other Number Systems—Aids to Understanding Mathematics," *8:* 350-356, November, 1961.
70. Zweng, Marilyn J., "Division Problems and the Concept of Rate," *11:* 547-556, December, 1964.

Index